Protein Additives in Foodservice Preparations

Protein Additives in Foodservice Preparations

JOSEPH RAKOSKY, JR., Ph.d.
Food Industry Consultant
J. Rakosky Services
Morton Grove, Ill.

An avi Book
Published by Van Nostrand Reinhold
New York

An AVI Book
(AVI is an imprint of Van Nostrand Reinhold)
Copyright © 1989 by Van Nostrand Reinhold

Library of Congress Catalog Card Number 88-5409
ISBN 0-442-22676-4

Printed in the United States of America

Designed by Carla Bolte

Van Nostrand Reinhold
115 Fifth Avenue
New York, New York 10003

Van Nostrand Reinhold International Company Limited
11 New Fetter Lane
London EC4P 4EE, England

Van Nostrand Reinhold
480 La Trobe Street
Melbourne, Victoria 3000, Australia

Macmillan of Canada
Division of Canada Publishing Corporation
164 Commander Boulevard
Agincourt, Ontario M1S 3C7, Canada

16 15 14 13 12 11 10 9 8 7 6 5 4 3 2 1

Library of Congress Cataloging-in-Publication Data

Rakosky, Joseph, 1921–
    Protein additives in foodservice preparations/Joseph Rakosky, Jr.
        p. cm.
    Bibliography: p.
    Includes index.
    ISBN 0-442-22676-4
    1. Proteins in human nutrition.   2. Soy products.   3. Food
additives.   I. Title.   II. Title: Protein additives in foodservice preparations.
TX553.P7R28 1988
641.5'7—dc19   88-5409
                                                                   CIP

To Dr. L. J. Minor, food scientist, teacher, and businessman, through whose encouragement this book was written.

To my associates and colleagues, from whom I learned much over the years.

To my daughter, Beth Meyer, who not only read and corrected my manuscript, but through her desire to understand the subject matter, caused me to modify some of my explanations.

To my wife, Mary, who tolerated the time I spent in seclusion preparing this material.

Contents

5. BAKERY PRODUCTS 97

6. PASTA PRODUCTS 123

Preface

I have 30 years' experience working with soy products—their production and use in processed foods. Much of this time was spent in the marketing department of a large soy-processing company as director of technical marketing services. In this capacity, I became quite familiar with many competitive products and became adept at recognizing their advantages and disadvantages as compared to soy proteins. Because of this broad background in soy protein products, I have often used soy products in examples and explanations. However, there will be cases where one protein, other than soy, will have functional properties that others do not have. In these instances, I endeavored to bring out such differences. This text was written with the beginning foodservice student in mind. My goal was to give guidelines and necessary basic information to allow the student to make intelligent recipe-adjustment decisions when proteins are introduced into food preparations. I avoided deep technical explanations because it is not necessary for the foodservice student to have such detail. If such technical information is needed or desired, the student is encouraged to consult the references given and to seek out the depth desired.

In covering the subject of protein additives in foods, it is apparent that limits must be set as to what is a protein additive, that is, what is the lowest protein level acceptable for a product? I arbitrarily set that lower limit at 25 percent. For this reason, practically all of the cereal products are eliminated, except those specially processed concentrates and isolates that have their origins in certain cereal grains.

The introduction of new protein products is a frequent occurrence. Some have prospects of being used commercially in a relatively short time; others appear to have only curiosity appeal. Here, too, limits must be set. For the most part, I considered only those products that are being used most widely in the last several years. This should not be too much of a handicap since a newly developed product will probably be similar to one or more of the proteins already being used. If there are marked differences, the company promoting the product will be sure to point out that difference.

As protein additives are discussed in specific applications, the student will note that emphasis is placed on guidelines. Rarely do I give specific formulations. Every company supplying protein additives usually has model formulations for various applications. In most cases, these formulations are simply suggested starting points for developmental work. Because the company cannot anticipate conditions under which their products will be used, they will not warrant their product's performance. Thus, a disclaimer almost always is printed with the formulation, especially if the formulation is printed with the company logo. Because of this and because I do not endorse any company or product, I avoided offering suggested formulations. The student should contact companies supplying protein additives and ask them for samples of their products and formulations. In most cases, the companies will be anxious to comply with the request and will even offer assistance in arriving at an acceptable recipe.

By sharing my experiences, I trust that the guidelines and principles given will help the student to successfully utilize protein additives in various foods in a relatively short time.

Although this text was written with the foodservice student in mind, the material covered and the approaches used also should be helpful to food technologists working in developing countries. The suggestions, guidelines, and mathematical procedures should be helpful in guiding the technician in modifying native foods for the desired benefits, particularly in protein fortification and in making foods more affordable.

CHAPTER 1

Protein Additives: Use and Regulation

Foodservice in the United States is big business and is getting bigger. The National Restaurant Association (NRA) reported that foodservice sales more than doubled in the past decade: from $42.7 billion in 1970 to $114.0 billion in 1980. As reported by Ellis (1985), sales were estimated to be $191 billion for the year 1985, resulting in an annual growth rate of 10.87 percent. Based on this information, projected foodservice sales in 1990 will amount to $320 billion.

It is interesting to note that about two-thirds of the foodservice sales is in commercial feeding operations (Ellis 1985). For a breakdown of the part the various sectors play in making up the 1985 projection, in both the commercial and the noncommercial segments, see Table 1-1.

As might be surmised, all foodservice operations are very competitive and, as a result, the pressure is on to function profitably and to attract customers, particularly in the commercial segments. One way this can be done is to offer customers good, wholesome, tasty foods at reasonable prices. For this reason, ways and means are usually sought to keep costs in line without sacrificing appeal. This is especially true for institutional feeding operations, where businesses are usually forced to stay within budgetary limits that, more often than not, do not keep pace with inflation.

The overall cost of food and beverage purchases in 1981 was about 40 percent of gross sales. Employee wages and benefits amounted to about 30 percent, leaving another 30 percent for overhead and profit. (Percentages are based on data given in the NRA's fact sheet for 1981. Percentages were rounded off.) It does not seem likely that there can be very much left for profit if there is a large debt to be paid off for equipment, fixtures, buildings, taxes, and so forth. It is interesting to note from the 1985 projections by the NRA that the cost of food-service purchases was estimated to be $74.7 billion, which is slightly under the 40 percent figure.

One way to cut costs is to look at the efficiency of the operation. This might involve finding a more efficient use of employees, equipment, and even scheduling. Another way is to look at the cost of the food. Should the portions be cut? Is there a way to lessen costs of a particular food preparation? The latter question does not apply so much to retail operations as it does to institutional ones where fractional savings are significant, because large volumes are usually involved (see the following list for considerations in cutting foodservice costs).

Efficient use of
   Employees
   Equipment
   Scheduling
   Space
Cost of raw materials
Size of portions
Cost of food preparation
Substitution of ingredients
Cost of packaging
Cost of storage and delivery

When cost considerations are given to different food preparations, with few exceptions, the animal-protein ingredient is the most expensive. In many instances, it is virtually impossible to replace all the animal-protein product with a less expensive protein product if that product is ordered by a specific name, such as "filet mignon." However, in institutional feeding it would be doubtful that such an item would be served very often, if at all.

There are many ways that food preparation costs can be cut. In this text we will focus on what can be done to improve products and cut costs through the use of various protein additives.

FOOD ADDITIVES AND INGREDIENTS

When considering food formulations and recipes, we invariably are confronted with the terms *additive* and *ingredient*. When is a food an additive? When is it an ingredient? It is unlikely that there will be any confusion over the term *ingredient*. It is more likely that *additive* will be confusing in the minds of many, particularly when there is a school of thought that believes "all additives are bad

**Table 1-1 Estimated 1985 Sales by
Foodservice Outlets**

	Estimated Sales ($ billion)
Commercial Segments	
Separate eating places	107.4
Hotels and motels	7.0
Recreational	5.6
Retail hosts	5.4
Separate drinking places	1.2
Subtotal	126.6
Noncommercial Segments	
Primary and secondary schools	12.3
Colleges and universities	5.4
In-plant and in-office	12.6
Vending machines	11.6
Health-care facilities	12.9
Military	5.2
Airlines	2.5
Other noncommercial	1.9
Subtotal	64.4
TOTAL	191.0

Source: Ellis 1985.

because they are chemicals." The implication is that all chemicals are bad. It would appear that this definition fails to acknowledge that food in its natural state is made up of chemicals, both inorganic and organic (Fig. 1-1).

To most people in the food business, additives are needed because of their beneficial effects. Hence, they are considered to be good. But it is possible to use an additive to achieve a beneficial effect in one instance and an adverse effect in another. A good example of this is the use of a preservative that is toxic to both bacteria and man. Fortunately, using such additives is unlikely in food processing because of our strict laws.

The term *additive* will mean different things to different people. We need to understand these meanings not only because we will be discussing additives but also because we need to be familiar with the regulations governing the use of additives.

According to *Webster's Ninth New Collegiate Dictionary* (1983), an additive is "a substance added to another in relatively small amounts to impart or improve desirable properties or suppress undesirable properties." An ingredient is "something that enters into a compound or is a component part of any combination or

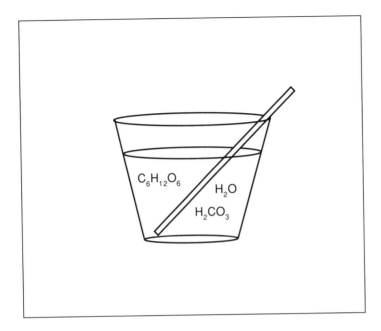

Figure 1-1. Chemical cocktail (sweetened soda water).

mixture." It follows that an additive is an ingredient, but an ingredient is not necessarily an additive because of the quantity of the material being used in the formulation or recipe. Even this does not hold true, however, because there are certain "ingredients" used in small quantities that, if left out, would cause the preparation to fail. Leavening agents are good examples. Obviously, there are no clear-cut differentiations.

This text will consider examples where a food protein product will be used as an additive in a formulation to achieve a beneficial effect, yet that same product can be the major component in another formulation. A good example is gelatin, which can be a minor component in giving body to a soup but is a major component in a gelatin dessert.

When considering additives from the health-safety standpoint, it is an extremely complicated situation for regulatory agencies to come up with legal definitions. Nevertheless, such a definition is given in Section 201(s) of the Federal Food, Drug and Cosmetic Act (1979):

> The term "food additive" means any substance the intended use of which results or may reasonably be expected to result, directly or indirectly, in its becoming a component or otherwise affecting the characteristics of any food (including any substance intended for use in producing, manufacturing, packing, processing, preparing, treating, packaging, transporting, or holding food; and including any source

of radiation intended for any such use), if such substance is not generally recognized, among experts qualified by scientific training and experience to evaluate its safety, as having been adequately shown through scientific procedures (or, in the case of a substance used in food prior to January 1, 1958, through either scientific procedures or experience based on common use in food) to be safe under the conditions of its intended use; except that such term does not include—

(1) a pesticide chemical in or on a raw agricultural commodity; or
(2) a pesticide chemical to the extent that it is intended for use or is used in the production, storage, or transportation of any raw agricultural commodity; or
(3) a color additive; or
(4) any substance used in accordance with a sanction or approval granted prior to the enactment of this paragraph pursuant to this Act, the Poultry Products Inspection Act (21 USC 451 and the following) or the Meat Inspection Act of March 4, 1907 (34 Stat. 1260), as amended and extended (21 USC 71 and the following); or
(5) a new animal drug.

According to the act, a food additive is any substance that can become a component of a food. This would include substances purposely or inadvertently added that will affect the food in some way. Also, the additive may be intentionally or unintentionally added during any part of processing and subsequent food handling. An interesting inclusion is radiation that may be a part of the process. In the definition, there are certain exclusions because they are regulated in a specific way.

Generally, most of the protein additives discussed in this volume have prior sanction approval, are "Generally Recognized as Safe" (GRAS), or are currently being considered for GRAS inclusion. In the latter case, qualified experts can declare a substance GRAS. It then can be used in a food, unless, of course, it can be shown that the product is unsafe or is questionable. This is the basis on which many of the products found in health-food stores find their way to the shelves.

For the most part, foodservice operators need not concern themselves about using additives if they use well-known, widely accepted products or if they deal with reputable suppliers.

Value of Additives in Food Products

The only reason a person would consider using a protein additive, or any additive, is because its use would result in a benefit in some way.

• Would the food taste better?
• Would it be more juicy and flavorful?
• Would it look more appealing?

- Would it hold up better under stress, such as during freeze/thaw cycles?
- Would it have a longer shelf life?
- Would it be more nutritious?
- Would it have fewer calories?
- Would it cost less to make the preparation without lowering its quality?

An affirmative answer to one or more of these questions, or other questions, would be reason enough to use a protein additive. The more benefits that an addition can achieve, the greater the reason to use it. Obviously, in considering the benefits, an increase in cost must be weighed against the benefits: Is it worth it?

When looking at the various benefits, note that protein additives have special properties that can be put into three categories:

1. Functional benefits
2. Nutritional benefits
3. Economic benefits

Functional properties are those characteristics of a protein additive that provide the benefits through the way they work or "function" within a food system. Functional properties, or functionality, have been defined by Pour-El (1981, p. 2) as "any property of a food or food ingredient except its nutritional ones that affects its utilization." This definition would include both desirable and undesirable properties. Obviously, a food processor would not like to use an additive that is undesirable, but it is good to know what undesirable traits, if any, are associated with an additive. Such knowledge would be invaluable to a food technologist who is considering the use of a protein product in some food application.

For a protein to give functional benefits, we must take advantage of its functional properties, that is, its color, flavor, solubility, or dispersibility; its ability to act as an emulsifier and/or an emulsion stabilizer; its cohesive and adhesive properties; its film-forming properties; and its gelation, coagulation, and binding properties.

With one or more of these functional properties, a protein additive can produce one or more beneficial effects in a food system.

The following are possible functional benefits of a protein additive in a food system. The protein additive may

- Improve conditions to simplify processing.
- Act as an emulsifier.
- Act as an emulsion stabilizer.
- Increase the viscosity.

- Become an essential ingredient.
- Result in longer shelf life of the product.
- Increase eye appeal.
- Have a more desirable texture.
- Have an interesting flavor and/or improve taste.
- Act as a binder of particles, fat, and/or water.

The following are possible nutritional benefits in a food system. The protein additive may

- Lower the calorie content of the food.
- Increase the protein level.
- Improve the protein quality by balancing the amino acid profile.
- Improve the nutritional profile through the addition of other vitamins and minerals.

The following are possible economic benefits in a food system. The protein additive may

- lower cost by replacing a more costly product with a less expensive one.
- lower cost by lessening the amount of rework that is normally done.
- lower cost by increasing the yield.

Cost may well be an overriding factor because, if an additive adds greatly to the cost without producing an appropriate benefit, the use of the additive may be ruled out. The desire of all food technologists is to keep the cost as low as possible without sacrificing quality. In most cases, a decision must be made relative to the quality desired versus the cost when protein additives are being considered.

The three categories covered very briefly here will be discussed in greater detail in Chapters 3 and 4.

REGULATORY AGENCIES AND FOODSERVICE

As in all businesses, foodservice operators are under the watchful eye of regulatory agencies and, in many cases, the facilities are subject to inspections to see whether or not the operation is run according to the law.

When we think about regulatory agencies, we usually think of the Food and Drug Administration (FDA) and, in some cases, the Food Safety and Inspection Service (FSIS) of the U.S. Department of Agriculture (USDA). Both of these agencies are concerned with food operations that are involved in interstate commerce. Because most foodservice operations are conducted on a local level, the

FDA and FSIS are not involved, except in some special instances. In most cases, the regulatory agencies of concern usually are local boards of health, such as state, county, city, or village agencies. Nevertheless, there are many foodservice businesses that do come under federal regulations. For this reason, as well as because many of the local agencies follow federal standards, it is advisable to be somewhat familiar with the federal agencies that watch over food-processing businesses.

Besides these agencies, there are several others that, as a rule, have jurisdiction over interstate food operations: the U.S. Department of Commerce, National Marine Fisheries Service; the Environmental Protection Agency, (1) Office of Water Supply and (2) Office of Pesticide Programs; and the U.S. Department of Labor, Occupational Safety and Health Review Commission.

A brief description of each of the pertinent agencies is summarized in the following list (Rakosky 1982).

The Food and Drug Administration has regulatory authority over the products, distribution, labeling, and selling of foods, drugs, and cosmetics.

The Food Safety and Inspection Service is responsible for agricultural products, particularly animal products. Its interests include food safety, sanitary practices, standards, labels, and grading. It also has jurisdiction over foods containing meat, such as soup.

The National Marine Fisheries Service is partly responsible for assuring the quality of seafoods consumed in this country. It also offers a voluntary inspection service.

The Office of Water Supply, in cooperation with state and regional authorities, with which it helps establish regulations, acts to safeguard our drinking water supply.

The Office of Pesticide Programs is responsible for the proper control of pesticides to protect both human life and the environment.

The Occupational Safety and Health Review Commission is concerned with employee safety as provided for in the Occupational Safety and Health Act of 1970 (OSHA). The act was passed in an effort to reduce the incidence of injuries, illnesses, and deaths among workers in carrying out their jobs.

The Food and Drug Administration (FDA)

Most of the federal agencies work with each other in a cooperative effort. Although each has its own areas of responsibility, the FDA most often sets the stage for the others. The other agencies rarely conflict with FDA regulations because Congress gave the FDA the authority to police food operations when it passed the Federal Food, Drug and Cosmetic Act (as amended in 1979).

For the purpose of getting a feel for this act and for the authority of FDA, three important sections of the act will be considered: food standards, adulteration, and misbranding.

> Sec. 401 (341). Whenever in the judgment of the Secretary such action will promote honest and fair dealing in the interest of consumers, he shall promulgate regulations fixing and establishing for any food, under its common or usual name so far as practicable, a reasonable definition and standard of identity, a reasonable standard of quality, and/or reasonable standards of fill of container . . .

The act goes on listing certain exceptions. Under this section of the act, the FDA can require special names for protein ingredients in labeling and, in the case of standard foods, it can tell the processor what can and cannot be used as an ingredient. In many cases, the law has restrictions on amounts as well.

Standard of Identity

The act gives the FDA the authority to "promulgate regulations" and publish *Standards of Identities* on various food products. These standards are covered in the *Code of Federal Regulations* (9 *CFR*, parts 130 to 169). Later chapters will refer to a number of the Standards of Identity as they apply to the subject covered.

Common or Usual Name for Nonstandard Foods

There is another part in sec. (401) of the act that gives the FDA the authority to establish Common or Usual Name for Nonstandard Foods. This regulation (9 *CFR*, part 102) differs from the Standard of Identity regulation (9 *CFR*, part 130) in that it does not set a compositional standard. Instead, "It simply provides nomenclature that identifies a similar group of foods and describes their material characteristics." In the case of a food that is formulated to simulate another food, the FDA has a provision that, if the formulated food product is equal nutritionally to the simulated food, the formulated product does not need to be labeled as "imitation." However, if it is nutritionally inferior, then it must be labeled as an "imitation" product.

The FDA published a "Tentative Final Regulation" entitled, Common or Usual Names for Vegetable Protein Products and Substitutes for Meat, Seafood, Poultry, Eggs, or Cheeses Which Contain Vegetable Protein Products as Sources of Protein (*FR* 1978). Most of the provisions covered in this tentative regulation would affect much of what is covered in this text. As of the end of 1988, the FDA has not finalized this regulation. On the other hand, the FDA does use it as a guideline in answering inquiries about labeling.

One aspect of the regulation that manufacturers of protein products follow is in the naming of their products. Rather than a quote of the regulation, a brief description of the pertinent parts will be given.

If a product has less than 65 percent protein content on a moisture-free basis, the product must be named with the generic name plus the word *flour* or *granules*, as the case might be. Whether it is a flour or granular product is determined by particle size. Examples are soy flour, peanut flour, and cottonseed flour; soy granules or peanut granules. The trade rarely uses the word "granules" in the generic names. Instead, they refer to these products as grits, such as soy grits.

If the product has more than 65 percent but less than 90 percent protein on a moisture-free basis (mfb), it can be called a _____ protein concentrate. The blank can be filled in with the generic name.

If the product contains 90 percent protein or more (mfb), it can be called a _____ protein isolate or an isolated _____ protein.

When products are textured from one of the above products, the word *textured* should precede the product name, for example, textured soy flour and textured peanut protein concentrate.

Adulteration

The second section of the Federal Food, Drug and Cosmetic Act is concerned with adulterated food, which is covered under sec. 402 (342).

A food shall be deemed to be adulterated—

(a) (1) If it bears or contains any poisonous or deleterious substance which may render it injurious to health. . . .

(3) if it consists in whole or in part of any filthy, putrid, or decomposed substance, or if it is otherwise unfit for food; or (4) if it has been prepared, packed, or held under insanitary conditions whereby it may have become contaminated with filth, or whereby it may have been rendered injurious to health; or (5) if it is in whole or in part, the product of a diseased animal or of an animal which died otherwise than by slaughter; or (6) if its container is composed, in whole or in part, of any poisonous or deleterious substance which may render the contents injurious to health. . . .

(b) (1) If any valuable constituent has been in whole or in part omitted or abstracted therefrom; or (2) if any substance has been substituted wholly or in part therefor; or (3) if damage or inferiority has been concealed in any manner; or (4) if any substance has been added thereto or mixed or packed therewith so as to increase its bulk or weight, or reduce its quality or strength, or make it appear better or of greater value than it is.

(c) If it is, or it bears or contains, a color additive which is unsafe within the meaning of section 706(a).

From the foodservice viewpoint, product adulteration can be considered as:

- A threat to health
- A dilution of a product in one or more ways
- A removal of valuable constituents
- An aesthetically unfit practice

There are four broad categories for adulterants, which are shown in the following list (Rakosky 1982).

Disease-producing organisms
    Bacteria, yeasts, molds, protozoa, and parasites
Chemicals
    Poisons, dyes, sprays, paints, greases, oil, and so on
Objects
    Glass, sand, nails, wood, and so on
Filth
    Any foul, obnoxious material waste, or dirt

If dilution of a product is performed with the intention of defrauding the consumer through the use of water, a bulking agent, or some other diluting material, the act states that the food product is adulterated. Thus, adding water to milk and selling it as whole milk is a violation because the product is considered adulterated. This is considered an infraction of the law under the section of the act covered by misbranding.

If a valuable constituent is removed from a product without informing the consumer, it also is a violation of the act. However, this does not mean that a product is adulterated if, for example, a vitamin is destroyed when that product is processed. Again looking at milk, if a portion of the butterfat is removed and the milk is sold as whole milk, the act is violated. The milk is considered adulterated unless, of course, the product is properly labeled as to its fat content; however, it cannot be called whole milk.

According to the act, a product is considered to be adulterated if the food is aesthetically unfit as a food. This would occur if the food were allowed to decompose or spoil to some degree and then further processed as an edible product. The thought here is that the bacteria are destroyed by the heat involved and therefore the food should be safe. It may or may not be safe. As far as the law is concerned, the product is adulterated. Keep in mind that the toxin produced by the organism responsible for staph poisoning is thermostable, that is, the toxin can still cause problems even though the organisms are killed by heat. This is just one reason why the FDA does not permit a food operation to function in an insanitary manner, even though the food is later cooked. A good thing to remember is that "garbage sterilized does not make it edible."

In reading section 402 of the act, it can be seen that *the FDA need not prove that a product is, in fact, adulterated. All the inspector needs to do is to show that adulteration is possible under the conditions observed.*

Misbranding

The proper branding or labeling of foods is the third responsibility that the Federal Food, Drug and Cosmetic Act gives to the FDA. This comes under the heading "Misbranded Food."

> Sec. 403 [343]. A food shall be deemed to be misbranded—
> (a) If (1) its labeling is false or misleading in any particular, or (2) in the case of a food to which section 411 (Footnote—) applies its advertising, is false or misleading in a material respect or its labeling is in violation of sec. 411(b)(2).
> (b) If it is offered for sale under the name of another food.
> (c) If it is an imitation of another food, unless its label bears, in type of uniform size and prominence, the word "imitation" and, immediately thereafter, the name of the food imitated.
> (d) If its container is so made, formed, or filled as to be misleading.
> (e) If in package form unless it bears a label containing (1) the name and place of business of the manufacturer, packer, or distributor; and (2) an accurate statement of the quantity of the contents in terms of weight, measure, or numerical count. . . .

There is much more to this section of the act, but the above quote should be enough to see how much authority the FDA has in controlling the misbranding of a food product.

The U.S. Department of Agriculture (USDA)

The are three agencies in the U.S. Department of Agriculture (USDA) that may become involved in foodservice operations in one way or another: the Agricultural Marketing Service, the Food and Nutrition Service, and the Food Safety and Inspection Service.

The Agricultural Marketing Service (AMS)

The Agricultural Marketing Service administers broad standardization, grading, voluntary and mandatory inspection services, market news, regulatory services, and related programs. In one aspect of its work, the AMS is responsible for underwriting the quality of much of the nation's food supply. In doing this, they most often work in food plants where grading is required.

In many instances, certain institutions contract for a food preparation that conforms to specifications. They may also require that an inspector from the AMS be present in the food plant to make sure the product meets those specifications. Obviously, the added cost for this service is borne by the institution.

This type of service is often required by some schools when they place orders for food preparations to be used in their school lunch programs.

The Food and Nutrition Service (FNS)

The Food and Nutrition Service administers the food-assistance programs with state and local cooperation. These include the Food Stamp Program, the Child Nutrition Program, and the Food Distribution Program. Of importance here is the Child Nutrition Program, including school lunch, as a foodservice operation. Although many schools operate their own kitchens, many are turning to outside foodservice companies for help, either to administer the program or to supply the schools with meals.

When selling food products to schools under these programs, suppliers must obtain prior approval from the FNS to be placed on an approved list. This is necessary for the government to make sure that the foods in question will supply the nutrients required in the specifications. Making sure that the food meets FNS specifications is a necessity for the school to qualify for matching funds.

The Food Safety and Inspection Service (FSIS)

The Food Safety and Inspection Service was established in 1981. Over the years, it has been known by various names, but its responsibilities have remained essentially the same. Before 1981 it was known as the Food Safety and Quality Service (FSQS), and before 1977 it was known first as the Meat Inspection Department (MID) and then as the Animal and Plant Health Inspection Service (APHIS).

The FSIS is responsible for the wholesomeness, safety, and proper labeling of meat and poultry products. It achieves this by actual in-plant inspections and by monitoring all distribution channels in an effort to prevent violations of the laws and to test the products for adulteration or the presence of unsafe drugs and chemical residues. In carrying out its responsibilities, the agency works with state departments of agriculture, the FDA, and other governmental agencies when necessary.

Under the Federal Meat Inspection Act and the Poultry Products Inspection Act, the FSIS inspects all meat and poultry shipped interstate and through foreign commerce for use as human food. Included are processed products such as sausages, frozen dinners, canned meats, and soups made with meat and poultry, as well as raw meat and poultry. Generally, the FSIS regulates all food items that contain more than 2 percent poultry and/or 3 percent meat products. For items containing less than these amounts, regulation is controlled by the FDA.

Some states conduct their own meat and poultry inspection programs. The 1967 Wholesome Meat Act and the 1968 Wholesome Poultry Product Act require these programs to be at least "equal to" the federal inspection program. Only meat and poultry sold intrastate may be inspected in a state program. If states cannot maintain standards equal to federal inspection requirements, the Meat and Poultry Inspection Program must assume responsibility for intrastate inspection.

Of special interest is that, unlike with the FDA, prior approval from the FSIS must be obtained before meat or poultry processing can begin. This means that plans for the processing plant must be submitted for approval and when the plant is completed it must be inspected to see if it and its equipment conform to FSIS requirements.

Prior approval is also required for all labels. Not only must the label contain specific information but also the name of the product must be appropriate. When establishing these requirements, the agency is concerned about consumer misinformation. There are standards of identity for most processed meat products. Those that do not meet these standards are most often referred to as nonstandard products. Hamburger and beef pattie are examples of standard items whereas meat pattie is an example of a nonstandard item.

The FSIS also requires prior approval of all ingredients that will be used in meat products, and, in most cases, it sets limits on their use. Thus, if a product is not approved, it cannot be used in meat and poultry products. Because of this requirement, there are limitations in the use of protein additives. These restrictions will be discussed in Chapter 7, "Processed Meats."

The label-approval process requires that the formulations and the method of processing be disclosed to the FSIS to be certain that the label is appropriate. Data accumulated from approved labels, with regard to the ingredients and their amounts and to the processing methods, are used to help establish standards for meat content as well as additive, fat, and moisture limits.

THE *FEDERAL REGISTER* AND THE *CODE OF FEDERAL REGULATIONS*

As was just discussed, there are two major federal agencies that regulate food products and their manufacture, distribution, and sometimes sales. Laws and policy decisions are often changed and/or revised, making it difficult for food processors to keep abreast. Most often this information is distributed in announcements in a trade association newsletter, by word of mouth, or, if he or she is on the premises, through a local inspector. However, there is an official channel used to keep everyone up to date. The federal government makes public announcements of any changes in the law or in policy interpretations in a publication called the *Federal Register*.

The *Federal Register (FR)* is published every weekday except Saturdays, Sundays, and legal holidays. To subscribe to the *FR*, contact the Superintendent of Documents, U.S. Government Printing Office, Washington, D.C. 20402.

The government uses the *FR* to publish not only new regulations and legal notices but also presidential proclamations, executive orders, and any other notices that the agencies wish to make public. References to such notices appear in one of several ways. References can be cited by date and page number or by volume and page number. An example is the following published notice: "National School Lunch Program; Special Food Service Programs for Children—Appendix A; Alternate Foods for Meals." The specific citation could be *Federal Register*, April 12, 1973, page 9234; it could also be referred to as 38 *FR* 9234 or *FR* 38:9234.

There is a second publication called the *Code of Federal Regulations*, or, as it is more commonly known, the *CFR*. The *CFR* is a set of books numbered from 1 through 50. Instead of being called volumes, they are designated as *Titles*. Each governmental agency is referred to by a particular title number; for example, meat regulations come under *Title 9—Animal and Animal Products*, and the FDA regulations come under *Title 21—Food and Drugs*. As changes are made in the regulations, they are announced in the *Federal Register*. In many cases, proposed changes are also announced in the *FR*, thereby giving an individual, a company, or any interested group a chance to comment on the proposal before it is made official. Once the regulation becomes official, it becomes a part of a particular *CFR*, which is updated each year. Therefore, a person can keep up to date by purchasing a *CFR* of interest each year rather than by subscribing to the *Federal Register*, which can become quite voluminous. However, there are companies that subscribe to the *FR* because it is in their best interest to keep abreast of changes in the law. Most suppliers of protein additives have one or more individuals on their staff who read the *FR* on a regular basis and are in a position to help their customers if certain information is needed. Keep this fact in mind: Not only will a supplier help a customer or potential customer in giving helpful information on the utilization of a product, but also it is in a position to give up-to-date information on pertinent regulations.

Since references by number are often made to specific regulations, it is necessary to understand a few points. Certain reference numbers pertaining to the Federal Food, Drug and Cosmetic Act (as amended 1972) were used earlier in this chapter, such as sec. 201 (321) and sec. 401(a). When reference is made to certain sections of the *CFR*, reference numbers will again be used; for example, part 136 of 21 *CFR* is concerned with bakery products. Specific regulations under this part are referred to as section 136.110 (bread, rolls, and buns.) A more proper way of referring to the specific section would be 21 *CFR* 136.110, which makes it simple. Unfortunately, many people refer just to the section, and unless a person is familiar with the numbers being used, the neophyte will not know whether the reference is to the act or to the *CFR*. Usually, these references are *CFR* citations.

Another point to be brought out is that the *CFR*s are broken down into chapters. In 21 *CFR*, chapter 1 concerns the Food and Drug Administration. Under the subject of meat products (9 *CFR*), chapter 3 concerns those regulations that come under the jurisdiction of the FSIS. Thus, all reference numbers in the FDA regulations listed under chapter 1 will go from 100 to 199. In the same way, those for meat inspection will be in the 300 series. This system makes regulations much easier to find.

Much of this will become clearer when we cover the regulations in the various applications. A further and more detailed discussion of 9 *CFR* is given in Chapter 7.

PROTEIN SOURCES

Theoretically, it is possible to obtain proteins in rather pure form from almost any plant or animal matter. Whether or not it is practical to obtain proteins from these sources for commercial purposes is another matter. The following list includes a number of potential sources.

Animal
    Animal meal
    Blood
    Connective tissue
    Eggs
    Fish meal
    Milk
    Muscle
Plants
    Leaves
    Microorganisms
    Stems
    Roots
    Seeds
      Cereal
      Germinated
      Legume
      Oilseed

Animal Sources

Of the animal sources, all those listed are being utilized in some way. Animal and fish meals are being used extensively in animal feed products because they are so rich in protein and are relatively inexpensive. The same is true of blood meal, but as is known, blood is also used in some sausages as an ingredient. However, when used for this purpose, the product must be prominently labeled; the word *blood* must be part of the product's name.

Potentially, blood is composed of certain extractable components (fractions) that are quite functional and would have value in certain food systems. Thus far, such fractional products are not being used in foods in the United States.

Connective tissue contains a great deal of collagen, which is converted into gelatin by a series of hot water extractions.

Eggs are composed of two main components that are most often dried into shelf-stable products, which are also used as food ingredients. These products are dried egg white and egg yolk solids.

Milk is a complex mixture of several proteins as well as a number of other important components. The solids content of milk is composed of three main fractions: proteins, milk sugar or lactose, and butterfat. Of importance from the nutritional aspect, milk is a good source of calcium, vitamins, and minerals.

The protein portion of milk is in reality composed of several different types of protein: about four-fifths is casein, a little under one-fifth is lactalbumin, and the rest is minor proteins and enzymes. Be aware that both casein and lactalbumin proteins are composed of still other fractions. For a more complete breakdown of these fractions, please refer to the National Dairy Council's *Newer Knowledge of Milk and Other Fluid Dairy Products* (1979).

The chief protein products obtained from milk that are used as protein ingredients are dried whole milk, nonfat dry milk, whey protein concentrate, and dried buttermilk, as well as variations of these fractions. These products may be obtained as secondary ones from a particular process. A good example of this is the whey obtained in making cheeses.

Muscle as a source of protein is of value in certain food preparations, particularly in processed meat products. In this application, extraction and processing of the food product take place at the same time, that is, there is no isolation of the extracted protein. The sausage process is a good example of this.

Vegetable Sources

Included in vegetable sources are the various parts of plants, such as leaves, stems, roots, fruits, and seeds. Of these parts, seeds are the richest sources for proteins, fats, and carbohydrates. This is nature's way of concentrating nutrients for use when the seed germinates. Some seeds are very rich in protein, some in fat and others in carbohydrates. Oilseeds are often good sources of both oil and protein.

Proteins from microorganisms are also referred to as *single-celled protein* (SCP). One SCP product is yeast powder or yeast extract.

It is interesting to note a historical fact brought out by Satterlee (1981). During World War II blockades, both Germany and England were concerned about their protein supplies being cut off. As a result, both countries searched for ways to supplant their protein supply. "Germany chose yeast which could readily be produced via fermentations, while Britain chose leafy green plants as a protein resource to meet food and feed needs" (Satterlee 1981, p. 54).

COMMERCIALLY AVAILABLE PROTEINS

Animal Proteins

Milk

Dried milk protein products are abundant and widely used as food protein additives. These products are both functional and nutritious. Because of a U.S. price-support program for nonfat dry milk, some of these products are prohibitive in cost for some applications. Despite this handicap, they are still being used to a great extent.

In contrast, whey products, which are byproducts of cheese processing, are more attractive in price. In an effort to increase the protein content, processors use some elaborate processing methods to reduce the milk sugar content. This consequently increases costs somewhat.

Because of the prohibitive price of nonfat dry milk and the added processing costs, practically all the casein products available in this country are imported.

Gelatin

Gelatin is the protein obtained from white fibrous connective tissue from animals. "White connective tissue is the basis of the protective and structural organs of the mammalian body and the constituent collagen comprises about 60% of the total body protein. Bone, pork skins, hide splits and trimmings are the only raw materials from which gelatin is prepared" (Tourtellote 1974, p. 476).

Table 1-2 gives the typical composition of several animal protein products, including gelatin. It needs to be pointed out that gelatin is devoid of the essential amino acid tryptophane, and therefore it is not a complete protein. Because of this, it has a negative PER. Nevertheless, gelatin does have nutritional value, especially when combined with other proteins.

From the functional standpoint, gelatin has a number of properties that have value in food systems besides the well-known gelation property seen in gelatin desserts.

Egg Products

There are basically three types of dried egg products: whole, white, and yolk solids. These products are available in several different forms. The form needed depends on the way the product is to be used in various applications. For more about the preparation of eggs and egg products, refer to Bergquist (1974).

Table 1-2   Typical Composition of Some Common Dry Animal Protein Products

Product	Moisture (%)	Protein (%)	Fat (%)	Carbohydrate (%)	Crude Fiber (%)	Ash (%)
Milk products						
Whole milk[1]	2.47	26.32	26.71	38.42	0	6.08
Nonfat milk						
Regular[1]	3.16	36.16	0.77	51.98	0	7.93
Instantized[1]	3.96	35.10	0.72	52.19	0	8.03
Calcium-reduced[1]	4.90	35.50	0.20	51.80	0	7.60
Buttermilk, sweet cream[1]	2.97	34.30	5.78	49.00	0	7.95
Whey protein concentrate[2]	5.0	25–80	1–10	<60	—	2–15
Casein[2]	7.0	88	1	—	—	4
Caseinate[2]	3–5	90–94	0.7–1.0	—	—	6–7
Egg products						
Whole[1]	4.14	45.83	41.81	4.77	0	3.45
Stabilized (glucose reduced)						
Whole[1]	1.87	48.17	43.95	2.38	0	3.63
White, flakes[1]	14.62	76.92	0.04	4.17	0	4.25
White, powder[1]	8.54	82.40	0.04	4.47	0	4.55
Yolk[1]	4.65	30.52	61.28	0.39	0	3.16
Fish protein concentrate						
Whole fish[3]	2.0	78.0	0.3	0	—	19.7
Fillets[3]	3.0	93.0	0.1	0	0	3.9
Fillet wastes[3]	3.0	71.0	0.2	0	0	25.8
Gelatin[3]	13.0	85.6	0.1	0	0	1.3

[1] USDA/ARS 1976.
[2] Hugunin 1982.
[3] USDA/ARS 1963.

Fish Protein Concentrate (FPC)

FPC is essentially a fish meal product, except that great care is taken in making the product for human consumption, which is not the case for animal feeds. First, the product is manufactured under good sanitary conditions. Second, an effort is made to make the product more aesthetically attractive, that is, to remove the head, interior organs, and other undesirable parts. And third, much of the bone material is removed to avoid the problem of a high fluorine content.

The processing method used to obtain FPC is essentially an extraction in which water and lipids are removed. After extraction, the solvent (usually isopropyl alcohol) is removed and the residue is processed further into a dry, light-brown, flour-type product. Although the process is such that it is not very

Table 1-3 Typical Composition of Some Common
Dry Vegetable Protein Products

Product	Moisture (%)	Protein (%)	Fat (%)	Carbohydrate (%)	Crude Fiber (%)	Ash (%)
Cereal Products						
Wheat gluten (vital)[1]	6.0	75–80	1.0	—	—	1.0
Wheat germ meal or flour[2]	7.7	36	0.1	48.3	2.5	5.4
Wheat gluten meal or flour[2]	6.5	79	1.0	11.5	1.0	1.0
Corn germ isolate[3]	—	73	—	3	0.08	4.3
Legumes						
Pea flour[4]	0	50.4	3.5	37.2	3.8	5.1
Pea protein concentrate (from curd)[5]	0	81.4	3.7	9.3	0.3	4.6
Oilseeds						
Cottonseed flour (liquid cyclone process)[6]	2.7	64.2	0.4	23.0	2.2	7.4
Peanut						
Flour (defatted)[6]	8.6	68.6	0.6	13.1	3.8	5.3
Flakes (full-fat)[7]	1.8	29.4	51.7	11.3	—	2.4
Flakes (partially defatted)[7]	3.5	41.0	30.7	17.1	—	3.3
Flakes (defatted)[7]	6.9	58.7	0.2	22.7	—	4.7
Soybean						
Enzyme active flour[8]	8.0	52.0	1.0	30.0	3.0	6.0
Soy flour and grits[8]	8.0	52.0	1.0	30.0	3.0	6.0
Natural full-fat[9]	3.4	41.0	22.5	26.3	1.7	5.1
Refatted soy flour						
Low fat[2]	6.0	50.0	6.0	29.8	2.5	5.7
High fat[8]	6	44	16	26.5	2.5	5
Lecithinated soy flour[2]	6.0	45.0	16	25.3	2.5	5.2
Soy protein concentrate[2]	4.9	67.6	0.3	18.8	2.6	4.8
Soy protein isolate[8]	5.0	91.5	0.5	2.5	0.5	4.5
Textured products	(Composition essentially same as parent material)					
Torula yeast[5]	6.0	45.0	7.0	29.0	5.0	8.0

[1] Sales literature 1981.
[2] J. Rakosky files (unpublished and published material).
[3] Neilsen et al. 1973.
[4] Sumner et al. 1981.
[5] Gebre-Egziabmer and Sumner 1983.
[6] Wadsworth et al. 1979.
[7] *Food Processing*, "Peanut Flakes," 1976.
[8] Sales literature 1981.
[9] *Soy Protein Fact Sheet* 1971.

functional, it is a highly nutritious product from the protein-quality stand-point.

Table 1-2 shows the composition of several types of FPC. Of particular note is the ash content. The high ash content is a good indicator for the presence of much bone material; thus, the calcium content should be relatively high.

Vegetable Proteins

Theoretically, it is possible to obtain protein products from any number of vegetable products, including alfalfa, cereal grains, legumes, and oilseeds. Whether or not products are obtained from these sources depends on a number of factors, such as practicality, cost, availability, inherent problems, nutritional value, and functional value. The overall determining factor is the amount of protein at an attractive cost; desirable properties and compatibility in form, color, and taste.

The technical literature is rich in reports of work done in obtaining protein products from the various vegetable sources. There are a number of potentially valuable sources if only certain undesirable properties were eliminated. Of particular note is sunflower meal and the protein products obtained from it.

As Satterlee (1981) pointed out, when sunflower flour is used with other foods, it can impart a yellow-green color depending on the pH. This certainly is not a desirable characteristic. This defect should be eliminated eventually.

From the practical standpoint, it is difficult to compete with the various soy protein products from the aspect of availability, nutrition, functionality, and cost. Unfortunately, with soy flours there is the problem of a "beany flavor" that limits the level of use and/or causes the processor to consider one or more of the upgraded products, which adds to the cost.

The functional properties of wheat gluten, which other products cannot du-plicate, give it a unique place among the various protein products. In all like-lihood, it will continue to have this particular advantage.

With single-celled proteins, preparations from yeast maintain a unique po-sition because there is little if any competition from other single-cell sources. Yeast preparations are used not only as protein products but also as flavoring ingredients. One of the problems concerning nutritionists is the relatively high nucleic acid content of SCP. This is of importance to those individuals who need to be on a low-purine diet. (Purine is a constituent of nucleic acid.) Many processors are using procedures to greatly reduce the nucleic acid content of their products.

Table 1-3 shows the typical compositions of the more common vegetable protein products.

Note that, in most cases, the textured products will have the same analytical composition as the parent substance, especially if additives are not used in its processing. About the only expected variation is a change in the moisture content.

REFERENCES

Berquist, D. H. 1974. "Eggs and Egg Products." In *Encyclopedia of Food Technology,* ed. A. H. Johnson and M. S. Peterson, 351–61. Westport, Conn.: AVI Publishing.

Bookwalter, G. N., G. C. Mustakas, W. F. Kwolek, J. E. McGhee, and W. J. Albrecht. 1971. "Full-Fat Soy Flour Extrusion Cooked; Properties and Uses." *J. Food Sci.* 36:5–9.

Code of Federal Regulations. 1984a. *Title 9. Animal and Animal Products,* chapters I–IV. Washington, D.C.: U.S. Government Printing Office.

———. 1984b. *Title 21. Food and Drugs. Parts 100–169 and 170–199,* 2 vols. Washington, D.C.: U.S. Government Printing Office.

Ellis, R. F. 1985. "Forecast $191 Billion in Sales for Foodservice Industry in 1985." *Food Proc.* 46 (Aug.):39–40.

Federal Food, Drug and Cosmetic Act. As amended 1979. USDHEW/FDA 79-1051. Washington, D.C.: U.S. Government Printing Office.

Federal Register. 1978. "Tentative Final Regulations (FDA)." *Fed. Reg.* 43:30472–91.

Food Processing. 1976. "Peanut Flakes—Duplicate Texture/Taste of Egg, Meat and Dairy Products." *Food Proc.* 37 (Jan.):42–3.

Gebre-Egziabmer, A. and A. K. Sumner. 1983. "Preparation of High Protein Curd from Field Peas." *J. Food Sci.* 48:375–88.

Hugunin, A. G. 1982. "Dairy-Based Ingredients and Their Use as Alternatives to Traditional Sweeteners in Formulated Foods." In *Chemistry of Foods and Beverages: Recent Developments,* ed. George Charalambous and George Inglett, 235–49. New York: Academic Press.

Neilsen, H. C., G. E. Inglett, J. S. Wall, and G. L. Donaldson. 1973. "Corn Germ Isolate—Preliminary Studies on Preparation and Properties." *Cereal Chem.* 50:435–43.

Newer Knowledge of Milk and Other Fluid Dairy Products. B300-2. 1979. Rosemont, Ill.: National Dairy Council.

Pour-El, A. 1981. Protein-functionality: Classification, definition and methodology. In *Protein Functionality in Foods,* ed. John P. Cherry, 1–19. ACS Symposium Series 147. American Chemical Society, Washington, D.C.

Rakosky, J. 1982. *A Common Sense Guide to Food Plant Sanitation—Why Have a Sanitation Program?* Morton Grove, Ill.: J. Rakosky Services.

Sales literature. 1981. Decatur, Ill.: ADM Foods.

Satterlee, L. D. 1981. "Proteins for Use in Foods." *Food Tech.* 35 (6):53–70.

Soy Protein Fact Sheet. 1971. Chicago (now Fort Wayne, Ind.): Chemurgy Div., Central Soya Co.

Sumner, A. K., M. A. Neilsen, and C. G. Young. 1981. "Production and Evaluation of Pea Protein Isolate." *J. Food Sci.* 46:364–66, 372.

Tourtellote, D. 1974. "Gelatin." In *Encyclopedia of Food Technology*, ed. A. H. Johnson and M. S. Peterson, 476–78. Westport, Conn.: AVI Publishing.

USDA/ARS. 1963. *Composition of Foods, Agricultural Handbook No. 8*. Washington, D.C.: U.S. Government Printing Office.

————. 1976. *Composition of Foods—Dairy and Egg Products—Raw—Processed— Prepared. Agricultural Handbook No. 8-1*. Washington, D.C.: U.S. Government Printing Office.

Wadsworth, J. I., R. E. Hayes, and J. J. Spadaro. 1979. "Optimum Protein Quality Food Blends." *Cereal Food World* 24:274–86.

CHAPTER 2
Proteins, Amino Acids, and Derivatives

All living matter is composed of water, organic compounds, and inorganic compounds. The latter, usually minerals (except for bone), are present in minor amounts. Other than water, organic compounds are present in major amounts. Organic compounds are unique because their basic structures are composed of chains and/or rings of carbon-to-carbon links, or skeletons, to which other elements are attached. The prevalent attached element is hydrogen, followed by oxygen and nitrogen. Sulfur and phosphorus also play significant parts, as do some of the trace elements.

The predominant organic compounds found in living organisms are *proteins, fats,* and *carbohydrates*. Fats and carbohydrates are composed essentially of just carbon, hydrogen, and oxygen. A characteristic difference between the two is that fats are soluble in solvents such as petroleum, ether, and hexane; carbohydrates are not. Also, based on oxygen content, carbohydrates contain a higher percentage of oxygen. Proteins, too, are composed essentially of carbon, hydrogen, and oxygen, but in addition they contain a major amount of nitrogen, about 16 percent. They also contain a small amount of sulfur, which plays a significant role. Since the chief concern in this text is with protein products, remarks will be confined primarily to this class of organic compound.

The word *protein* means "first" or "primary" substance/compound. Proteins are considered primary because they are common to all living cells, in one or more forms, as vital constituents. Proteins are complex nitrogenous compounds that have large molecular weights, ranging from about 5,500 for insulin to as high as 40,000,000 for some of the more complex proteins, such as tobacco mosaic virus.

It is interesting to note that there are as many different proteins as there are species of plants and animals; even within an organism itself, there are many different proteins. The question is, How is it possible that there can be so many different types? The answer lies in the fact that proteins are made up of individual units called *amino acids*. There are some 20 different common amino acids that are linked together, in various combinations, as *polymers,* which are giant molecules formed by the linkages of many molecules. These polymeric chains can be of varying lengths with varying combinations of amino acids, resulting in an astronomical number of proteins.

Our present interest in proteins is their use as functional, nutritional, and cost-effective additives in foods. Since their particular characteristics can be quite different, making a choice for their use in some food systems can be difficult. Fortunately, there are not many proteins that are commercially available, as we saw in Chapter 1; hence, their selection is not as difficult as it may seem.

To appreciate the various protein additives and to better understand their properties, we need to look at them in some detail.

AMINO ACIDS

Amino acids are organic compounds of varying complexity that are composed of two reactive groups, an *amino group* ($-NH^2$) and a *carboxyl, or acid, group* ($-COOH$); hence the name amino acid. There are 20 amino acids that occur most often in proteins. These are of the *alpha* type; that is, the amino group is attached to the alpha (first) carbon atom next to the carboxyl group. For the most part, the various amino acids differ from one another by the chemical radical that is also attached to the alpha carbon. To help us understand the structures of amino acids and how they differ from one another, we will refer to this side group as "R." Thus, the model amino acid should look like the following structure:

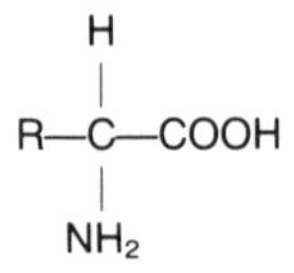

$$
\begin{array}{c}
H \\
| \\
R-C-COOH \\
| \\
NH_2
\end{array}
$$

Depending on of what the "R" group consists, each amino acid has a specific name. The "R" group can range from a simple hydrogen atom to a more complex organic radical. In hydrogen, the amino acid formed is called *glycine*. When the side group is a methyl group, the acid is *alanine*. Tables 2-1, 2-2, and 2-3 give

Table 2-1   Amino Acids with Nonpolar R Groups

Name	R Groups

Model Amino Acid

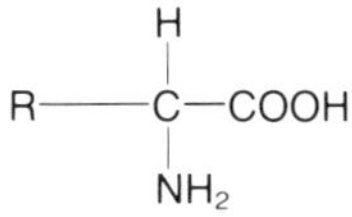

$$R-\overset{\overset{H}{|}}{\underset{\underset{NH_2}{|}}{C}}-COOH$$

Amino Acids with Nonpolar R Groups at pH 6.0 to 7.0
(Shown in the Ionized Forms.)

Alanine

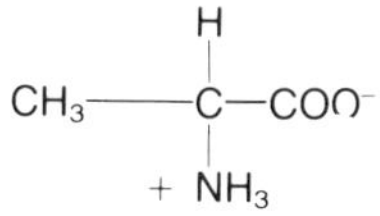

$$CH_3-\overset{\overset{H}{|}}{\underset{\underset{+\ NH_3}{|}}{C}}-COO^-$$

Valine

$$\overset{CH_3}{\underset{CH_3}{\overset{|}{CH}}}-\overset{\overset{H}{|}}{\underset{\underset{+\ NH_3}{|}}{C}}-COO^-$$

Leucine

$$\overset{CH_3}{\underset{CH_3}{\overset{|}{CH}}}-CH_2-\overset{\overset{H}{|}}{\underset{\underset{+\ NH_3}{|}}{C}}-COO^-$$

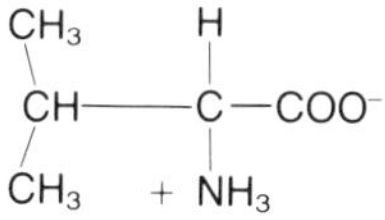

Isoleucine

$$CH_3-CH_2-\underset{\underset{CH_3}{|}}{CH}-\overset{\overset{H}{|}}{\underset{\underset{+\ NH_3}{|}}{C}}-COO^-$$

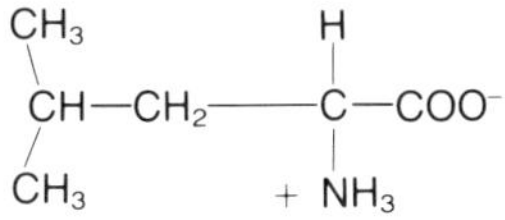

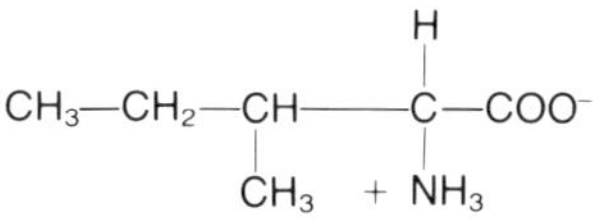

Proline

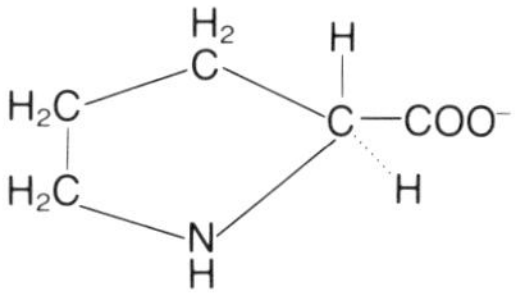

Phenylalanine

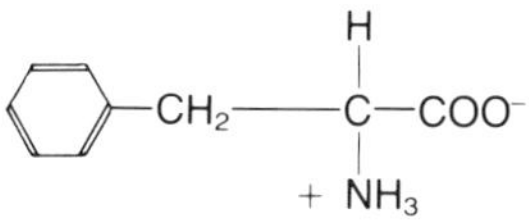

$$\langle \ \rangle-CH_2-\overset{\overset{H}{|}}{\underset{\underset{+\ NH_3}{|}}{C}}-COO^-$$

Tryptophane

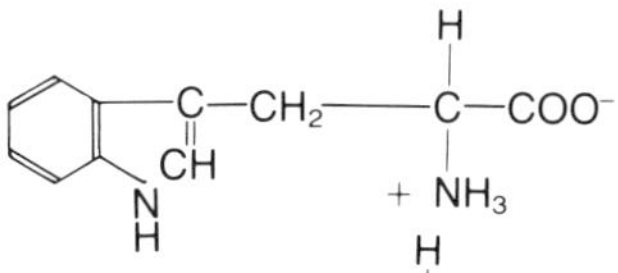

Methionine

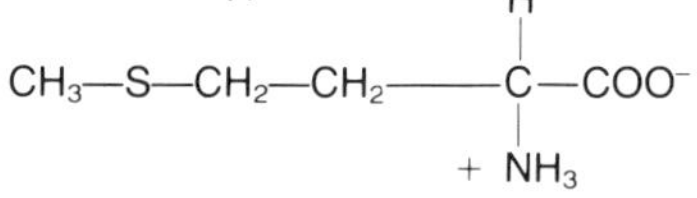

$$CH_3-S-CH_2-CH_2-\overset{\overset{H}{|}}{\underset{\underset{+\ NH_3}{|}}{C}}-COO^-$$

Source: Adapted from Lehninger 1975.

Table 2-2 Amino Acids with Uncharged Polar R Groups

Glycine

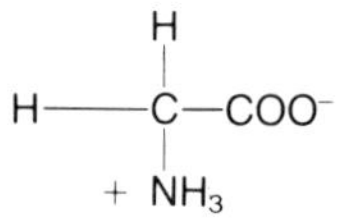

$$H\text{———}\underset{\overset{|}{+NH_3}}{\overset{\overset{H}{|}}{C}}\text{—COO}^-$$

Serine

$$HO\text{—}CH_2\text{———}\underset{\overset{|}{+NH_3}}{\overset{\overset{H}{|}}{C}}\text{—COO}^-$$

Threonine

$$CH_3\text{—}\underset{\overset{|}{H}}{\overset{\overset{OH}{|}}{C}}\text{———}\underset{\overset{|}{+NH_3}}{\overset{\overset{H}{|}}{C}}\text{—COO}^-$$

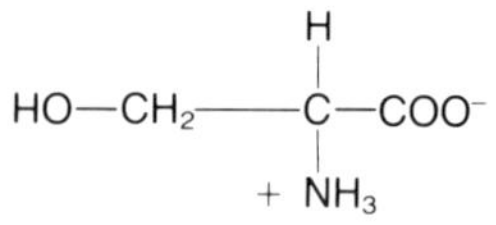

Cystine

$$HS\text{—}CH_2\text{———}\underset{\overset{|}{+NH_3}}{\overset{\overset{H}{|}}{C}}\text{—COO}^-$$

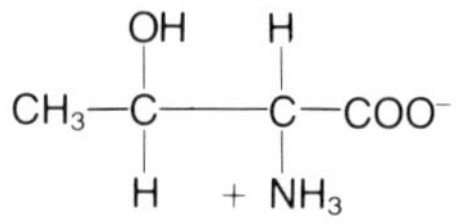

Tyrosine

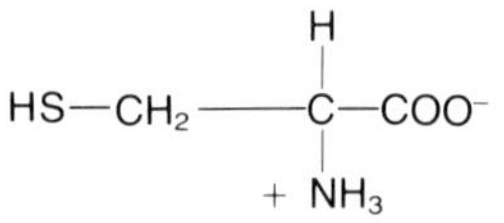

$$HO\text{—}\langle\!\!\bigcirc\!\!\rangle\text{—}CH_2\text{———}\underset{\overset{|}{+NH_3}}{\overset{\overset{H}{|}}{C}}\text{—COO}^-$$

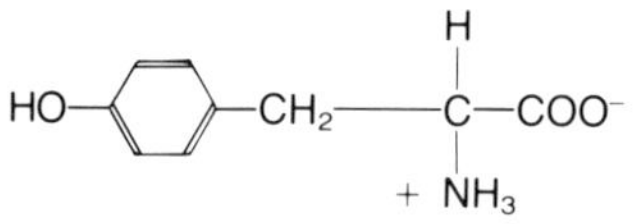

Asparagine

$$\underset{O}{\overset{NH_2}{\underset{\parallel}{C}}}\text{—}CH_2\text{———}\underset{\overset{|}{+NH_3}}{\overset{\overset{H}{|}}{C}}\text{—COO}^-$$

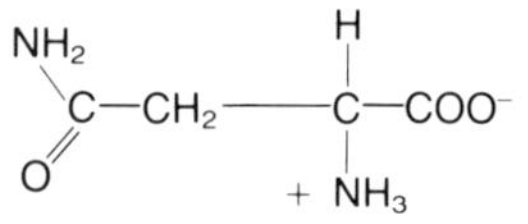

Glutamine

$$\underset{O}{\overset{HN_2}{\underset{\parallel}{C}}}\text{—}CH_2\text{—}CH_2\text{———}\underset{\overset{|}{+NH_3}}{\overset{\overset{H}{|}}{C}}\text{—COO}^-$$

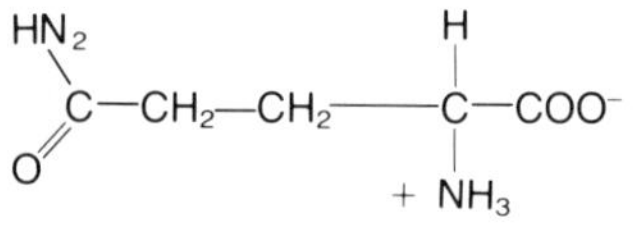

Source: Adapted from Lehninger 1975.

Table 2-3   Amino Acids with Charged Polar Groups at pH 6.0 to 7.0

Acidic Amino Acids (Negatively Charged at pH 6.0)

Aspartic acid

$$
\begin{array}{c}
{}^-O \\
\diagdown \\
C-CH_2\text{------}\overset{\displaystyle H}{\underset{\displaystyle +NH_3}{\overset{|}{\underset{|}{C}}}}-COO^- \\
\diagup \\
O
\end{array}
$$

Glutamic acid

$$
\begin{array}{c}
{}^-O \\
\diagdown \\
C-CH_2-CH_2\text{------}\overset{\displaystyle H}{\underset{\displaystyle +NH_3}{\overset{|}{\underset{|}{C}}}}-COO^- \\
\diagup \\
O
\end{array}
$$

Basic Amino Acids (Positively Charged at pH 6.0)

Lysine

$$
H_3N^+\text{---}CH_2\text{---}CH_2\text{---}CH_2\text{---}CH_2\text{------}\overset{\displaystyle H}{\underset{\displaystyle +NH_3}{\overset{|}{\underset{|}{C}}}}-COO^-
$$

Arginine

$$
H_2N\text{---}\overset{\displaystyle }{\underset{\displaystyle +NH_2}{\overset{\parallel}{\underset{}{C}}}}\text{---}NH\text{---}CH_2\text{---}CH_2\text{---}CH_2\text{------}\overset{\displaystyle H}{\underset{\displaystyle +NH_3}{\overset{|}{\underset{|}{C}}}}-COO^-
$$

Histidine

$$
\begin{array}{c}
HC\!=\!C\text{---}CH_2\text{------}\overset{\displaystyle H}{\underset{\displaystyle +NH_3}{\overset{|}{\underset{|}{C}}}}-COO^- \\
\underset{+}{HN}\quad NH \\
\diagdown \quad \diagup \\
C \\
H
\end{array}
$$

Source: Adapted from Lehninger 1975.

the names and show the structures of the 20 alpha amino acids that occur in natural proteins. These tables also categorize the amino acids into four types based on the characteristics of the "R" group: nonpolar, uncharged polar, positively charged polar, and negatively charged polar types.

Attention should be directed to the amino acid proline because its alpha amino configuration is a little different from the others. In this case, a ring is formed with the nitrogen in the alpha position. This is referred to as an *imino group.*

Before considering the way amino acids are linked to form protein molecules, we should look at the way they behave under acid and alkaline conditions. Amino acids have both acidic and basic characteristics due to their amino and carboxyl groups. They are referred to as *amphoteric* compounds, which, besides being acid and basic in character, also are capable of yielding both hydrogen and hydroxyl ions.

At a pH of 2 to 3 (acidic), a hydrogen ion reacts with the amino group, giving it a positive charge:

$$
\begin{array}{c}
H \\
| \\
R-C-COOH \\
| \\
H-N-H \\
\quad | \quad \oplus \\
H
\end{array}
$$

At an alkaline pH of about 10, the charge of the amino acid molecule becomes negative:

$$
\begin{array}{c}
H \\
| \\
R-C-COO^{\ominus} \\
| \\
NH_2
\end{array}
$$

In the intermediate pH range of 4 to 9, the amino acid exists as a dipolar ion, also referred to as a *zwitterion* (having both positive and negative charge):

$$
\begin{array}{c}
H \\
| \\
R-C-COO^{\ominus} \\
| \\
H-N-H \\
\quad | \quad \oplus \\
H
\end{array}
$$

Peptide Bonds

Amino acids are linked through the amino group of one amino acid with the carboxyl group of another by *peptide bonds*. When these bonds form, the hydrogen of the amino group is removed along with the $-OH$ of the carboxyl group to form water:

$$
\underset{\substack{|\\H}}{\overset{\substack{H\;\;R\;\;O\\|\;\;\;|\;\;\;||}}{H-N-C-C}}-OH \;\;\; \underset{\substack{|\\H}}{\overset{\substack{H\;\;\;\;\;R\;\;O\\|\;\;\;\;\;|\;\;\;||}}{H-N\;\;\;\;-C-C}}-OH \rightarrow \;\;\; \underset{\substack{|\\H}}{\overset{\substack{H\;\;R\;\;O\\|\;\;\;|\;\;\;||}}{H-N-C-C}}-\underset{\substack{|\\H}}{\overset{\substack{H\;\;R\;\;O\\|\;\;\;|\;\;\;||}}{N-C-C}}-OH + H_2O
$$

When two amino acids are joined through a peptide bond, the resulting newly formed compound is called a *dipeptide*. A combination of three amino acids linked by peptide bonds is known as a *tripeptide*. Larger chains are referred to as *polypeptides*, which can be depicted by the following general formula:

$$
\underset{\substack{|\\H}}{\overset{\substack{H\;\;R\;\;O\\|\;\;\;|\;\;\;||}}{H-N-C-C}}-\left[\underset{\substack{|\\H}}{\overset{\substack{H\;\;R\;\;O\\|\;\;\;|\;\;\;||}}{N-C-C}}\right]_n \underset{\substack{|\\H}}{\overset{\substack{H\;\;R\;\;O\\|\;\;\;|\;\;\;||}}{-N-C-C}}-OH
$$

If n equals one, the formula is that of a tripeptide. Peptides that have more than one amino acid represented by n most often are referred to as polypeptides.

PROTEIN CHARACTERISTICS

Proteins may be composed of extremely long peptide chains or of any number of chains that may be cross-linked through a *disulfide bond*. With a single polypeptide chain, at what length can we assume that the molecule is a protein rather than a polypeptide? There is no simple answer to this question. As so often is the case in biological classifications, "there are no sharp breaks in nature."

Molecular weights of proteins can range from about 5,500 to 40,000,000. It is of interest to point out that the egg white enzyme called lysozyme is a protein composed of one long polypeptide chain having a molecular weight of 13,800. The hormone insulin is a simple protein composed of two polypeptide chains linked by two disulfide bonds; one chain consists of 21 amino acids and the other chain consists of 30 amino acids, for a total of 51. Insulin was the first protein to have its structure determined (Fig. 2-1). The tobacco mosaic virus,

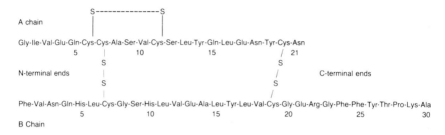

Figure 2-1. Amino acid sequence of bovine insulin. (*Source:* Lehninger, 1975. *Biochemistry,* 2d ed. New York: Worth Publishers.)

which is one of the largest known-molecular-weight proteins, is composed of 2,130 chains (Lehninger 1975).

To give us some idea of the many different proteins that can be formed from the various amino acids, we will go through a simple exercise by considering the number of possible combinations for something as simple as a dipeptide.

As previously mentioned, dipeptides are composed of two amino acids linked through a peptide linkage. On either end of the simple chain, there is a free amino group and on the other end there is a free carboxyl group. These are referred to as *N-terminal* and *C-terminal* amino acids. To keep our example simple, we will refer to the two amino acids in the dipeptide as *A* and *B*. When looking at all possible combinations for these two amino acids, the following will be noted: *AA, AB, BA,* and *BB.* At first glance it would appear that *AB* and *BA* are the same, but they are not. When considering the free terminal groups of the two amino acids, we need to look at the combinations in a little more detail.

The *A* and *B* amino acids can be depicted as *aAc* and *aBc,* representing the free amino and carboxyl groups with the small letters *a* and *c*. In our illustration, the combinations can now look like *aABc* and *aBAc.* The *a* and *c* are not shown between the two amino acids because they no longer exist as such; they are now a part of the peptide bond. The two dipeptides are different.

Taking the illustration one step further, we now will look at a tripeptide composed of the same two amino acids, *A* and *B.* The possible combinations are *AAA, AAB, ABA, BAA, ABB, BBB, BBA, BAA,* and *BAB.*

Instead of going through this exercise with larger combinations, we can use a simple mathematical formula to arrive at the total number of possible combinations:

$$X^Y = \text{Total number of possible combinations}$$

$$X = \text{Number of amino acids in a chain}$$

$$Y = \text{Number of amino acids to be used}$$

In the first example, the formula is 2^2 combinations, or a total of 4. In the second example, it is 3^2 combinations, or a total of 9.

Taking the low-molecular-weight protein insulin as an example, using the 51-amino-acid chain composed of 17 amino acids, it is possible to have 51^{17}, or 1.07×10^{29}, certainly an astronomical number of possibilities. Is it any wonder that proteins can be different? It is important to remember this when using one protein for another in a food application, especially from the standpoint of its functional properties. When looking at the problem in this light, it is almost impossible to substitute one protein completely for another in all applications. More will be said about this later.

PROTEIN STRUCTURE

We already have some idea about the structure of proteins. They are, in reality, polymers of amino acids and can be quite complex. To help us to understand some of the functional properties and other characteristics of proteins, we need to consider their structures. However, before doing so it is necessary to become familiar with the various attractive forces that come into play when proteins are formed.

The most common force that holds organic molecules together is the *covalent bond*. Typical of this bond is the sharing of electrons between two adjacent atoms. Carbon has four electrons that can be shared as four covalent bonds. Hydrogen has one such electron to share, and oxygen has two. Consequently, one carbon atom can share four of its electrons with four hydrogens to form methane; it can share all four electrons with two oxygens to form carbon dioxide; it can share its electrons with two hydrogens and one oxygen to form formaldehyde; and it can share its electrons with another carbon to form a carbon chain. Similar sharing takes place with other atoms that are a part of the protein molecule.

Ethyl Alcohol

In ethyl alcohol, all the atoms are held together by covalent bonds. The covalent bond is an extremely strong one and is not as easily broken as some of the others that we will now consider.

The *ionic bond,* in which unlike charges attract each other, is the next strongest bond. A good example is the attraction between the free amino and the carboxyl group at the ends of the polypeptide chain. Other examples are the acidic and basic polar side chains of lysine, arginine, histidine, aspartic acid, and glutamic acid residues:

$$
\overset{O}{\underset{||}{-C}}-O^{\ominus} \cdots\cdots\cdots {}^{\oplus}H-\overset{H}{\underset{|}{\underset{H}{N}}}- \quad \overset{O}{\underset{||}{-C}}-O^{\ominus} \cdots\cdots\cdots N{=}\overset{\overset{\oplus}{H}}{\underset{|}{C}}-
$$

The next bond is the *hydrogen bond,* which forms when hydrogen is shared between two negatively charged atoms:

$$
\overset{|}{-C}{=}O \cdots\cdots H{-}\overset{|}{N}-
$$

Last is the *hydrophobic interactive force,* which takes place between two similar nonpolar radicals:

$$
\overset{|}{\underset{|}{-C}}-CH_3 \quad CH_3-\overset{|}{\underset{|}{C}}- \qquad \overset{|}{\underset{|}{-C}}\text{—}\hexagon\hexagon\text{—}\overset{|}{\underset{|}{C}}-
$$

If there are attracting forces, then there should also be repelling forces. The most obvious one is the repelling force between two like ionic charges. There is also a repelling force that takes place between nonpolar groups.

Each of the previously discussed forces has an influence on the way a particular protein will be structured. This will become more apparent shortly.

Simple Proteins

The simplest type of protein is one that is formed by a long polypeptide chain. The only type of bonding considered for this simple protein is the covalent bond. Carbon has four covalent bond locations equally spaced around it but they are not in a flat plane as they are so often shown. If each bond location is considered a point, then the formation of a tetrahedron can be visualized as consisting of four equilateral triangles.

If an attempt is made to string a series of these tetrahedrons from peak to peak, it would be impossible to form a straight chain. For this reason, it is better to depict the polypeptide chain as follows, realizing that there is a three-dimensional effect:

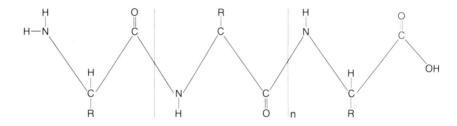

The covalent bond between carbons allows the chain on either side to turn, or revolve, giving the complete chain a snakelike action. This allows the chain to fold back on itself, but at the peptide linkage there is no turning because of the partial double-bond nature of the peptide.

When this twisting and turning of the chain occurs, it allows attracting groups to approach one another. If the attractive force is great enough to resist a pulling away of the adjoining sections, then that configuration tends to stabilize. It is possible for a chain to fold back on itself a number of times and for separate chains to join through these same attraction forces to build large protein agglomerates.

Complex Proteins

Proteins become more complex when the chains get extremely long and fold back on themselves and remain in that form because of the matching of various attracting radicals. The same thing takes place with individual chains. Branching also makes the protein more complex.

The sulfur-containing amino acids cysteine and cystine play an important role in the formation of complex protein structures. If cysteine is oxidized by removing the hydrogen, then two cysteine molecules join to form one molecule of cystine. In reverse, if cystine is reduced by adding hydrogen, then one molecule forms two molecules of cysteine:

$$
\begin{array}{ccc}
\text{COOH} & \text{COOH} & \text{COOH} & \text{COOH} \\
| & | & | & | \\
\text{H}_2\text{N}-\text{C}-\text{H} & \text{H}-\text{C}-\text{NH}_2 \quad \text{NH}_2-\text{C} & & \text{C}-\text{NH}_2 + \text{H}_2 \\
| & | & | & | \\
\text{CH}_2-\text{S}-\text{H} \quad \text{H}-\text{S}-\text{CH}_2 & & \text{CH}_2------\text{S}-\text{S}------\text{CH}_2 \\
\text{2 Cysteines} & & \text{Cystine}
\end{array}
$$

This same sort of reaction takes place within a peptide chain if conditions are right and if two sulfur radicals are close enough to form the disulfide bond. Likewise, two parallel chains can join through such peptide bonds. Both examples can be seen in the structure of bovine insulin shown in Fig. 2-1.

It is important that there are many structures produced not only because of the patterns formed when amino acids are linked through the peptide bond and the disulfide bonds, but also because there are strong attraction and repellent forces that help form a unique protein molecule.

PROTEIN CLASSIFICATION

In attempting to classify proteins, chemists postulate various schemes based on protein structures. These structures were postulated with attempts to classify them. They range from simple chains to helical (coiling), sheetlike, and so on. These structures are categorized as primary, secondary, tertiary, and quaternary. To go into detail on these types is not warranted for our purposes.

Although proteins may be classified according to their structure, functionality, and solubility characteristics, the latter has been used for the longest period of time. This method is of greatest value and should help in a consideration of proteins as food additives. In some cases, protein structure also may be taken into consideration.

Taken as a whole, proteins can be placed in two broad categories: *fibrous* and *globular*. Lehninger (1975, p. 60) points out that, "The fibrous proteins consist of polypeptide chains arranged in parallel along a single axis, to yield long fibers or sheets. Fibrous proteins are physically tough and are insoluble in water or dilute salt solutions. They are the basic structural elements in the connective tissue of higher animals." These are the proteins that make up tendons, cartilage, bone matrix, skin, hair, feathers, horn, nails, hooves, and even silk.

Lehninger goes on to say that globular proteins are polypeptide chains that "are tightly folded into compact spherical or globular shapes. Most globular proteins are soluble in aqueous systems. They usually have a mobile or dynamic function in the cell" (1975, p. 60). They can be considered to be the active proteins in the body or the more functional ones, such as enzymes, hormones, and antibodies.

An earlier classification of the globular proteins (Mertz 1959) is worth considering in view of some of the properties that will be mentioned when functionality is considered. Mertz divided the globular proteins into two types according to their solubility in distilled water—soluble and insoluble. Albumin is the best example of the soluble type; the best example of the insoluble type is globulin. According to the *Concise Chemical and Technical Dictionary* (Bennett 1974) *albumin* is defined as "native protein, soluble in water and dilute salt solutions; the term loosely refers to the white of egg." *Globulin* is "native protein, insoluble in water and soluble in dilute salt solutions and alkalis." These characteristics will be important in later discussions.

Another class of proteins is called *conjugated*. These proteins include both the fibrous and globular types, but they have nonprotein (prosthetic groups) attached to them. Pigmented chicken feathers may be thought of as an example of the conjugated fibrous type, whereas hemoglobin and casein are examples of the conjugated globular type. The prosthetic group for the first example is heme, and for casein the protein is combined with phosphoric acid.

Remember that "there are no sharp breaks in nature." This becomes very significant to anyone who attempts to categorize or classify anything in nature: chemical compounds, animal and plant species, and even food categories. There are always gray areas to be considered; some things do not fit into either category or else have characteristics of several categories. Classification attempts are simply ways to organize related subjects into categories so the overall picture can be understood.

MODIFIED PROTEINS

It is apparent that various properties and characteristics of proteins depend very much on the structure of each protein. Thus, if structure is altered in any way, we would expect to see one or more characteristics altered. If that alteration is somewhat radical, such as what occurs with protein foods during cooking, that protein is said to be irreversibly *denatured*.

When used as additives, proteins may be purposely altered or modified to give them characteristics that are better suited for a particular use. Modification may

- Improve digestibility.
- Improve or change functionality.
- Remove or destroy unwanted factors.
- Stabilize a protein.
- Improve nutritive properties.
- Improve flavor.
- Improve appearance.
- Develop color.
- Change solubility characteristics.

To understand what modifications can do for protein additives, we will consider three modifying methods: heat, chemical, and enzyme. When looking at these methods, we can generalize that "what applies to one protein will apply to another, for the most part." We must realize that, although each method will act in a similar way on all proteins, the end result may not functionally be the same. As we discuss the methods, this will become more apparent. An important point to consider is that once the principle is understood, a technique may be selected to obtain an additive that may be more suitable for a particular application.

Heat Modifications

Heat is the most commonly used method to modify proteins. It is used to cook foods to make them more digestible and more nutritious, to make them more tender and easier to chew, and to develop pleasing flavors.

In baked items, heat is used to "set" the structure of the dough or the egg white of a meringue. In sausages, heat in the smokehouse is used to denature, or set, the protein structure to lock in the emulsified fat and other ingredients.

There are many other examples where heat is essential in the preparation of foods, but here we want to consider how heat can be used to modify protein additives to obtain a beneficial effect. As an illustration, we will look at soy proteins. What applies to this consideration should also apply to other oilseed proteins and may well apply to other protein products as well.

In soybean processing, immediately after the oil is extracted with solvent, the resulting meal or defatted flake is still wet. This solvent can be removed by vacuum and/or heat in some form. This is a critical step for the protein, particularly if moist heat is applied. Moist heat has a pronounced effect on protein functionality; the protein is gradually denatured in a time/temperature relationship. An easy way to determine what effect heat had on the protein is to determine its solubility, particularly its solubility in water. When performed under set laboratory conditions, the technologist determines how much of the protein is soluble. The higher its solubility, the less the protein had been subjected to heat denaturation. Solubility is usually expressed as a percent of the total protein present. This may be referred to as *Water-Soluble Protein* (WSP) or as *Protein Dispersibility Index* (PDI). Sometimes the solubility is expressed in terms of nitrogen and is called the *Nitrogen Solubility Index* (NSI).

Solubility is expressed in terms of nitrogen because proteins are high in nitrogen content, with an average of about 16 percent. A widely accepted laboratory procedure used in the analysis for protein is to determine the nitrogen content of the product and then convert that finding into protein by multiplying by 6.25 or by dividing by 0.16. With solubility expressed as a percent of the total, it makes little difference if the results are expressed in terms of nitrogen or protein.

Table 2-4 Terminology of Solubility Methods for Assessing Heat Treatment of Soy Flours and Related Products

Term	Abbreviation	Calculation[1]
% Water soluble nitrogen[2]	WSN	$\dfrac{\text{Ml alkali} \times \text{N} \times 0.014 \times 100}{\text{Wt of sample}}$
% Nitrogen solubility Index[2]	NSI	% Total nitrogen in sample
% Water dispersible	WSP	% WSN $\times$ 6.25
% Protein solubility Index[2]	PSI	$\dfrac{\text{% WSP} \times 100}{\text{% Total nitrogen in sample} \times 6.25}$
% Water dispersible protein[3]	WDP	$\dfrac{\text{Ml alkali} \times \text{N} \times 0.014 \times 100 \times 6.25}{\text{Wt of sample}}$
% Protein dispersibility Index[3]	PDI	$\dfrac{\text{% WDP} \times 100}{\text{% Total nitrogen in sample} \times 6.25}$

[1] Calculations are based on Kjeldahl analysis of extracts where N = normality of alkali, 0.014 = millequivalent weight of nitrogen, and 6.25 = nitrogen to protein conversion factor.
[2] Based on AOCS Method Ba 11-65 (AOCS 1970).
[3] Based on AOCS Method Ba 10-65 (AOCS 1970).
Source: Courtesy of Wolf and Cowan 1971.

However, there are variances due to the subtle differences used by the various methods to solubilize the protein. See Table 2-4 for comparisons of the methods used and note how they differ.

To have a fuller appreciation of what is meant when it is said that a protein product has an NSI of a particular percentage, we will consider an egg-cooking exercise.

Egg white is 100 percent soluble in water. If the egg white is cooked so that it is completely denatured, it will appear as a soft white material. If it is placed in water, it will not dissolve, no matter how much it is stirred; it has 0 percent solubility. If the egg white is mildly cooked, as in the early stage of frying, part will be denatured and part will still have a watery appearance. It is conceivable that a stage can be reached where the egg white will be 50 percent soluble, that is, when half of the egg white will dissolve. This same thing can and does take place in the preparation of an oilseed protein. In fact, moist heat will have the same effect on almost all proteins.

Solubility determinations, such as NSI and PDI, on proteins can be quite meaningful. The solubility information obtained tells how much heat treatment the protein received, and it gives some idea about that protein's functionality. This point cannot be stressed enough. Its importance will be brought out when various applications are discussed in later chapters.

Proper use of heat on soy products performs a very important function. Unheated soy proteins have an antinutritional factor called the *trypsin inhibitor* (TI). This factor, which is protein in nature, inhibits the enzyme trypsin from breaking down protein in the early stage of digestion. The proper use of moist heat will destroy the TI, thereby making the protein more readily usable by the body; the protein is then of greater value. If too much heat is used on soy products, the protein is altered to the point where it cannot be utilized by the body. Much of what was learned about the proper use of heat on soy proteins was learned from animal nutritionists as they tried to develop efficient feeds.

Enzyme Modifications

Proteases, enzymes that break peptide bonds, have been used to change protein functionality for a long time. Originally, enzymes that occurred naturally in foods were used. When beef is allowed to age under specific conditions, the naturally occurring enzymes in the meat function to tenderize the product by autolytic proteolysis (Brissey and Goeser 1963). In other cases, microorganisms were used (and still are used) to perform specific enzymatic tasks. Cheese processing is a typical example. "With increased knowledge of what enzymes are and how they work, their deliberate isolation and addition to food systems became widely practiced" (Phillips and Beuchat 1981, p. 275).

Protease acts on the protein molecule by catalyzing the hydrolytic break at a peptide linkage. Through this action, the protein molecule is broken down into smaller units, or peptides. This action tends to make the protein more hydrophilic—more soluble in water. As the molecules become more soluble, they tend to foam more. Unfortunately, as the foaming property increases, foam stability tends to decrease. But this can be overcome by the addition of another protein or even of the same protein that has not been enzymatically altered. Unaltered protein will act as a stabilizer.

Whipping agents and/or egg white substitutes can be prepared through the use of a protease on, for example, soy protein. Patents were granted on these techniques in 1949 and 1950: Burnett and Gunther (1949); Turner (1949); and Sair and Rathman (1950). In the process, soy protein is treated by pepsin at a pH of about 2.0 and at a temperature of 100°F to 110°F for about 1.5 hours. The enzymatic action is stopped by raising the pH to 5.2. On centrifugation, the solids are separated from the clear liquid containing the modified protein, which is then spray dried.

In this process, the enzyme-modified product is functional in acidic systems. Hence, this is a method to prepare a protein-type product to be used in acid systems that are not normally tolerated by an unaltered protein. The same thing applies to systems that have a fairly high concentration of a divalent ion such as calcium. If the calcium ion is of high enough concentration, it will precipitate protein.

Water-binding capacity for a protein can also be increased by a protease that is active around a neutral pH. This probably takes place because of the increased numbers of amino and carboxyl groups that are freed when the peptide bonds are broken. Proteases are of value in baking where they are used to act on the wheat gluten in order to improve the handling properties of doughs.

Before leaving the subject of enzyme modification of proteins, we should explore another area where enzymes have value. Certain enzymes can be used to build up a protein, that is, to synthesize peptide bonds. This is known as the *plastein* reaction. These products tend to become insoluble as they grow larger.

The proteases used most often in these reactions have been pepsin and papain. The substrates, substances being acted on, used by various investigators have been soy, casein, zein (corn protein), gluten, milk whey, and egg albumin. See Phillips and Beuchat (1981) for references.

Two important benefits were found in producing plasteins. The first was in removing the bitter peptides from enzyme hydrolysates of soy protein (Phillips and Beuchat 1981). According to Fujimaki et al. (1977), the bitter principals were attributed to the aromatic or aliphatic side-chain amino acids in the peptides. When the hydrolysates were subjected to the plastein reaction, this bitterness was eliminated. It is not known exactly how this was accomplished.

The second, a nutritional benefit, was achieved when a limiting amino acid was incorporated into a protein. A plastein was synthesized by the use of papain from a ten-to-one mixture of a soybean hydrolysate and a methionine ethyl ester. The methionine content of the product was 7.22 percent, which was about six times the level of the hydrolysate. Rat-feeding studies showed the product to be greatly improved (Yamashita et al. 1971).

There are other types of enzymes that can be used to modify proteins. There is aminopeptidase, which breaks the peptide bond of a terminal amino acid that has a free amino group, and there is carboxypeptidase, which acts on the peptide bond of the amino acid that has a free carboxyl group. Some specific enzymes will break peptide bonds next to a particular amino acid. There are more, but the ones mentioned are sufficient to show that many modifications are possible. Although the food scientist is aware of these activities, a limited amount of work has been done in this area, particularly in commercial preparations. About the only one that is used commercially today is the whipping agent or egg white replacer made from soy protein.

Chemical Modifications

In some ways, chemical modifications are similar to enzyme modifications. Peptide bonds can be broken by acid hydrolysis. If the hydrolysis is carefully controlled, the protein molecule partially breaks down into peptides similar to the whipping agent preparation.

Two differences have been observed. Usually in an enzymatic preparation, a bitter note often develops, attributed to the exposure of certain hydrophobic groups attached to some of the amino acids. If these groups are located within the chain, bitterness seems to lessen. Also, in acid hydrolysis, a flavor tends to develop that gives it a meaty characteristic, such as that found in hydrolyzed vegetable protein (HVP).

By means of chemical reagents, it is possible to break certain bonds, such as the disulfide bond; through the use of specific salts, other bonds also may be broken. Chemical changes can be made by adding particular reactive groups and masking others. All products resulting from these chemical modifications are assumed to have different functional properties.

For greater detail on these various modification methods, refer to Feeney and Whitaker (1977).

ENZYMES

Enzymes are a unique class of proteins that are produced by all living cells. They are unique because they are organic catalysts that initiate and control biological reactions. This type of activity makes them essential for all living cells—from the simplest to the most complex.

Enzymes as catalysts perform their specific function at very low levels of concentration, and they are able to do this free of the living cell. For this reason, it is entirely possible that enzymes can accompany special protein products as they are processed from their native state. This is important to the food technologist because the presence of certain enzymes can be undesirable if the enzyme catalyzes an unwanted reaction.

The following are a few examples of the catalyzed reactions that can take place with specific enzymes:

- Disaccharides can be split into monosaccharides.
- A terminal amino acid can be split off from the end of a protein or a polypeptide chain. This can be specific for the free carboxyl end or the free amino end.
- A peptide bond can be broken at a specific location.
- Certain bonds, such as the disulfide bond, can be broken.
- A carboxyl group can be removed from an amino acid.
- Enzymatic browning can take place.
- Pigments can be decolorized.
- A free amino group can be split off from an amino acid.
- Fats can be broken down into glycerol and fatty acids.

- Fats can be oxidized.
- Flavors can develop.

These are just a few of hundreds of examples. They are sufficient for us to realize that enzymes do many things that may benefit us, or that they may affect a food adversely in a number of ways, even from the nutritional standpoint. For these reasons, it is important to the food technologist to have some knowledge about enzymes.

Composition

Enzymes are globular proteins that fall into one of three categories: (1) a simple globular type, (2) a globular metalloprotein type, and (3) a globular protein or a metalloprotein type complexed with a nonprotein group. In the latter case, the protein portion is called an *apoenzyme,* while the nonprotein portion is called a *coenzyme.* The combination is referred to as a *holoenzyme.* In some specific cases, the coenzyme portion of a holoenzyme may be one of the B vitamins, such as thiamine, riboflavin, nicotinic acid, pantothenic acid, or pyridoxine, or they may be another simple compound, such as glucose, phosphate, or a methyl radical. They also may be more complex. However, in most cases coenzymes are dialyzable and can be removed reversibly from the protein portion of the molecule. There are situations in which the coenzyme is so tightly bound to the apoenzyme that it cannot be removed by dialysis; more drastic procedures are then needed if the two components are to be separated.

Naming Enzymes

Several methods are used in naming enzymes. In most cases, they are named for the substrate on which they act. Either the entire name or a major part of it is used, to which the suffix *-ase* is added, producing names such as carbohydrases, proteases, and lipases. We can be more specific by adding the origin to the name, such as salivary amylase, bacterial protease, and gastric protease. This is important because the same type of enzyme from different origins may have slightly different activities.

Because there are enzymes that are highly specific in their action on some particular portion of a molecule, another way of naming them is to use the substrate followed by the type of activity that is achieved, such as glucose oxidase and ascorbic acid oxidase.

Enzymes were not always named by these schemes. In fact, as far as we are aware, no scheme was used in the early days of enzyme research. Most of the names simply were coined. Because of their constant use over the years, some of these names are still being used, such names as pepsin, rennin, and trypsin.

Using the current naming scheme, these enzymes should be called gastric protease, gastric caseinase, and pancreatic protease, respectively.

In 1972, an international commission on enzyme nomenclature recommended placing enzymes in six major classes and sets of subclasses. It also recommended that a classification number be used. The six major groups are as follows:

1. Oxido-reductases (oxidation-reduction reactions)
2. Transferases (transfer of functional groups)
3. Hydrolases (hydrolysis reactions)
4. Lyases (addition to double bonds)
5. Isomerases (isomerization reactions)
6. Ligases (formation of bonds with ATP cleavage)

For further information on this classification system, refer to Lehninger (1977).

Factors Affecting Enzyme Activity

As we discussed earlier, there are many factors that affect the functionality of proteins, which occurs when protein structure is disturbed or is partially altered. These same factors affect enzymes to a greater degree because even slight changes in structure may have pronounced effects on enzyme activities.

In the usual chemical reactions, the speed of the reaction doubles for every 10°C rise in temperature. For most enzyme-catalyzed reactions, this occurs at low temperatures, but, as the temperature rises, the rate falls off because of the adverse effect heat has on the enzyme. Most enzymes show an optimum activity between 30°C and 50°C. There are some enzymes that will function at higher temperatures, such as those that are produced by thermophilic bacteria, although most enzymes will be destroyed at a temperature of 60°C (140°F). It is the destruction of vital enzymes that kills microorganisms when they are subjected to pasteurizing temperatures.

Enzymes are greatly influenced by the pH of their environment, as are most proteins. They are most active at a specific pH, which is referred to as the optimum pH. As the pH changes on either side of the optimum pH, activity falls off rapidly.

Certain metallic ions are essential to some enzymes and actually take part in a reaction. Obviously, if the essential metal is tied up, the enzyme will not function.

Enzymes are affected by substances called *inhibitors*. In the preceding paragraph, we pointed out the adverse effect when an essential metal is made unavailable. If a substance is added that will tie up that metal (a chelating agent), then that substance can be considered an inhibitor.

There are other types of inhibitors. If the enzyme comes in contact with a compound that is similar in structure to the substrate but is not attacked or altered by the enzyme, that is called a *competitive inhibitor*, that is, it competes with the substrate for the active site on the enzyme molecule.

There is also the *noncompetitive inhibitor*, which will bind on the enzyme at a location other than the active site. It seems that it inactivates the enzyme by distorting or deforming the enzyme. According to Lehninger, "the most common type of noncompetitive inhibition is given by reagents that combine reversibly with some functional group of the enzyme (outside the active site) that is essential for maintaining the catalytically active three-dimensional conformation of the enzyme molecule" (1975, p. 201).

REFERENCES

Bennett, H. 1974. *Concise Chemical Dictionary*. New York: Chemical Publishing.

Brissey, G. E., and P. A. Goeser. 1963. "Aging, Curing and Smoking of Meats." In *Food Processing Operations—Their Management, Machines, Materials, and Methods*, vol. II, ed. M. A. Joslyn and J. J. Held, 600–34. Westport, Conn.: AVI Publishing.

Burnett, R. S., and J. K. Gunther. 1949. Preparation of Whipping Composition and the Resulting Product. U.S. Pat. 2,489,173 (Nov. 22).

Feeney, R. E., and J. R. Whitaker, ed. 1977. *Food Proteins—Improvement Through Chemical and Enzymatic Modification*. Advances in Chem. Series 160. Washington, D.C.: American Chemical Society.

Fujimaki, M., S. Arai, and M. Yamashita. 1977. "Enzymatic Protein Degradation and Resynthesis for Protein Improvement." In *Food Proteins—Improvement Through Chemical and Enzymatic Modification*. Advances in Chem. Series 160, ed. R. E. Feeney and J. R. Whitaker, 156–84. Washington, D.C.: American Chemical Society.

Lehninger, A. L. 1975. *Biochemistry*, 2d ed. New York: Worth Publishers.

Mertz, E. T. 1959. *Elementary Biochemistry*. Minneapolis: Burgess Publishing.

Official and Tentative Methods, 3d ed. 1970. Champaign, Ill.: American Oil Chemist Society.

Phillips, R. D., and L. R. Beuchat. 1981. "Enzyme Modification of Proteins." In *Protein Functionality in Foods*. ACS Symposium Series 147, ed. J. P. Cherry, 275–98. Washington, D.C.: American Chemical Society.

Sair, L., and R. Rathman. 1950. Preparation of Modified Soy Protein. U.S. Pat. 2,502,029 (Nov. 28).

Stryer, L. 1981. *Biochemistry*. San Francisco: W. H. Freeman.

Turner, J. R. 1949. Modified Soy Protein and the Preparation Thereof. U.S. Pat. 2,489,208 (Nov. 22).

Yamashita, M., S. Arai, S. Tsai, and M. Fujimaki. 1971. "Plastein Reaction as a Method for Enhancing the Sulfur-Containing Amino Acid Level of Soybean Protein." *J. Agr. Food Chem.* 19:1151–54.

CHAPTER 3

Nutritional Considerations

Not too many years ago, foodservice operators used protein additives in food preparations primarily for functional and economic benefits. They were not, however, willing to pay for any nutritional benefits; they expected them as bonuses. Today, the nutritional benefits are becoming increasingly important in the eyes of consumers because consumers are more interested in nutrition and are willing to pay for it. Many are now asking food processors for factual information concerning the nutritional properties of food preparations.

Nutritional considerations are even more important in certain institutional sectors of the business, particularly in school lunch and other governmental feeding programs. Thus, it is important that foodservice operators have some fundamental knowledge about nutrition, particularly as it concerns the foods they prepare.

Much of the material in this chapter is quite basic, but it is written with a purpose. The stage is being set not only for common understanding but also for those who do not wish any more than just the basics. This approach is invaluable when explaining nutrition to the uninitiated who lack a technical background but need a knowledge of nutrition basics for their work. There is no reason why this approach should not be effective in educating foodservice help.

Since the chief concern of this text is protein additives, we will concentrate on this aspect when discussing the basics of nutrition.

BASIC NUTRITION

As we consider nutrition basics, we ask, "What is the meaning of the word *nutrition?*" According to *Webster's Ninth Collegiate Dictionary,* nutrition is "the act or process of nourishing or being nourished: the sum of the processes by which an animal or plant takes in and utilizes food substances." This can be expanded by adding that nutrition is the process in which nutrients are taken into a plant or animal and then are converted into living tissue or are used to maintain life. In this expanded version, we use the word *nutrient.* What is a nutrient? According to the dictionary, it means "furnishing nourishment." Our definition is the following: "A nutrient is any food or group of constituents that aids in the support of life when consumed."

Nutrients can be placed in two broad categories. *Inorganic nutrients* are oxygen, water, and minerals; *organic nutrients* are more complex, primarily compounds of carbon that are produced by living matter, such as carbohydrates or sugars, fats or oils, proteins, and vitamins.

Inorganic Nutrients

Oxygen is a nutrient that is taken for granted because it is so plentiful. About $\frac{1}{5}$ of the air we breathe is oxygen. Normally, we do not think of oxygen as a nutrient; however, it is a most important one. It is taken into the body via the lungs, where it enters the blood quickly and is distributed to all locations within the body to take part in the metabolic process at the cellular level. The body obtains energy from the food that is broken down by a process whereby hydrogen is transferred in orderly steps; during each step, a little energy is released, until all the utilizable energy contained in the food is realized. The process ends when oxygen is the final acceptor of hydrogen, resulting in the formation of water. Oxygen also accepts carbon in breakdown of food to form carbon dioxide, which, of course, is released in the lungs. Oxygen is so important to us that we can live but a few moments without it.

Water is another nutrient that is taken for granted. It, too, is a most essential nutrient. Being deprived of water is not as critical as being deprived of oxygen because, depending on conditions, we can live for a number of days without water.

Water is the most abundant constituent in our bodies. Depending on our size and age, we may consist of from 50 to 80 percent water on a weight basis. The turnover rate of water in the adult is about 6 percent of body weight. In the infant it is 15 percent. On average, only 54 percent of our water intake comes from what we drink, and another 37 percent comes from the foods we eat. We obtain about 9 percent of our water needs through metabolic means, for example, when oxygen accepts hydrogen.

Mayer and Goldberg (1980) made a point of how critical water is to the body by relating what happens when there is a water loss. A 10 percent loss causes severe symptoms of dehydration; a 20 percent loss is fatal. In contrast, the body can lose about 50 percent of its weight, which includes all of its reserve of carbohydrate (glycogen) and fat and half of its lean protein tissue before it is in danger of starving to death.

Water has a number of important functions in our body. It

* Transports nutrients
* Takes part in chemical reactions
* Takes part in physiological reactions
* Helps regulate body temperature
* Maintains the shape of body cells
* Lubricates and cushions the body
* Transports waste by-products
* Makes foods palatable

Minerals are a vital 5 percent of human and animal nutrition that serve as a foundation for body metabolism. Only small amounts are needed and may be consumed as salts, or they may accompany some of the more complex foods. Minerals can be placed in two categories, based on the amounts that are needed in the body. (This is an area of nutrition that may change as we become more sophisticated in our laboratory techniques.)

1. *Major:* Calcium, phosphorus, magnesium, sodium, potassium, iron, copper, cobalt, iodine, sulfur, zinc, and fluorine.
2. *Minor:* Aluminum, silicon, bromine, manganese, molybdenum, chromium, and selenium.

Organic Nutrients

Organic nutrients are compounds that are produced by living plants and animals. They are composed of such basic elements as carbon, hydrogen, and oxygen, and may or may not contain other elements. Because organic compounds are chiefly carbon, they are also referred to as carbon compounds.

Although organic compounds are produced by living plants and animals, in many instances compounds can be chemically made that are an exact duplicate of the natural product. When one of these compounds is consumed in place of the natural product as a food, the body will use it. It makes little difference to the body if the compound is a manufactured nutrient or a natural one.

Carbohydrates or Sugars

Carbohydrates are carbon compounds that are produced by green plants from carbon dioxide and water in the presence of light by a process called photosynthesis. Carbohydrates are composed of carbon, hydrogen, and oxygen.

Carbohydrates are compounds that may range from simple sugars, such as glucose, fructose, and galactose (Fig. 3-1), to complex polysaccharides, such as starch and cellulose. There are other carbohydrate forms between these two extremes, the most common of which are the disaccharides (sucrose or table sugar); maltose; and lactose, or milk sugar (Fig. 3-2). Note that sucrose is made up of glucose and fructose, maltose is composed of two glucose molecules, and milk sugar is composed of glucose and galactose.

The polysaccharide starch is composed of long chains of glucose. There are two forms of starch, the straight chain form called *amylose* and the highly branched form called *amylopectin*.

Carbohydrates are broken down in the body into simple sugars and are utilized as energy sources. The simple sugars are utilized quickly, whereas the more complex sugars take a little more time. When there is an excess of sugar in the body, it is converted into a polysaccharide called *glycogen*. Glycogen differs from starch because it is more readily broken down in the body, again as a quick energy source. But the body has a limited capacity to store glycogen. Because of this, excess sugar is more often converted into fat, which builds up in the body as a stored energy source.

There are complex forms of carbohydrates that are not broken down in the body, and are important in normalizing bowel movement. As a class, these are referred to as dietary fiber. Dietary fiber is defined as including all the components of a food that are not broken down by enzymes in the human digestive tract to produce small molecular compounds (*Food Tech.*, "Dietary Fiber," 1979, p. 35). The earliest recognition of the value of fiber was that it provided bulk in the diet, which aided the passage of food through the intestine. Today, we are learning that there are other benefits. It is thought that fiber tends to prevent the buildup of toxic, irritating compounds in the large intestine by absorbing these compounds and/or increasing bowel mobility.

Fats and Oils

Fats and oils, like carbohydrates, are composed of carbon, hydrogen, and oxygen. Unlike carbohydrates, fats are not soluble in water but are soluble in a solvent, such as ether. Fats and oils also differ from carbohydrates in that there is much less oxygen present.

The terms *fats* and *oils* are often used interchangeably. The only difference between the two is whether they are solids or liquids at room temperature. Oils are liquids and fats are solids. As a class of compounds, both are also known as *lipids*.

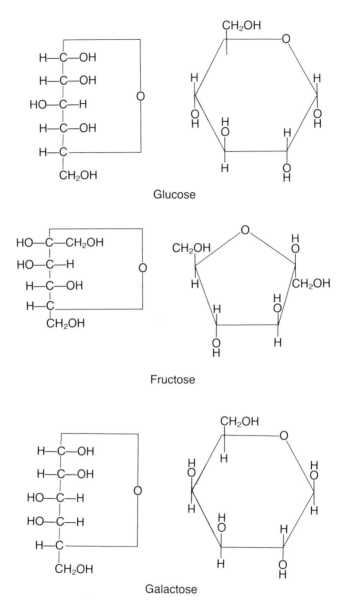

Glucose

Fructose

Galactose

Figure 3-1. Three common monosaccharides (ring structures).

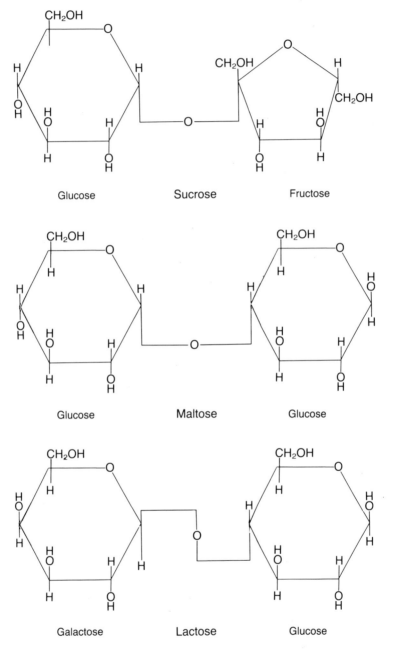

Figure 3-2.   Three common disaccharides.

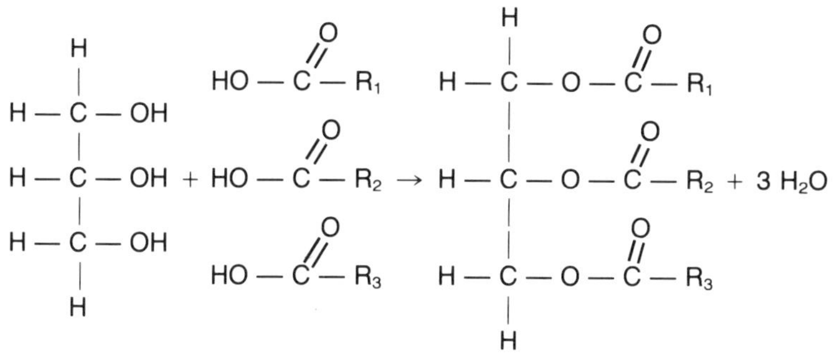

Glycerine   + 3 Fatty acids   →   Fat/oil   +   3 Waters

Figure 3-3. Fat/oil formation from glycerol and fatty acids.

Fats and oils are composed of two types of molecules called *fatty acids* and *glycerol* (Fig. 3-3). The fatty acid molecule is much like an amino acid except no amino group is present. For the various types of fatty acids, see Fig. 3-4. Another difference is that the chain is longer and not branched. Note in fig. 3-3 that glycerol is much like a sugar molecule except that it contains a chain length of only three carbons.

Fats and oils are good energy sources. However, they are not broken down as rapidly as carbohydrates. They are ideal as long-term energy sources. Fats produce a little more than twice the energy that carbohydrates do on a unit-weight basis, and they are stored in the body for later use. The average fat content in a human is about 15 percent.

Saturated

$$Stearic\ acid\ (C_{17}\ H_{35}\ COOH)$$
$$CH_3\ (CH_2)_{16}—COOH$$

Monounsaturated

$$Oleic\ acid\ (C_{17}\ H_{33}\ COOH)$$
$$CH_3—(CH_2)_7—CH=CH—(CH_2)_7—COOH$$

Polyunsaturated

$$Linoleic\ acid\ (C_{17}\ H_{31}\ COOH)$$
$$CH_3(CH_2)_4—CH=CH—CH_2—CH=CH—(CH_2)_7—COOH$$

$$Linolenic\ acid\ (C_{17}\ H_{29}\ COOH)$$
$$CH_3—CH_2\ CH=CH—CH_2—CH=CH—CH_2—CH=CH—(CH_2)_7—COOH$$

Figure 3-4. Types of C_{18} fatty acids.

Table 3-1 *Food and Nutrition Board, National Academy of Sciences–National Research Council Recommended Daily Dietary Allowances,*[1]
Revised 1980
(Designed for the maintenance of good nutrition of practically all healthy people in the United States)

	Age (years)	Weight (kg)	Weight (lb)	Height (cm)	Height (in)	Protein (g)	Fat-Soluble Vitamins — Vitamin A (μg RE)[2]	Vitamin D (μg)[3]	Vitamin E (mg α-TE)[4]
Infants	0.0–0.5	6	13	60	24	kg × 2.2	420	10	3
	0.5–1.0	9	20	71	28	kg × 2.0	400	10	4
Children	1–3	13	29	90	35	23	400	10	5
	4–6	20	44	112	44	30	500	10	6
	7–10	28	62	132	52	34	700	10	7
Males	11–14	45	99	157	62	45	1,000	10	8
	15–18	66	145	176	69	56	1,000	10	10
	19–22	70	154	177	70	56	1,000	7.5	10
	23–50	70	154	178	70	56	1,000	5	10
	51 +	70	154	178	70	56	1,000	5	10
Females	11–14	46	101	157	62	46	800	10	8
	15–18	55	120	163	64	46	800	10	8
	19–22	55	120	163	64	44	800	7.5	8
	23–50	55	120	163	64	44	800	5	8
	51 +	55	120	163	64	44	800	5	8
Pregnant						+ 30	+ 200	+ 5	+ 2
Lactating						+ 20	+ 400	+ 5	+ 3

[1] The allowances are intended to provide for individual variations among most normal persons as they live in the United States under usual environmental stresses. Diets should be based on a variety of common foods in order to provide other nutrients for which human requirements have been less well defined.

[2] Retinol equivalents. 1 retinol equivalent = 1 μg retinol or 6 μg β carotene.

[3] As cholecalciferol. 10 μg cholecalciferol = 400 IU of vitamin D.

[4] α-tocopherol equivalents. 1 mg d-α tocopherol = 1 α-TE.

[5] 1 NE (niacin equivalent) is equal to 1 mg of niacin or 60 mg of dietary tryptophane.

[6] The folacin allowances refer to dietary sources as determined by *Lactobacillus casei* assay after treatment with enzymes (conjugases) to make polyglutamyl forms of the vitamin available to the test organism.

Table 3-1 *Food and Nutrition Board, National Academy of Sciences–National Research Council Recommended Daily Dietary Allowances,[1] Revised 1980 (Designed for the maintenance of good nutrition of practically all healthy people in the United States) (cont.)*

Water-Soluble Vitamins							Minerals					
Vitamin C (mg)	Thiamine (mg)	Riboflavin (mg)	Niacin (mg NE)[5]	Vitamin B$_6$ (mg)	Folacin[6] (μg)	Vitamin B$_{12}$ (μg)	Calcium (mg)	Phosphorus (mg)	Magnesium (mg)	Iron (mg)	Zinc (mg)	Iodine (μg)
35	0.3	0.4	6	0.3	30	0.5[7]	360	240	50	10	3	40
35	0.5	0.6	8	0.6	45	1.5	540	360	70	15	5	50
45	0.7	0.8	9	0.9	100	2.0	800	800	150	15	10	70
45	0.9	1.0	11	1.3	200	2.5	800	800	200	10	10	90
45	1.2	1.4	16	1.6	300	3.0	800	800	250	10	10	120
50	1.4	1.6	18	1.8	400	3.0	1,200	1,200	350	18	15	150
60	1.4	1.7	18	2.0	400	3.0	1,200	1,200	400	18	15	150
60	1.5	1.7	19	2.2	400	3.0	800	800	350	10	15	150
60	1.4	1.6	18	2.2	400	3.0	800	800	350	10	15	150
60	1.2	1.4	16	2.2	400	3.0	800	800	350	10	15	150
50	1.1	1.3	15	1.8	400	3.0	1,200	1,200	300	18	15	150
60	1.1	1.3	14	2.0	400	3.0	1,200	1,200	300	18	15	150
60	1.1	1.3	14	2.0	400	3.0	800	800	300	18	15	150
60	1.0	1.2	13	2.0	400	3.0	800	800	300	18	15	150
60	1.0	1.2	13	2.0	400	3.0	800	800	300	10	15	150
+20	+0.4	+0.3	+2	+0.6	+400	+1.0	+400	+400	+150	[8]	+5	+25
+40	+0.5	+0.5	+5	+0.5	+100	+1.0	+400	+400	+150	[8]	+10	+50

[7] The recommended dietary allowance for vitamin B$_{12}$ in infants is based on average concentration of the vitamin in human milk. The allowances after weaning are based on energy intake (as recommended by the American Academy of Pediatrics) and consideration of other factors, such as intestinal absorption.

[8] The increased requirement during pregnancy cannot be met by the iron content of habitual American diets nor by the existing iron stores of many women; therefore the use of 30–60 mg of supplemental iron is recommended. Iron needs during lactation are not substantially different from those of nonpregnant women, but continued supplementation of the mother for 2–3 months after parturition is advisable in order to replenish stores depleted by pregnancy.

Source: Reprinted with permission from the National Academy Press, Washington, D.C.

Proteins

As mentioned in the previous chapter, proteins are essential components of living cells that are used by the body to build up tissues, especially muscle. To do this job effectively, the body uses certain amino acids. Proteins are a minor energy source. They are used for energy only after other body needs are provided.

Proteins are composed of amino acids, which in turn are composed primarily of the elements carbon, hydrogen, and nitrogen. Other elements may be present to a lesser extent. Because the nitrogen content is about 16 percent, proteins are often referred to as nitrogen compounds.

Proteins differ as to the amounts and types of amino acids present. Even within the organism, on a cellular level, there are protein differences. Depending on the types and amounts of amino acids present, certain proteins are of higher nutritional quality than others. The body needs less of the higher-quality protein to serve its needs than the lower-quality one. Because of this, nutritionists recommend specific amounts of protein, depending on age and sex, as a daily dietary intake.

We will delve into proteins in more detail in the section entitled "Protein Quality."

Vitamins

Vitamins are organic nutrients that are needed in minute quantities. Their compositions are varied and are of two broad types: fat-soluble and water-soluble. The *fat-soluble vitamins* are A, D, E, and K. The *water-soluble vitamins* are C, folic acid, thiamine, riboflavin, niacin, B_6, B_{12}, and other B vitamins.

Vitamins are accessory factors that help the body perform its vital functions. For the most part, necessary vitamins are found in food. A balance is achieved when we eat a variety of foods that have different vitamin contents.

NUTRIENT EVALUATION

We rely heavily on nutritionists to give us guidelines on what is a proper diet. They arrive at these recommendations over the years through observation and controlled research studies in both humans and animals.

The recommendations come to us in what is referred to as the Recommended Daily Allowances (RDA). Table 3-1 shows this information as it was published by the Food and Nutrition Board, National Academy of Sciences—National Research Council (*Recommended Dietary Allowances 1980*). The recommendations are broken down according to age and sex.

There is another table of similar nature called the U.S. RDA, which is used by the Food and Drug Administration in enforcing its regulation on nutritional labeling. It is considered the legal standard, a simple guideline that is needed for the general population. Since in nutritional labeling it is necessary to show percentage compositions based on standards, such a standard was set up to cover all age groups that would most likely consume the food (see Table 3-2).

Protein Quality

Proteins differ from one another in structure and in function, but how do they differ in nutritional value? When a protein is consumed as a food, the body breaks it down into its constituent amino acids, which are then used as building blocks to form specific proteins needed at some location within the body. They may be used to build or to replace tissues and/or organs; they may be used in some special bodily function. Whether or not the body is successful in making a needed protein depends on the availability of the required amino acids. If a particular protein is being constructed, as, for example, muscle, then the best protein source would be another muscle because it should be of similar composition. If the food source is something entirely different, there may be a problem in having the right combinations of amino acids to do the job. It is possible that the protein source might be limiting in one or more amino acids, or even devoid of a needed amino acid.

From the standpoint of body needs, there are two types of amino acids: essential and nonessential. There are eight essential amino acids for man, as shown in the following list. These amino acids are considered essential because they must be consumed as such, as a part of our food intake. On the other hand, nonessential amino acids are either quite plentiful or are synthesized. In the case of infants and small children, histidine is also considered to be an essential amino acid. Histidine can be synthesized, but not in sufficient quantities in rapidly growing bodies. The following amino acids are essential for man:

Isoleucine
Leucine
Lysine
Methionine (Cystine has a sparing action on methionine.)
Phenylalanine
Threonine
Tryptophane
Valine
Histidine (Needed by infants.)

Mention was made of limiting amino acids. These are the amino acids in a food that are present in sufficient amounts for body needs. This is of significance when there is a lack of one or more amino acids to supply body needs.

Table 3-2   U.S. Recommended Daily Allowance

Nutrient and Unit of Measurement	U.S. RDA[1]
Protein (optional), grams (g)	65[2]
	45
Vitamin A, international unit (IU)	5,000
Vitamin C, milligram (mg)	60
Thiamine, milligram (mg)	1.5
Riboflavin, milligram (mg)	1.7
Niacin, milligram (mg)	20
Calcium, gram (g)	1
Iron, milligram (mg)	18
Vitamin D (optional), international unit (IU)	400
Vitamin E, international unit (IU)	30
Vitamin B_6, milligram (mg)	2
Folic acid, milligram (mg)	0.4
Vitamin B_{12}, microgram (mcg)	6
Phosphorus, gram (g)	1
Iodine (optional), microgram (mcg)	150
Magnesium, milligram (mg)	400
Zinc, milligram (mg)	15
Copper, milligram (mg)	2
Biotin, milligram (mg)	0.3
Pantothenic acid, milligram (mg)	10
Potassium, gram (g)	[3]
Manganese, milligram (mg)	[3]

[1] U.S. Recommended Daily Allowance for adults and children 4 or more years of age.
[2] If the protein efficiency ratio of protein is equal to or better than that of casein, the U.S. RDA is 45 grams.
[3] No U.S. RDA has been established for either potassium or manganese; daily dietary intakes of 2.5 grams and 4.0 milligrams, respectively, are based on the 1979 Recommended Dietary Allowances of the Food and Nutrition Board, National Academy of Sciences, National Research Council.
Source: Taken from 21 *CFR* 104.20.

To have a better understanding of limiting amino acids, we will use an analogy (Cravens 1970). In the analogy, a barrel will be constructed of staves that may be looked on as amino acids. Each stave represents a specific amino acid, with its length representing the amount. If the stave is too short, it will be considered as limiting. The staves that are too long may be looked at as having too much of a particular amino acid. The barrel illustrated in Fig. 3-5 shows three types of staves, too long, too short, and of sufficient length. The barrel will hold liquid

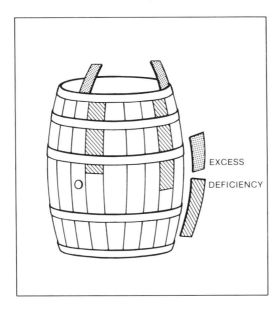

Figure 3-5. Barrel illustration depicting amino acid requirements in nutrition. (*Source:* Idea suggested by Cravens 1970.)

only up to the level of the shortest stave. It is obvious that this stave (or amino acid) must be built up, fortified, or extended. It may be looked at as the limiting factor in building the barrel, as it is a limiting amino acid in building body protein.

The excess of an amino acid shows it to be above the top of the barrel, where it can be trimmed. We might visualize burning the excess in a fire to receive warmth, or, in the case of a human, the body can use the excess for energy.

It is obvious that appropriate amounts of each amino acid are needed to build a particular structure. In this analogy it can be seen that a barrel can be built from another barrel. For an animal, the best nutrition is another whole animal. Because this is not our way of life, good results are achieved when we obtain our nutritional requirements from many different sources. Before examining these possibilities, we need to look at some protein sources and see what their limiting amino acids are.

As a general rule, most cereal grains are limiting in lysine. Corn is limiting in both lysine and tryptophane. Soy protein is limiting in methionine, but has an excess of lysine. If the cereal grain proteins are combined with soy proteins and consumed as a combination, the protein quality of the combination will be better than with either one alone. In this particular instance, the cereal protein supplements the sulfur amino acid in soy protein and the soy supplements the lysine for the cereal. In the case of corn and soy, soy will also help supplement a deficiency of tryptophane in the corn.

Bressani (1975) has shown in a convincing way how corn and soy complement each other in a protein-quality test known as the PER. Various combinations of corn and soy were made and fed to test animals to obtain growth responses. The results of this study are shown in Fig. 3-6. The optimum combination for corn protein and soy protein seems to be 40/60 by weight. Using whole ground corn meal with a protein level of 9.2 percent (USDA/ARS 1963) and soy flour at 50 percent protein, the 40/60 combination requires about 434 pounds of corn meal and 120 pounds of soy flour—roughly about a four-to-one combination. This concept is the one followed today in making protein blends for feeding programs being used in many of the developing countries.

Figure 3-6 illustrates how one protein product will help another when the combination is consumed as food. It does this because an amino acid deficiency in one protein can be partially or wholly made up by an excess of that particular amino acid in another protein, when the two are consumed together. This is why nutritionists tell us to eat a variety of foods, which is sound advice from the standpoint not only of protein but also of essential elements.

There is another way in which a deficiency in an amino acid can be eliminated: by adding the proper amount of the needed amino acid to the food. This is done in animal-feeding rations and in infant formulations. As a general rule, it is not done ordinarily in food preparation because it is more economical to combine food sources to make up for the needed deficiency.

Quality Evaluation

Protein quality can be measured in a number of ways. For our purpose, it is unnecessary to go into these methods in any great depth. The methods we will cover are protein efficiency ratio and amino acid score.

Protein Efficiency Ratio (PER).   The PER is perhaps the most widely used method for evaluating protein quality. It is the official method for both the FDA and the USDA.

The evaluation is made using laboratory rats that just have been weaned; they are test animals that are in a rapid growing stage. The rats are fed a diet that is complete with every known nutrient except protein. The test protein product is added to the basal diet so that the concentration is about 10 percent. Usually, 10 rats are fed this diet for a period of 28 days. An accurate accounting of the protein consumed and the weight gained is recorded. At the end of the feeding period, the test is concluded and a determination is made of the amount of protein consumed and the weight gained. The ratio determined is based on 1 gram of protein. If the average gain is 2 grams for every gram of protein consumed, then the PER is said to be 2. Since there are a number of variables that can affect the outcome of the test, a standard protein, casein, is also run. The PER of

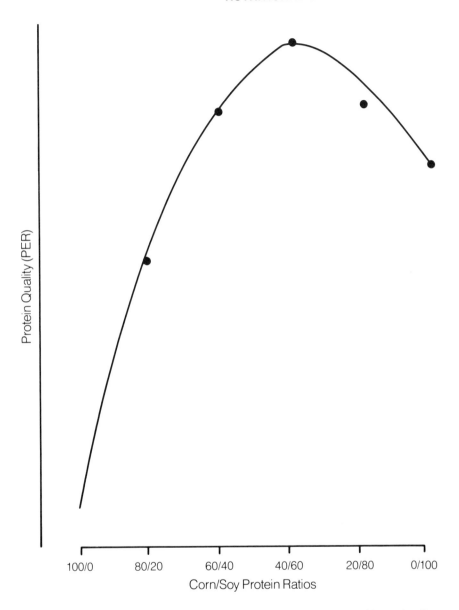

Figure 3-6. Protein quality of corn/soy combinations as measured in rat-feeding studies. (*Source:* Adapted from INCAP 75-363.)

casein is widely accepted as being 2.5. If in the evaluation casein is different from 2.5, the percentage change necessary to bring it to 2.5 is used on the test protein as well. Whenever PERs are given, a statement is usually made that the values are corrected, if they have been adjusted to a casein standard. See Table 3-3 for some typical PERs.

This method has a number of shortcomings, but we have no generally accepted method that can replace it. One of the criticisms is that rats have a different amino acid requirement than humans do. Humans need eight essential amino acids; rats need ten. Rats have a particular requirement for arginine, which is not considered essential in the human diet. Any food limiting in arginine would have a low PER, but it could be an excellent food for humans if the remaining amino acids are present in optimum amounts. Another criticism is that rats are fur-bearing animals; we are not. This affects the requirements for the sulfur-containing amino acids, which are needed for the growth of fur.

Because the basal diet is complete for all nutrients except protein, which must be added to achieve a 10 percent level, certain problems may result. For example, if the protein source is fairly low, as it is in a cereal product, a large amount of the food product must be added to get a level of 10 percent. This will then dilute the other nutrients in the basal diet and add too much starch. To overcome this, the protein becomes concentrated, which may have an adverse effect on the protein.

The same situation is present in an oilseed. Even though the protein level is quite high, the level of oil can have an adverse effect on the test; hence, the oil often is removed. When making these adjustments, the protein can be affected so that a true nutritional evaluation is not possible.

Another criticism of the method points out that since the test is based on feeding protein only, the significance of the results when we normally eat several proteins at a meal seems questionable. Despite this criticism, as well as the others mentioned above, the method is useful and widely accepted in evaluating proteins.

There are some people who believe another test animal should be used, such as the pig. The pig has a digestive system similar to ours and has similar nutritional requirements, and tests show that certain food products produce far better results in the pig.

Amino Acid Score (AAS). Because the value of a protein food depends on its amino acid content, some idea of its protein quality could be obtained by noting its amino acid content, particularly by noting the degree to which an amino acid is limiting.

Both the Food and Nutrition Board (FNB) and the Food and Agriculture Organization/World Health Organization (FAO/WHO) of the United Nations published recommended amino acid pattern requirements. These are shown in

Table 3-3   Protein Efficiency Ratios (PERs) of Various Food Products

Food Products	PER	Food Product	PER
Beans (average, dried)	1.9[1]	Oats	
Beef		Rolled	1.5[1]
Ground	2.5[2]	Flour	1.94[5]
Lean (15% fat)	2.96[3]	Peas	
Tissue (partially defatted)	1.7[3]	Dried	0.7[1]
Blood protein isolate	2.8[2]	Flour (field peas)	1.8[8]
Chicken meat		Peanuts	
(hand deboned)		Shelled	1.6[1]
Raw	3.13[3]	Flour	1.72[5]
Cooked	3.00[3]	Potato flour	1.68[5]
Corn		Rice	
Whole	1.4[4]	Whole	2.4[1]
Meal	0.7[4]	Polished	1.9[1]
Gluten meal	0.42[5]	Flour	1.35[5]
Protein isolate	0.28[5]	Sesame	
Cottonseed		Seed	1.2[1]
Meal	2.3[2]	Flour	1.17[5]
Flour	1.70[5]	Soy	
Egg		Flour (defatted, heated)	1.8[1]
Whole	3.2[4]	Flour (extruded)	2.0[1]
Egg white	2.5[4]	Protein concentrate	2.2[1]
Fish	3.1[1]	Protein isolate	1.3–1.8[4,7]
Fish protein concentrate	2.5[1]	Sunflower seed	1.5[1]
Gelatin	neg[1]	Wheat	
Milk		Bran flour	1.2[4]
Whole	3.2[1]	White flour	0.7[4]
Nonfat dry milk	2.9[1]	Durum flour	0.9[4]
Casein	2.5[1]	Protein concentrate	1.4[1]
Whey	2.9[4]	Gluten	1.3[1]
Whey protein concentrate	2.74[6]	Yeast protein concentrate	1.8[4]
Lactalbumin	2.4[4]		

[1] *The Growing Challenge* 1977.
[2] Sutton et al. 1978.
[3] Lee et al. 1978.
[4] Hsu et al. 1978.
[5] Steinke et al. 1980.
[6] Happich et al. 1975.
[7] Hopkins 1979.
[8] *Food Product Development*, "New Pea Flour," 1980.

Table 3-4   Amino Acid Pattern Needs

	Rat	FAO/WHO	FNB
Isoleucine	4.6	4.0	4.2
Leucine	6.2	7.0	7.0
Lysine	7.5	5.5	5.1
Total Sulfur Amino Acids (Methionine and Cystine)	5.0	3.5	2.6
Total Aromatic Amino Acids (Phenylalanine and Tyrosine)	6.7	6.0	7.3
Threonine	4.2	4.0	3.5
Tryptophane	1.3	1.0	1.1
Valine	5.0	5.0	4.8
Histidine	2.5	1.4	1.7
Arginine	5.0	—	—

Table 3-4 along with the rat requirement pattern. There are marked differences among the three.

Since it would appear that protein quality is dependent on the presence of each of the essential amino acids in the proper amount, then the degree to which the most limiting amino acid is lacking would determine the quality of that particular protein. If a protein has all the essential amino acids in at least the amounts given in the table, then it can be considered a good protein, as far as humans are concerned. It will have an AAS of 100. If the most limiting amino acid is half of that shown in the table, then its score would be 50. Table 3-5 compares amino acid scores based on the two patterns.

Even this approach has its limitations. What about digestibility? If the protein is not completely digested, it cannot be used efficiently. There may even be other factors influencing protein quality that we are overlooking. Obviously, the best determination is the in vivo determination in which a human subject responds directly; but, unfortunately, this is not always practical.

Limiting Amino Acids

In rat-feeding studies, whole egg protein was found to produce the highest PER of all the proteins tested. Some nutritionists believe that the amino acid profile of whole egg would be ideal when comparing the amino acid contents of various proteins, that is, to obtain an AAS. Table 3-6 lists a few food items with their amino acid scores.

The table reveals that, relative to egg, the foods checked were deficient in one or more amino acids. Of special interest is the apparent deficiency of methionine in human milk. For the sake of comparisons, the table also includes the FAO/WHO and FNB patterns to see how they compare with the egg pattern.

Table 3-5   Amino Acid Scores Compared

Food Item	Amino Acid Scores[1]	
	FAO/WHO Pattern[2]	FNB Pattern[3]
Milk, human	100	97
Milk, cow	94	100
Nonfat dry milk	100	100
Egg	100	100
Casein	97	100
Beef muscle	100	100
Pork tenderloin	96	100
Fish	100	91
Oats	62	67
Rye	71	76
Rice	69	75
Cornmeal	53	55
Sorghum	51	55
White flour	36	39
Wheat germ	74	82
Wheat gluten	31	33
Groundnut flour (peanut)	64	68
Soy flour	91	100
Sesame seed	45	49
Sunflower seed	56	61
Cottonseed meal	88	84
Potato	71	70
Navy bean	57	77
Soy protein isolate	77[3]	100

[1] FAO/WHO = Food and Agriculture Organization/World Health Organization; FNB = Food and Nutrition Board of the National Academy of Sciences.

[2] Scores from *The Growing Challenge* 1977.

[3] Scores calculated by the author.

Both are markedly deficient compared to whole egg. All this leads us to believe that the amino acid profile of egg is not the best pattern to follow when considering protein quality for humans. This also casts further doubt on using the rat to evaluate proteins for human nutrition.

In some cases, amino acids such as lysine, tryptophane, and methionine may be added to foods that are particularly deficient. Normally, this is a straightforward approach, but complications can arise. For example, methionine if present to great amount can be toxic. Because of this danger, the FDA requires that

Table 3-6 Amino Acid Scores Based on the Whole-Egg
Amino Acid Pattern

Food Item	Score	Limiting Amino Acid
Human milk	74	Methionine/Cystine
Cow's milk	58	Methionine/Cystine
Soy flour	56	Methionine/Cystine
White flour	29	Lysine
Standard Patterns		
FAO/WHO	59	Tryptophane
FNB	62	Methionine/Cystine

the amino acid content of whole egg be used as a standard. When any amino acid fortification is used, the total level of any one particular amino acid cannot exceed that found in whole egg.

Another limiting factor to be considered in using methionine as an additive is its flavor. Fairly high levels of methionine as an additive result in an objectionable flavor. This objection, coupled with its high price, seriously hampers the widespread use of methionine in food, except for animal feeds and in infant formulations.

COUNTING CALORIES

The major components of food—protein, fat, and carbohydrates—contribute energy to the body when they are digested and absorbed. The energy values are in terms of *calories*. The unit customarily used by nutritionists for measuring the energy needs of the body are 1,000 calories, or one *kilocalorie*. A more popular term for the kilocalorie is the *Calorie* (spelled with a capital C). The Calorie is defined as the amount of heat required to raise the temperature of 1 liter of water from 15°C to 16°C.

It is important for the foodservice technologist to have a working knowledge in calculating the Caloric content of a food preparation, particularly because of consumer interest in nutrition. There are an increasing number of restaurants that provide the Caloric content of the meals on the menu. In addition, there is a trend toward using nutrient density, which is nothing more than listing the nutrients based on the Caloric content, usually per 100 Calories. This probably will be the approach used in nutritional labeling.

To illustrate, consider the iron content of a club steak and lima beans. A 100-gram portion of a club steak has 454 Calories and 2.3 milligrams of iron. For each 100 Calories, the steak contains about 0.5 milligrams of iron. One cup of lima beans has 118 Calories and contains 3.1 milligrams of iron. For each 100 Calories, there are 2.6 milligrams of iron. (A usual serving of lima beans is about $\frac{1}{2}$ cup, or 59 Calories and 1.5 milligrams iron.) However, there is another factor that is not addressed: the nutritional *availability* of iron. In some vegetable products, the iron may be tied up so that it is unavailable. Nevertheless, the example is given to illustrate the concept of nutrient density, which can apply to grams of protein per 100 Calories or to any other nutrient.

Although there are many things to be considered when making calculations for the Caloric content of foods, such as digestibility and specific values for nutrients of a particular origin, a reasonable estimate can be made that is acceptable to most people.

For purposes of calculation, each gram of carbohydrate and protein is equal to 4 Calories; each gram of fat is 9 Calories. Water and minerals do not contribute to the Caloric content of foods. The same can be said of vitamins, since they are present in minute amounts.

Calculating Caloric Content

1. If the protein, fat, and carbohydrate contents of a food are listed as percentages, then consider each value given as units per 100 units of food. Since units are only relative values, we will now consider units as grams. In some cases, nutritional data on foods are based on a serving portion in terms of weight or volume. In most of these cases, the analytical data are given in grams, thereby making the calculation easier.
   a. Domestic Swiss cheese
      Protein—27.5 percent
      Fat—28.0 percent
      Carbohydrates—1.7 percent
   b. Low-fat milk
      (Serving size: 1 cup)
      Protein—8 grams
      Fat—5 grams
      Carbohydrates—11 grams
2. Take the protein and carbohydrate contents of the food (as found by analysis),* multiply by 4, and note this value.
   a. $4(27.5 + 1.7) = 116.8$
   b. $4(8 + 11) = 76$

---

*Normally, carbohydrate analysis is not made. It is usually arrived at by difference, that is, add protein, fat, water, ash, and fiber and subtract this total from 100 to arrive at the sugar or carbohydrate content. The amount of sugar added to a formulation can also be used, but cooking or baking losses must be taken into consideration. Another problem is that the difference procedure will include dietary fiber, which does not contribute Calories to the food.

3. Multiply the fat content by 9 and add this value to that found for the protein and carbohydrate.
   a. $28.0 \times 9 = 252$
      $252 + 116.8 = 368.8$
      or 369 Calories/100 grams of cheese.
   b. $5 \times 9 = 45$
      $76 + 45 = 121$ Calories per cup of milk.
4. Example b can be considered finished because it gives the caloric content of a serving size. For Example a, we need to convert to a serving size of 1 slice or 1 ounce. When converting, use one of the following conversion factors:
      1 ounce = 28.35 grams
      100 grams = 3.527 ounces
      1 pound = 453.6 grams
   a. Since 28.35 grams is 28.35 percent of 100 grams we can multiply the 369 Calories by 28.35 percent.
      $369 \times 0.2835 = 104.6$
      Or we can divide by 3.527.
      $369/3.527 = 104.6$
      Hence, one slice = 105 Calories.
5. Because it might be more convenient to work in pounds and ounces, change the Caloric content found in step 3 for 100 grams by multiplying this value by 4.54, which gives the Caloric content per pound of product.
6. Once this figure is obtained, it is a simple matter to find the Caloric content of slices, ounces, or portions by dividing the Calories in a pound of product by the number of units per pound.

REFERENCES

Bressani, R. 1975. "Nutritional Contribution of Soy Protein to Food Systems." *J. Amer. Oil Chem.* 52:254A–62A.

Cravens, W. W. 1970. Personal communication. Fort Wayne, Ind.

Food Product Development. 1980. "New Pea Flour Uses in Snacks, Cereals, Pasta." *Food Prod. Dev.* 41 (Aug.):86–7.

Food Technology. 1979. "Dietary Fiber. A Scientific Status Summary by the Institute of Food Technologists' Expert Panel on Food Safety and Nutrition and the Committee on Public Information." *Food Tech.* 33:35–9.

The Growing Challenge. 1977. Shawnee Mission, Kan.: ADM Milling.

Happich, M. L., R. A. Whitmore, S. Feairheller, M. M. Taylor, C. E. Swift, and J. Naghski. 1975. "Composition and Protein Efficiency Ratio of Partially Defatted Chopped Beef and of Partially Defatted Beef Fatty Tissue and Combinations With Selected Proteins." *J. Food Sci.* 40:35–9.

Hopkins, D. T. 1979. "How Should Protein Quality for Humans Be Determined?" In

Soy Protein and Human Nutrition, ed. H. L. Wilcke, D. T. Hopkins, and D. H. Waggle, 299–301. New York: Academic Press.

Hsu, H. W., N. E. Sutton, M. O. Banjo, L. D. Satterlee, and J. G. Kendrick. 1978. The C-PER and T-PER Assays for Protein Quality." *Food Tech.* 32(12):69–73, 68.

Lee, Y. B., J. G. Elliott, D. A. Rickansrud, and E. C. Hagberg, 1978. "Predicting Protein Efficiency Ratio by the Chemical Determination of Connective Tissue Content in Meat. *J. Food Sci.* 43:1359–62.

Mayer, J., and J. Goldberg. 1980. "Water Outweighs Protein, Vitamins as Body's Most Important Nutrient." *Chicago Tribune* (Thurs., Sept. 11), Sec. 7:15.

Recommended Dietary Allowances, 9th ed. 1980. Washington, D.C.: National Academy of Sciences.

Steinke, F. H. 1979. "Measuring Protein Quality of Foods." In *Soy Protein and Human Nutrition,* ed. H. L. Wilcke, D. T. Hopkins, and D. H. Waggle, 307–323. New York: Academic Press.

———, E. E. Prescher, and D. T. Hopkins. 1980. "Nutrition Evaluation (PER) of Isolated Soybean Protein and Combinations of Food Proteins." *J. Food Sci.* 45:323–7.

Sutton, M. O. 1978. Cited by Hsu et al. *Food Tech.* 32:68, 69–73.

USDA/ARS. 1963. *Composition of Foods.* Agricultural Handbook No. 8. Washington, D.C.: U.S. Government Printing Office.

Chapter 4
Functional Properties and Economics

Nutritional benefits are important reasons for using protein additives in foods, but there are other benefits that may be more motivating to the foodservice operator, such as functionality and economics. These may be more appealing because they seem to be more obvious. Both of these benefit areas will be discussed in some detail, with greater emphasis placed on functionality. The discussion on economics will be fairly short because this aspect will be covered in more detail in the chapters covering specific applications.

When discussing functionality, every effort will be made to keep the information simple and practical. For those who wish to delve into the subject in greater detail, see the following references: Cherry (1981); Schultz and Anglemier (1964); Whitaker and Tannenbaum (1977); and Paul and Palmer (1972).

FUNCTIONAL PROPERTIES

In Chapter 1, functionality was discussed very briefly. As stated in the definition by Pour-El (1979, 1981), functionality is any property of a food or food ingredient, except its nutritional one, that affects its utilization. Obviously, this can mean those properties that are either beneficial or detrimental in the food system where the protein additive is being used. It is important to be aware of both detrimental properties and beneficial properties, at least from the standpoint of avoidance and/or corrective action.

What are some of the beneficial functional properties, other than nutritional, that proteins may possess? Some typical properties are provided in the following list.

Improve
  Color
  Shelf life
  Taste
  Texture
Increase
  Total solids
  Viscosity
Bind
  Fat
  Particles
  Water
Surfactant
Emulsifier
Stabilizer

How does a foodservice technician select a particular protein to achieve the desired effect? Unfortunately, there is no simple answer and there is no simple test. A protein can be characterized by simple laboratory tests, but the results of such information cannot always be related to specific effects.

Each protein is a unique molecule with its own particular characteristics. It is true that there are certain similar characteristics proteins share, but there are many more that will be dissimilar in many ways, particularly in terms of the way they might function in various foods. It is almost an impossibility to find two proteins of different origins that will be alike in a number of functional characteristics, so it is practically impossible to substitute one protein for another in all applications, unless some adjustments are made in each situation. Very often, such adjustments may never be entirely satisfactory.

Knowing this, how can we look for a protein product to perform an expected function? One way is to draw from past experiences where certain results were always achieved. Another is simply to try one or more products and note the changes. Guidance may be gleaned from technical literature, but even here we cannot be sure that the performance will turn out as expected. Although there is a great deal of science involved in the use of protein additives, we need to be aware that art, too, plays an important role.

There is another important fact to remember: If expected results are not achieved with one company's product, try another. The same results cannot always be obtained with competitive products. This statement will be appreciated when it is realized how minor processing differences will have significant influences on functionality. Obviously, this need not be carried to an extreme. However, before it is concluded that a particular generic product (the same type) will not function as expected, two or three competitive products should be tried.

Classification

It is difficult to classify protein products based on their properties because they do not fit into neat little groups. There are always gray areas that defy categorization. Nevertheless, it is often advantageous to make such classifications, recognizing that gray areas do exist. Some type of classification is necessary to permit a person to look at the various properties in some logical manner.

In a classification scheme, there are four broad types of properties for protein additives: physical, chemical, functional, and nutritional. We cannot overlook the fact that both physical and chemical properties have a bearing on functionality. For example, the physical form of a product may affect its solubility, which in turn may determine how the product must be added in a food formulation. Even the color of the product will have a bearing. It may be good and appropriate in one case but bad or inappropriate in another.

Usually, chemical properties provided by the supplier are nothing more than proximate analyses. Sometimes other laboratory findings are included, but not always. If the protein level is low for the type of protein being considered, we can assume that there will be other components present that may or may not affect functionality. Most certainly, the level of protein present will be a factor. The ash content, being composed of one or more elements, may be an important consideration, especially when it is known that some elements, particularly certain metals, may have an adverse effect on the system.

There are many things that may interact to affect the functionality of a protein additive. It may seem like we are facing an impossible task in considering such additives. However, this is no different than working with most food additives and ingredients. These are just some of the problems that a chef encounters regularly, but through his or her early training and experience, he or she knows what to avoid and what to follow.

Functional properties may be broken down into two broad areas: *enzymatic* and *nonenzymatic*. The enzymatic properties will be of relatively minor importance to us. We will encounter protein products that will have some enzyme activity. In some cases, that activity will be beneficial, in others it will be a problem with which we must deal. Only to this extent will we be discussing enzymatic properties. This will become clearer when we discuss lipoxygenase activity in specific applications. In some cases the enzyme is beneficial, in others it is a problem.

Under the nonenzymatic heading, there are a number of subheadings in which all the various functional properties can be placed. For our purpose we will use only three: *sensory, hydrational,* and *surfactant.*

Sensory properties are readily recognized by our senses: color, texture or form, taste, and flavor.

Hydrational properties are those that a protein exhibits when combined with water. How does it wet? Is it dispersible or soluble? What effect does heat have on the dispersibility and solubility? Will the protein form a gel? Under what conditions? How much water does it bind? And, when dispersed in water, how does the dispersion flow, or what is the viscosity of the dispersion?

Surfactant properties are associated with water, but with one difference—these properties exhibit activity at an interface, that is, at the boundary between two imiscible substances: water and oil, water and air, water and the container, particles suspended in water, and so forth.

Using the above three broad categories as a guide, we will now examine the various functional properties of proteins.

Sensory Properties

Color. As pointed out by Blouin et al. (1981), color is probably the first property of a food that is noticed, and in many cases a person will make some judgment as to the quality of the food based on its color. Obviously, past experience plays an important part in making such a judgment.

Most of the widely used protein additives have colors that range from white to tan. If any other color is encountered, it is usually due to the presence of color-containing components that may be impurities. They may or may not be an undesirable factor, depending on the type of color and its intensity.

Cottonseed flour has good potential in many applications, but there may be a problem with color in certain applications, such as in biscuits at a level of 20 percent when the color of the final product is yellow-brown (Blouin et al. 1981). There is some indication that the presence of other food ingredients and/or metal ions will also influence color, not only with cottonseed protein products but also with others.

Sunflower flour also has a color problem apparently caused by the hull of the seed. Although it is relatively easy to remove the hull from the kernel, the high oil content of the hull makes it impractical to do so (Khan et al. 1980). One of the components responsible for color in sunflower is chlorogenic acid, which responds to changes in pH. "At various pH levels, the meal turns from white, pH 3; to beige, pH 6; to green, pH 9; to brown, pH 12" (Burns et al. 1972, p. 288).

Heat. Heat, particularly moist heat, may cause color development in many types of protein products due to the Maillard reaction. The color is the result of a reaction between lysine and a reducing sugar such as glucose, maltose, or lactose. Maltose is the disaccharide composed of two glucose molecules, which is formed in the enzymatic breakdown of starch. The reaction can be catalyzed under alkaline conditions. From the nutritional standpoint, the browning reaction detracts from the protein quality of a product, particularly cereals. Since lysine is already a limiting amino acid in cereals, it becomes even more limiting when it combines irreversibly with a reducing sugar. If another lysine-rich protein product, such as soy, is also present, it can offset the deficiency. If we wish to retain as much lysine as possible when working with a cereal product, there are a number of things that can be done or approaches that can be taken:

1. Avoid using reducing sugars. (Sucrose, or table sugar, is not a reducing sugar.)
2. Use a minimum amount of heat.
3. Add a lysine-rich protein source, such as soy.
4. Avoid alkaline conditions.
5. If color is desired, consider a color additive, such as caramel coloring.

Conversely, if we wish to develop the brown color, the Maillard reaction can be favored by adding reducing sugars, a small amount of sodium bicarbonate to achieve mildly alkaline conditions, and soy protein, and then using moist heat.

Texture and/or Form. From the sensory standpoint, texture and/or form of the product is the second most readily noticed property. In the preparation of a protein product, the physical form can be of several types. The simplest is achieved by grinding to a particular particle size, which is what is usually done in the preparation of a basic oilseed protein product. When the oil is removed from an oilseed, the resulting product is usually referred to as a meal. In the preparation step, the meal is ground into a flour or a grit. The only difference between the two products is particle size. Flour is a fine-ground product having a mesh size of 100 or finer. A grit or granular-type product is coarser than 100 mesh.

Other protein additive preparations are spray dried. In this case, the particle size is dependent on other factors, such as the type and size of the spray nozzles. In other cases, such as with egg white, the product may be in the form of a flake when it is dried on a roller or a belt.

In many cases, the various protein products may be made into one or more forms that may function in a different way, depending on the form being used or on particle size.

We will now consider a case when soy flour was used in a pureed baby food. It was rejected for this use because the product produced a sandy mouth feel, yet when the grit-type product was used, the product was found to be acceptable. It would appear that, in the latter case, the larger particles gave one the oral sensation of texture, whereas in the former instance it was simply sandy. Apparently, in one case the mouth feel was expected and in the other it was not.

The several forms previously discussed may not be satisfactory in all situations because their physical form may be incompatible in the food system in which they are being used. A good example is a protein product that is used as a meat extender, particularly for ground-meat products. In this case, the product is more compatible when it has a texture closely simulating the texture of the meat form. Texture is usually achieved by an extrusion cooking process. More will be said about these products in Chapter 7.

Taste and Flavor.   For the most part, protein products per se are bland. If they have flavors, it is usually due to the presence of accompanying volatiles that were not completely removed in preparation. In many cases, taste (sweet, sour, salty, or bitter) is the result of the chemicals used in preparation, such as salts, acids, and alkalines.

Flavors can develop in the preparation of protein products if the proteins are partially broken down as, for example, in hydrolyzed vegetable proteins. There are two ways this can happen. One may be an acid hydrolysis, the other an enzymatic breakdown, through the use of an enzyme preparation or by a fermentation process. Both of these approaches may be used to treat a protein additive to modify its functional properties. In many instances, we can tell which process is being used by tasting the preparation. If it has a salty taste, it probably was an acid hydrolysis, whereas if it has a bitter taste, it probably was an enzymatic preparation.

There is a flavor problem in some soy flours that is believed to be due to a naturally occuring enzyme called lipoxygenase. The enzyme oxidizes the residual fat in the product and causes the so-called "beany" flavor. In the earlier days of soy processing, this was more of a problem than it is today because processors know so much more about processing.

Hydrational Properties
As stated earlier, the hydrational properties are those that are associated primarily with water. "Water absorption or hydration is considered by some as the first and critical step in imparting desired functional properties to protein" (Hutton and Campbell 1981, p. 177). Interaction with water is, perhaps, the most important property proteins have, because without it the protein will not function.

Wettability.   Wettability is the ease with which a product will wet with water. This property can be very important to a user, particularly if special procedures are needed to solubilize a protein additive.

Some protein products are extremely difficult to wet for several reasons. If the powdery product has a high affinity for water, it will tend to ball up. A barrier is formed by the combination of protein and the water at the surface of a ball-like mass, which will not allow other water to pass through, thereby preventing the dry material on the inside from wetting. Special measures are needed to permit all the protein to come in contact with water. One approach is to use a whirling-type blade that will cut through the "balled" material. A Waring blender has blades that will do the job adequately, but the action should be at low speed to prevent whipping air in.

If the protein is being used in an emulsified fat system, it may be thoroughly dispersed in the melted fat before the other ingredients, including water, are added.

Another approach is to use the protein in its insoluble form, such as in its isoelectric state. This type of product will usually wet quite readily. After being thoroughly wetted and dispersed, it can be neutralized to form the soluble proteinate.

If the protein is in the form of larger spongy particles, this, too, may be used to speed up solubilization. Similar to this approach is the use of an agglomerated or instantized product. There are a number of patented approaches used to produce such products. One is to add water as fine droplets to the protein powder and mix well, causing the small particles to stick together in a random manner and form a spongelike particle after drying. When the agglomerated dry product is added to water, it will wet more readily.

In some cases, the protein may be spray dried or mixed with a surfactant such as a lecithin product, which has a beneficial effect that allows it to be wetted more easily.

Solubility and Dispersibility. These are terms that are often used interchangeably, even though there is a difference as defined by the physical chemist. The difference is essentially one of particle size when disassociated in water. For our purpose, we will consider the two terms to be synonymous.

In Chapter 2, we saw that proteins can be classified by their solubilities in various solvents, particularly in water and/or salt solutions. There are a number of factors that will affect the solubility of proteins in water. One is pH. Proteins are least soluble at their isoelectric point, which is often around pH 4.6. As the pH is changed on either side of the isoelectric point, solubility increases (Fig. 4-1). Moist heat also affects the solubility of proteins because of its denaturing effect.

Functionality is a function of solubility; that is, the more soluble the protein, the greater the chances for it to be more functional. This does not mean that a completely insoluble protein will be nonfunctional. In all likelihood, it will absorb water or fat and will contribute toward the total solids content of the food. It may even aid in making emulsions, especially if it is in the finely divided form. All of these can be considered functional properties by supposedly nonfunctional products. (In some cases, finely divided particles can cause foaming.) As a general rule, the soluble proteins will have more functional properties than the less soluble ones.

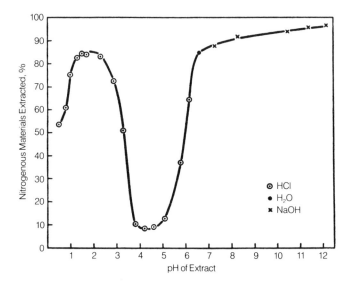

Figure 4-1. Extractability of protein in defatted soybean meal as a function of pH. (*Source:* Adapted from Smith and Circle 1938 by Wolf and Cowan 1971.)

The solubility characteristics of oilseed proteins, particularly soy, are usually given in the technical literature because this property is important. As we shall see shortly, the use of heat in the processing of soy products has a marked influence on protein solubility.

Influence of Heat on Solubility. In Chapter 2, we mentioned that moist heat affects the solubility of proteins. The denaturing effect on proteins is a function of temperature and time. This temperature/time relationship is interdependent; to achieve the same degree of denaturation, a higher temperature will require a shorter time and a lower temperature will require a longer time. Since many protein products are subjected to a certain amount of heat, which has a denaturing effect and influences the functionality of the product, it is often important to know to what degree denaturation has taken place. The determination is performed in the laboratory by checking the solubility of the protein and is reported in terms of percent soluble nitrogen or protein. The two most widely used methods are the Nitrogen Solubility Index (NSI) and the Protein Dispersibility Index (PDI). The influence of heat on protein solubility and on functional properties can be better appreciated if we look at a stage of soybean processing.

A most important step in processing defatted soybean flakes, following solvent extraction, is heat treating. It is important because the resulting protein is the parent substance for most of the specialty soy protein products used as food

Table 4-1 Characteristics of Defatted Soybean Flakes with Varying
          Degrees of Moist-Heat Treatment

Type	Heat Treatment	Protein Solubility (%)	Enzyme Activity	Trypsin-Inhibitor Activity	Taste
Enzyme active	Nil	70–90	Very high	Very high	Bitter/beany
White	Light	50–70	High	High	Bitter/beany
Cooked	Moderate	25–50	Moderate	Moderate	Beany
Toasted	Heavy	<25	Nil	Nil	Sweet/nutty

ingredients and additives. At this point, certain functional properties can be either destroyed or optimized for the various products arising out of the heat-treated, defatted soybean flakes.

After the oil is extracted and a defatted flake is obtained, it is necessary to remove the residual solvent. This operation is critical because if heat is used, the protein will become denatured to some degree, especially if there is some moisture present (which will likely be present in some residual amounts). If the desire is to obtain a product with the highest possible soluble protein content, then it is necessary to take special measures in removing the solvent. The two most common methods are using a vacuum or a superheated solvent. The latter technique is very effective because the vapors are "dry," causing excellent heat transfer. Through the judicial use of these methods, it is possible to obtain products that will have a PDI or an NSI in the range of 70 to 90 percent. Because there is so little denaturation, these products will have high enzyme activity. As a result, they are often called *enzyme active*.

When more moist heat is used in treating the extracted protein product, these products fall into three broad categories, according to the amount of heat used: light, moderate, and heavy. The respective solubility indices would be as follows: light is 50 to 70 percent, moderate is 25 to 50 percent, and heavy is less than 25 percent.

Moist-heat treatment also has an influence on the color of the resulting product. Some processors refer to these products as white, cooked, and toasted. Since color development is due to the Maillard reaction, which is induced by the heat, we get the range of products from white to toasted, a deep-brown color. To most of us toasting usually refers to the use of dry heat. Between these two extremes, we have the cooked product.

Table 4-1 compares the characteristics of the different flake products. A number of things can be noted, including the four degrees of heat treatment and the four ranges of protein solubilities. Since enzymes are proteins, their activities decrease as they are exposed to heat. For this same reason, trypsin-inhibitor activity drops off as the product is exposed to heat. Heat treatment also has an influence on the flavor of the product. The white product is bitter and beany, whereas the toasted product is sweet and nutty, with the moderately cooked product being midway between these two.

We need to ask, "What is the significance of these differences?" First, the white product is more functional because it has a higher degree of solubility. However, it is poor from a nutritional standpoint because the trypsin inhibitor will interfere with the proper utilization of the protein. The toasted product does not have this problem, but its functionality is limited because most of its protein is denatured.

As a general rule, neither the enzyme-active nor the white products are ever recommended in food systems that receive little if any cooking in their preparation, because their flavors are not the best and their trypsin-inhibitor activity is quite high. In food systems that receive little if any cooking, it is best to use a toasted product.

The active enzyme (lipoxygenase) of white products may be used in an application such as baking, where it can be employed for its functional properties. When the dough is then subjected to the heat of the oven, the effect will be similar to that obtained with cooked and toasted products, that is, the flavor will improve and most of the trypsin inhibitor will be destroyed.

In the preceding explanations, nothing was said about the moderately heated products. Obviously, these products fall between the two discussed. More will be said about the use of these protein products in the chapters that cover specific applications.

Heat-Altered Products. We now know that functionality and heat treatment are interdependent. Heat obviously affects the structure of the protein molecule. At one extreme is an undenatured protein; at the other is a completely denatured protein. It seems reasonable to assume that proteins at either extreme will differ in their functional properties. A practical way to look at this is as follows. Think of a product being composed of many proteins, each of which has a different sensitivity to heat and its own particular functional property. As heat is used to denature the more sensitive proteins, others will withstand the heat and become more dominant with their functional properties. Such heat treatment can and will change the characteristics of a protein product for better or for worse in a particular application.

Users of a particular soy flour have specified a product having an NSI that falls within a narrow range, plus or minus 10 percent. Such products functioned best in their particular application. Obviously, then, this is a consideration that should not be overlooked.

Several terms are used interchangeably for *water-holding capacity* (WHC). Two of the most common are *water-binding* and *water-absorption*. As we shall see shortly, Quinn and Paton (1979) also use the abbreviation WHC, but their use of WHC refers to *water-hydration capacity*. The terms all refer to the maximum amount of water a protein will take up and retain when used in foods. Care should be exercised in the use of the term *bound water* because it has a different meaning from water-holding capacity. Bound water is water held very tightly within the protein molecule that is removed only with great difficulty.

According to Hutton and Campbell (1981), there are a number of methods being used to measure water absorption in proteins. They narrowed the methods down to the following:

1. *Relative Humidity Method.* Water absorption is defined as the water absorbed by a dry powder with equilibration against water vapor at a known relative humidity.
2. *Swelling Method.* In this method, a small amount of sample is dusted on a wet filter paper fastened on a glass filter. "The filter is fitted on top of a thermostated funnel filled with water and connected to a horizontally located capillary. The uptake of water is followed in the capillary. . . . Swelling is defined as the spontaneous uptake of water by the additive" (Hutton and Campbell 1981, p. 179).
3. *Excess Water Method.* Here the protein is exposed to excess water for a short time and then is centrifuged. The supernatant liquid is discarded and the residue is weighed to determine the amount of water taken up.
4. *Water Saturation Method.* This method is similar to the excess water method, except an effort is made not to have any supernatant liquid after centrifugation, that is, to use just enough water to saturate the sample.

After using the swelling and excess water methods and finding problems in their use, Quinn and Paton (1979) proposed the fourth method, the water saturation method, which they found to be more reproducible and more reliable. They claimed that the method "more closely simulates actual food product application conditions" because limited water rather than excess water is used (Quinn and Paton 1979, p. 39). Table 4-2 shows the reproducibility of a number of determinations by three operators. Table 4-3 compares the excess water and the water saturation methods using eight different protein products.

Since the WHC of proteins is influenced by environmental conditions such as pH, temperature, salt concentration, and the presence of other materials, specific conditions should be stated when the WHC of a protein product is reported.

Wolf and Cowan (1971) remind us that soy proteins contain numerous polar side chains along their "peptide backbones," thus making them hydrophilic; as a result, when proteins absorb water, they tend to retain it in the finished food product. "Some of the polar sites such as carboxyl and amino groups are ionizable; thus, polarity can be changed by varying pH. Changing pH alters the water absorption properties of soy flour" (Wolf and Cowan 1971, p. 125). They

**Table 4-2   Water-Hydration Capacity Expressed as
Milliliters per Gram of Sample**

	Operator 1	Operator 2	Operator 3
Vital gluten	1.3–1.4	1.3–1.4	1.3–1.4
	1.3–1.4	1.3–1.4	1.3–1.4
	1.3–1.4	1.3–1.4	1.3–1.4
	1.3–1.4	1.3–1.4	
Devitalized gluten	2.0–2.2	2.0–2.1	2.0–2.1
	2.0–2.2	2.0–2.1	1.9–2.1
	1.9–2.1	2.0–2.1	2.0–2.1
	1.9–2.1	1.9–2.0	
		2.0–2.1	
Textured soy concentrate	2.7–3.0	2.7–2.85	2.7–3.0
	2.3–2.7	2.7–2.85	2.7–3.0
	2.7–3.0	2.7–2.85	2.7–3.0
	2.3–2.7	2.7–2.85	
Rapeseed concentrate	2.5–2.8	2.7–2.85	
	2.7–3.0	2.7–2.85	
	2.7–3.0	2.7–2.85	
	2.7–3.0	2.7–2.85	

Source: Courtesy of Quinn and Paton 1979.

Table 4-3   Water-Hydration Capacity Values of Various Materials

	Excess Water Method[1]	Proposed Method[2]
Pea concentrate	1.05	1.31
Promosoy 100 concentrate	3.10	3.00
Promine D isolate	3.50	3.85
Supro 620 isolate	6.70	5.50
Rapeseed concentrate	4.50	3.29
Caseinate	0	2.33
Egg white	1.30	0.67
Whey concentrate	0	0.97

[1] Method of Fleming et al. 1974.
[2] Values were obtained before the technique was standardized. The values are estimates of where
the WHC lies within the experimentally determined range.
Source: Courtesy of Quinn and Paton 1979.

then point out that at pH 8.5 a doughlike mass of soy flour absorbs about twice as much water as a dough in the pH range of 4.5 to 6.3. Although Wolf and Cowan talked about soy protein, we can assume that much of what was said applies to other proteins as well.

When looking at some of the data published by Hutton and Campbell (1977) on water-absorption studies of soy protein concentrate and soy protein isolate, we learned that pH and temperature have more of a beneficial effect on the WHC of protein products that are soluble than those that are highly denatured.

It is interesting to note that the solubility of a soy protein can be increased at its isoelectric point by the addition of salt. Wolf and Cowan (1971) stated that "the majority of soy proteins are globulins. This class of proteins is insoluble in water in the region of their isoelectric point but will dissolve in the isoelectric state when salts such as sodium or calcium chloride are added" (Wolf and Cowan 1971, p. 105). They go on to point out that these proteins are soluble on either side of the isoelectric point in the absence of salt.

When reviewing the work of Professor Reiner Hamm on beef protein, Fennema (1977) reported that minimum WHC occurs at about pH 5.0, the isoelectric point of actomysin, the major protein of muscle. As the pH is changed on either side of the isoelectric point, WHC increases dramatically. He also reported that at pH values above the isoelectric point, sodium chloride greatly increases the WHC of beef, whereas below the isoelectric point an opposite effect occurs. Fennema said that "a satisfactory explanation for this behavior can be devised once it is realized that anions (Cl in this instance) generally exhibit stronger interactions with proteins than do cations (Na in this instance)" (Fennema 1977, p. 81).

Fennema goes on to say that the WHC of muscle is greatly influenced by the ionic strength of the medium. When sodium chloride is added to ground beef, maximum WHC occurs at an ionic strength equivalent to that of about 5 percent sodium chloride by weight.

Viscosity is a term used to describe the flowability of a liquid that results from the combined effects of adhesion and cohesion. It is the internal friction between adjacent layers of liquid. Viscosity can be measured in a number of ways. The simplest method is to measure the flow of a liquid through a tube. The longer the liquid takes to flow through the tube, the more viscous the material. (Viscosity studies come under a branch of science referred to as Rheology. Rheological studies are concerned with the deformation and the flow of matter. It is important to know a little about the rheological characteristics of proteins in food applications because such knowledge helps us make the necessary adjustments to achieve desired effects.)

As a general rule, we can expect the viscosity of a protein solution to increase as the concentration of the protein increases. Viscosity also increases as solubility increases. We would not expect a protein dispersion to be more viscous at its isoelectric point than at some other pH. Likewise, in some cases viscosity was found to increase as the temperature of the dispersion is raised, but only to a point. Above a critical temperature, the viscosity will drop off. This information is based on the findings of Circle et al. (1964) when they studied some of these properties of soy proteins.

Circle et al. also reported that the viscosity of an unheated soy protein dispersion will drop dramatically if the pH of the dispersion is changed from 7 to 6. However, on heating, they found that the viscosity increased and was equal to that of dispersions at pH 7 and 8. When the pH rose to 9, the viscosity dropped off, probably due to some hydrolysis of the protein.

It is possible to cause the viscosity of a protein dispersion to drop off if the dispersion is subjected to a great amount of mechanical agitation, but on standing for a short time, the viscosity will return to its original level.

Circle et al. learned that lipids (soybean oil and lecithin) and polysaccharides (wheat starch, carboxymethylcellulose, and carrageenan) increased the viscosities of the unheated dispersions and of most of the gels. They reported that two reducing agents, sodium sulfite and cysteine, markedly reduced the viscosity of both unheated and heated dispersions. Other reducing agents did not give the same results.

The preceding general statements may not hold for all proteins under all conditions, but these guidelines can be of help when deciding how to make the necessary adjustments if they are needed.

Under certain conditions, proteins will form gels, which may or may not be an advantage in a food system. Almost everyone is familiar with gelatin, but fewer persons are familiar with some of the gels that can be formed from vegetable proteins. The property of gelation can be of value in a number of food applications.

According to Schmidt (1981), gelation is a protein aggregation phenomenon: a polymer–polymer and polymer–solvent interaction in which there are both attraction and repulsion forces that are so well balanced that a network or matrix is formed. He states that this matrix is capable of entrapping large amounts of water.

The two techniques that are considered the most important in forming gels in food-processing systems are the use of divalent cations (calcium and magnesium) and/or heat treatment. It is believed that gelation is a two-step heat-treatment process. The first step involves an unfolding or dissociation of the protein molecule; the second involves an aggregation step in which association and aggregation reactions occur, resulting in gel formation under appropriate conditions. Schmidt goes on to say that "in a general sense there are two basic types of heat-induced gel structures depending on the conditions involved. These gel types may be generally termed: 1) thermo-set (or 'set') or reversible and 2) thermoplastic or irreversible gels" (1981, p. 132). The thermo-set gel is one where the gel sets up on cooling, like the gelatin gel, and, of course, is reversible. The thermoplastic gel is one that will set up on heating and is irreversible. It is

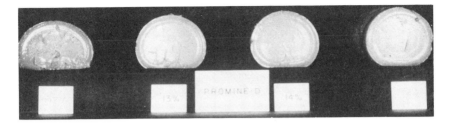

Figure 4-2. Photograph illustrating appearance of gels from 12%, 13%, 14%, and 15% sodium soy proteinate heated at 100°C for 30 minutes in no. 1 C-lined tinned cans.

possible for a protein product to form both types. This has been observed and reported for soy protein by Catsimpoolas and Meyer (1970).

The mechanisms involved in the gelation of proteins with cations are less defined than those suggested for heat-induced gelation, according to Schmidt (1981). Although this mechanism is difficult to explain, it has an extremely long history of usage. The Chinese produce tofu by this method, and they have been doing so for centuries. Tofu is made from soymilk by heating it to near boiling and then adding a divalent salt to produce a curd. The salt may be calcium, magnesium sulfate, or calcium chloride, or, in some cases, an acid may be used. The curd is washed in cold water to remove unwanted solubles and then is packed in water for distribution under refrigeration. Tofu can be considered a cheeselike product because in the production of dairy cheeses, complexes of calcium, phosphates, and casein also are formed.

Certain commercial preparations of soy protein isolates are produced that exhibit a gelation property. If these proteins are dispersed in water and heated above 160°F, they will form a gel that is irreversible. Figure 4-2 shows a photograph of one such product using protein concentrations of 12 to 15 percent. It can be seen that the gels are self-supporting. More will be said about these gels in Chapter 7.

Surfactant Properties

Surfactant properties are those that function at surfaces of *interfaces,* which are boundaries between immiscible substances such as gases, liquids, and solids. In our consideration of proteins, which usually are solubilized in aqueous systems, at least one of the phases will be water. Hence, the interfaces we are likely to encounter are those that exist between water and its container, water and air, water and any fine particles that may be dispersed in it, and, if there is an oil emulsion, water and oil.

Surfactants, or surface-active agents, tend to concentrate at interfaces and will function in a particular way in those areas. Certain proteins will function in such

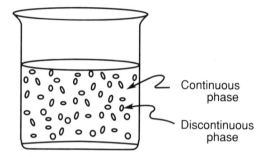

Figure 4-3. Continuous/discontinuous phases of an emulsion.

locations because their molecular structure may be composed of two parts that will have an affinity for the substances on either side of the interface.

When oil is emulsified in water, the emulsion is referred to as an oil-in-water (O/W) emulsion, where oil is in a discontinuous phase while the water is in a continuous phase. When water is emulsified in oil (W/O), the opposite is the case. It is possible to go from one type of emulsion to the other. A good example is cream being churned into butter. In the original situation, the cream is an O/W emulsion, but in the case of butter it is a W/O emulsion (Fig. 4-3).

Of special interest to us are food systems that contain both oil and water solutions of one type or another. Because both liquids are immiscible, special measures are needed to work with both in the same system. In most cases one liquid is finely dispersed in the other. The process of dispersing one in the other is called *emulsification*. The resultant product is referred to as an *emulsion*. While pure oil can be emulsified in pure water, such emulsions generally are not stable and will break in a relatively short time. Emulsification is easier and will be more stable if a proper surfactant is used.

As was previously stated, surfactants are compounds that have an affinity for the substances on either side of an interface. For oil and water, this means that one part is attracted to oil, while the other part is attracted to water. There are a number of terms used to denote the relationships of the emulsion components. In the example of oil-and-water emulsions, there are two classes of compounds that can be described through the use of certain prefixes. For water it is *hydro-* and for oil it is *lipo-*. Certain suffixes can be used to denote whether or not the substance has an affinity for or an aversion against. Hence, the suffix *-philic* means it has an attraction for, or an affinity for; on the other hand, *-phobic* means just the opposite, it has an aversion for, or does not have an affinity for, the substance. We can also think of these terms as meaning "loving" and "dreading." Thus, we use such terms as *hydrophilic, hydrophobic, lipophilic,* and *lipophobic.* Those substances having an aversion for water would be hydropho-

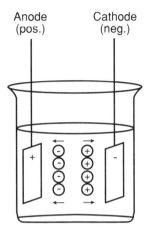

Figure 4-4.   Ion migration.

bic, and those having an aversion to oil would be lipophobic. Usually, a substance that is hydrophilic is lipophobic, and one that is lipophilic is hydrophobic.

Surfactants can also be classified as being *nonionic, cationic,* or *anionic,* depending on the nature of the hydrophilic group. These are terms that describe the "charge" on the lipophilic radical, that is, no charge (nonionic), positive charge (cationic), or negative charge (anionic). These terms will be better understood if we realize that the negative ions are attracted to an anode and positive ions are attracted to a cathode (Fig. 4-4).

One of the best known, commonly used surfactants is soap, the sodium salt of fatty acids. The fatty acid radical of soap is lipophilic, whereas at the site where the sodium is bound is hydrophilic. Soap acts at the interface between water and fat by forming a bond between the two. The molecules orient themselves so that the fatty acid end imbeds in fat, while the other end imbeds in water; the molecules of soap bridge across the interface between fat and water. When soap is used to clean a surface, this bridging action takes place and, as the water is moved along, the fat is carried with it. This is shown in Fig. 4-5.

Emulsions that are not stable may exhibit one of several conditions. These conditions are breaking, or coalescence; creaming; and flocculation (Fig. 4-6). *Breaking* is the spontaneous joining of the small droplets to form larger ones, which leads to a separation with one liquid floating on the other. This is what happens in some simple salad dressings that need shaking before use. *Creaming* is not emulsion breaking as such, but the emulsified oil will float en masse to the top, as when cream comes to the top in regular whole milk. Creaming usually occurs when the emulsion is fairly dilute and when the continuous phase has a

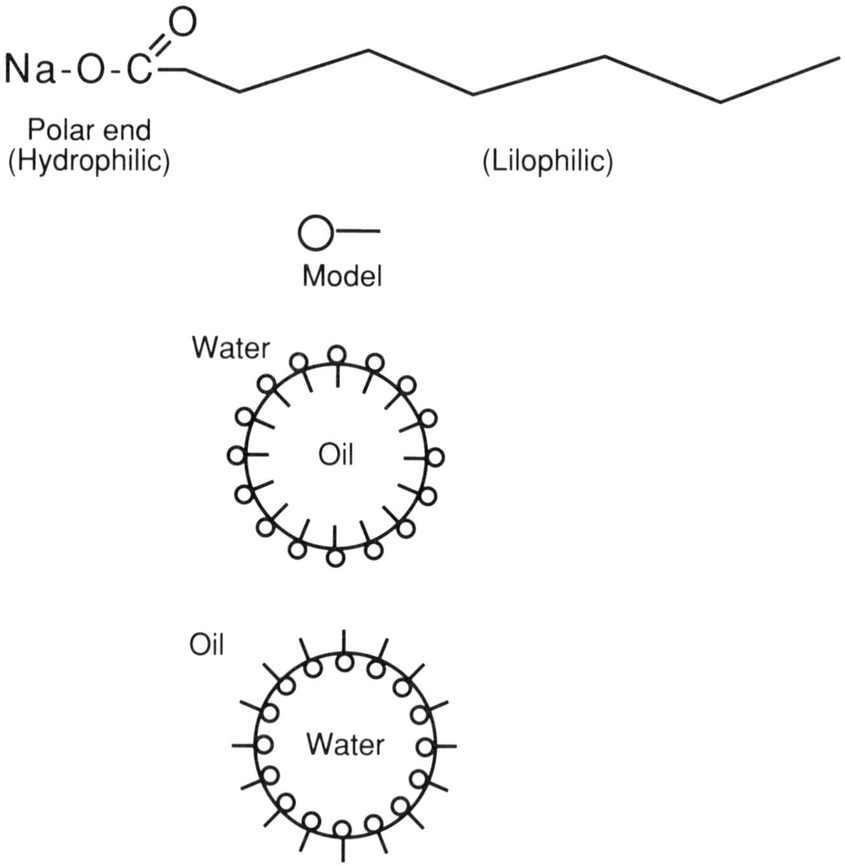

Figure 4-5. Soap/water/oil relationships.

low viscosity. *Flocculation* occurs when the dispersed droplets stick together, forming three-dimensional clusters. This also may be referred to as *feathering*, a defect that may occur with some coffee creamers. It would appear that the protein on the surface of the oil droplets sticks to others for one reason or another. In this case, the oil carries the floc to the top. Flocculation can happen if the protein is not of the proper type, making it susceptible to the presence of certain acids, divalent ions, and so on. To overcome this defect, it may be necessary to modify the protein, to use another type, to include another surfactant along with the protein, or to use certain salts and other buffers.

Liquids have a surface tension that tends to pull in on all sides, like a shrinking

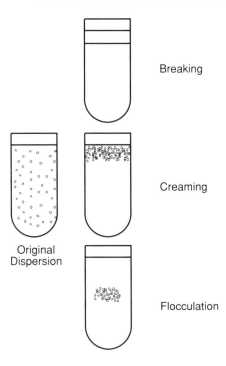

Figure 4-6. Diagrammatical representations of types of emulsion instability. (*Source:* Courtesy of Puski et al. 1974.)

skin, causing as little surface as possible to be exposed per unit volume. Since the structure that has the least surface area exposed per unit volume is a sphere, this is the shape that droplets tend to take.

In order for emulsification to take place, energy must be applied to the system, usually mechanical energy. This might be achieved by shaking, rapid stirring, whirling blades or propellers, colloidal mills, pressure homogenizers, or sound waves. In each of these, some type of shearing action must be used to reduce the size of the dispersed phase.

As pointed out by McWatters and Cherry, "Three separate mechanisms that appear to be involved in formation of a stable emulsion include: 1) reduction of interfacial tension, 2) formation of a rigid interfacial film, and 3) electrical charges" (1981, p. 217).

Surfactants will reduce the surface tension of a liquid, tending to allow the liquid to emulsify or to disperse more easily. Since they will also orient themselves on the surface of the dispersed spherical body, the surface tends to become more rigid, especially if other agents form layers or shells around the sphere

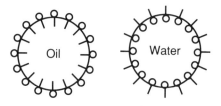

Figure 4-7.   Micelles.

called a *micelle* (Fig. 4-7). By the buildup of other materials that orient themselves on the surface of the micelle, charges may form that also will contribute to the stability of the emulsion. When all micelles have similar charges, they are held apart from one another. Emulsion technology can get quite complicated, especially if we consider all the theories that are put forward.

There are many things that affect the stability of an emulsion, especially when proteins are involved in the process. Any factors that affect the functionality of proteins will have some effect on the emulsion in which they are involved. These factors include the presence and/or the absence of salts, certain metals, temperature, or pH. Unfortunately, as reported by McWatters and Cherry, "No standardized tests exist for evaluating the emulsifying properties of proteins, and in many cases there seems to be little correlation between results obtained in model systems and those obtained in performance trials in food systems" (1981, p. 220).

According to Puski et al. (1974), the emulsifying properties of proteins depend on several factors. The amino acid composition and sequence determine the number of hydrophobic and hydrophilic side groups, which is very important. Only those hydrophobic and hydrophilic groups that are on the surface of the molecule take part in emulsification. Thus, those structures that determine the shape of the protein molecule have a major influence on emulsification properties.

The protein's interaction with various components and its solubility, the pH of the system, and the presence of certain salts as well as of other emulsifying agents are also important in influencing emulsifying properties. "Therefore, when such properties of proteins are discussed, we have to specify the whole system, and a statement such as "soybean proteins are good (or bad) emulsifying agents" can be misleading" (Puski et al. 1974, p. 1972).

In a number of emulsion systems, more stable emulsions can be obtained if a combination of emulsifiers is used together with certain buffering salts. Combinations of proteins and a number of the gums (for example, carrageenan) seem to have a synergistic effect. Water-soluble gums as a rule tend to stabilize O/W emulsions by increasing the viscosity and gelling characteristics. These agents appear to stabilize the emulsion by inhibiting coalescence. As far as viscosity is concerned, it should be noted that as the emulsion concentration increases, viscosity also tends to increase.

There are a number of factors that affect the stability of an emulsion. One is the size of the dispersed micelles. However, as the size is reduced, the surface area of the dispersed material is increased. This is an important consideration in some applications, such as the formation of a meat emulsion in making sausage. This will be covered in more detail in Chapter 7.

We will now use a simple example to show that as the emulsified particles are reduced in size, the surface area increases greatly. If a 1-inch cube is cut in half, 2 extra inches of surface are exposed. If these cubes are again cut in half, another 2 inches will be exposed. Thus, it appears that every time the remaining cubes are cut in half, or the number is doubled through this cutting action, an extra 2 square inches of surface will be exposed. This can be seen in Fig. 4-8.

Since we encounter spherical bodies rather than cubes in emulsions, we need to think in terms of spheres. It is fairly easy to calculate the surface area of an emulsion if we know the amount of liquid that is emulsified and the average diameter of the individual droplets. If 10 ml of oil are emulsified to the extent that the average droplet size is 0.1 μ, the total surface area will be 300 square meters (3,261 square feet). This fact can help us make certain judgments in the use of emulsifiers and additives. As a general rule, if the surface area is increased significantly more emulsifier will be needed. Also, if the balance is not proper between the two phases it is entirely possible that the emulsion will reverse, which could lead to disastrous results in a food system.

There are times when it is desirable to know with what type of emulsion we are working, whether it is O/W or W/O. Several simple tests can be performed that will allow us to determine this. One method uses powdered dyes that are soluble in water or in oil. The test is carried out by dusting a small amount of the dye over a small sample of the emulsion. If the color spreads throughout, then the continuous phase is of the type in which the dye is soluble. If it does not spread, then it is of the opposite type. One fat-soluble dye that will function well in this test is Sudan III. Some of the vegetable dyes can be used as water-soluble ones.

Another method that is also useful is to place a small amount of the emulsion on a plate or glass surface, add oil or water, and mix. Whichever material blends in evenly identifies the continuous phase. This can be observed using mayonnaise as the test emulsion. If water is used to mix with the mayonnaise, it will blend in very nicely, indicating that it is an O/W emulsion. If oil is used, it tends to mix with difficulty and looks like it has curdled. The same test can be performed using softened margarine. In this case, the oil blends and water does not. This test must be used with caution in those emulsions that can easily reverse their phases, such as with some creamy salad dressings.

When discussing the surfactant properties of proteins and a few basics of

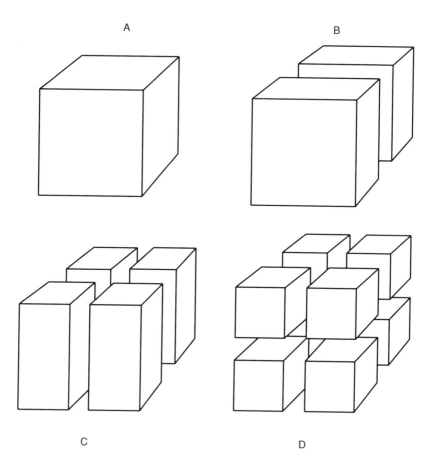

Figure 4-8. Visual—As a fixed volume is reduced in size the surface area increases. (Volume = 1 cubic inch. A = 6 square inches of surface area; B = 8 square inches of surface area; C = 10 square inches of surface area; D = 12 square inches of surface area.)

emulsion technology, we avoided many specifics. The specifics will be covered as needed in the rest of this text.

ECONOMICS

No matter what benefits a protein additive might have, the overriding factor is economic. If a benefit can be obtained with no adverse effects in using the protein for no additional cost, then that addition is attractive to foodservice management. However, if there is an additional cost, then management must weigh the benefit against that additional cost, that is, is the improvement worth the money?

Cost savings mean different things to different people. For instance, a home-maker is not interested in a savings of a few cents on a food that he or she feels is important, such as some animal product. This is not the case for someone who deals in large quantities, as in foodservice operations, where a savings of a fraction of a cent per portion is important. The significance of this shows up at the end of the fiscal year.

When selecting protein additives for beneficial economic returns, the food-service technologist should be aware of and on guard against making a snap decision based on the cost of an ingredient. Such judgments should not be made until that ingredient has been tried and all the factors have been considered. There are many instances when an ingredient that appears to be expensive results in a food product that costs less when the additive is used. Usually, these savings show up in the form of product yield. In other cases, the formulations were found to be superior in that there were fewer product failures and less of a need to rework products.

If a protein additive does increase cost, the question must be asked, "Is the noted improvement worth the extra cost?" Only management can answer that question after due consideration and, perhaps, after a little market testing.

Other than costly spices and flavoring, the most costly food ingredient is usually an animal protein product. If we are looking for a way to reduce costs, this is the ingredient to consider. The approach to be taken is to use a less expensive comparable ingredient, such as a vegetable protein, as a complete or a partial replacer. In taking this approach, a formulation adjustment probably will be needed. Guidelines for such adjustments will be given in the appropriate following chapters.

Unit-Protein Costs

Since our interest in using protein products is to get the greatest functionality out of them on a unit-cost basis, we need some way to assess comparative costs. Making cost comparisons on the additive per se is not satisfactory. It is better to do this on a unit-protein basis.

Table 4–4 Protein Factors to Determine Protein Price per Unit Weight

Animal Product		Vegetable Product	
Beef	5.0	Beans (dry)	4.5
Casein	1.0	Cornmeal	11.0
Cheese (Swiss)	3.5	Rice	15.0
Chicken/fish	5.0	Soy	
Dried skim milk	3.0	Defatted flour	2.0
Eggs (whole)		Protein concentrate	1.5
Fresh	7.5	Protein isolate	1.0
Dried	2.0	White flour	8.5

Note: Protein factor obtained by taking the reciprocal of the protein level of the food and rounding off to 0.5. (See text for explanation of usage.)

When making presentations on the use of soy proteins as valuable food additives, we often use charts showing price differences. The problem with this approach is that when a slide is made with today's prices, it is shortly out of date. When presentations are made in foreign countries, the problem is even greater. In these situations, the audience was familiar with only their own monetary and weight systems. How can we make it more meaningful? In arriving at a solution, we solved not only this problem but also the problem of changing prices. The approach is as follows.

A number of common animal and vegetable products are selected for comparative purposes. In each case, the reciprocal of the protein content is determined, with the result rounded off to a whole number, which we call a protein factor. Rounding off to whole numbers is done to make it easier for the audience to make some quick mental calculations. For our purpose, we will make the comparisons a little more accurate. Table 4-4 shows the same protein factor comparisons rounded off to the nearest one-half unit.

When using this table, all we need to do is to take the current price of a product and multiply it by the protein factor listed in the table, which gives the cost of protein on a per-unit-weight basis. Obviously, in making such comparisons no value is placed on the other components in the food. Our only interest is protein. For example, if nonfat dry milk (NFDM) costs $1.00 per pound, we find that the cost of the protein is $1.00 times the protein factor (three), or $3.00 per pound. In the case of a steak (beef) selling at $3.00 per pound, the cost of the protein is $16.50 per pound. From a practical standpoint, we would not want to compare the cost of protein in NFDM with that in a steak, particularly in a restaurant, but it does have practicality in other ways, such as comparing protein additive costs. This method is useful in foreign countries where local costs per unit weight can be compared with ease.

Rather than getting into specifics in giving practical examples at this time, we will defer these until they are discussed in the following chapters on various applications.

Product Image

A final point needs to be made about the conceived image of various protein products. For our comments on this subject, we will use soy flour as an example because the product is plentiful and inexpensive, and it is used quite extensively in foods.

In the earlier days of marketing soy flour, salespeople sold the product strictly on the basis of economics. They pounded away on the theme that its use would reduce costs, making all the other attributes secondary. As a result, soy flour took on the image of a "cheap product," and whenever we saw soy flour on the label we expected drastic cost reductions, which was unrealistic. Many food processors felt that they had quality products and, as such, they did not want their products to be associated with a "cheap" additive. It was not until this marketing concept changed, together with product improvement, that soy flour had a drastic image change.

This lesson needs to be carried over into foodservice operations, particularly concerning the use of additives. People take pride in saying that they have quality products, but what is quality? Quality to one person does not necessarily mean quality to another. Quality must be related to costs because as the quality of a product approaches perfection, costs rise drastically. A judgment must always be made as to the degree of quality we wish to achieve for a particular cost. This is a never-ending exercise.

REFERENCES

Blouin, F. A., Z. M. Zarins, and J. P. Cherry. 1981. "Color." In *Protein Functionality in Foods,* ACS Symposium Series 147, ed. J. P. Cherry, 21–39. Washington, D.C.: American Chemical Society.

Burns, E. E., L. J. Talley, and B. S. Brummet. 1972. "Sunflower Utilization in Human Foods." *Cereal Sci. Today* 17:287–9, 298.

Catsimpoolas, N., and E. W. Meyer. 1970. "Gelatin Phenomena of Soybean Globulins. I. Protein–Protein Interactions." *Cereal Chem.* 47:559–70.

Cherry, J. P., ed. 1981. *Protein Functionality in Food.* ACS Symposium Series 147. Washington, D.C.: American Chemical Society.

Circle, S. J., E. W. Meyer, and R. W. Whitney. 1964. "Rheology of Soy Protein Dispersions. Effect of Heat and Other Factors on Gelation." *Cereal Chem.* 41:157–72.

Fennema, O. 1977. "Water and Protein Hydration." In *Food Proteins,* ed. J. R. Whitaker and S. R. Tannenbaum, 50–90. Westport, Conn.: AVI Publishing.

Fleming, S. E., F. W. Sosulski, A. A. Kilara and E. Humbert. 1974. "Viscosity and Water Absorption Characteristics of Slurries of Sunflower and Soybean Flours, Concentrates, and Isolates." *J. Food Sci.* 39:188–191.

Hutton, C. W., and A. M. Campbell. 1977. "Functional Properties of a Soy Concentrate and a Soy Isolate in Simple Systems. Nitrogen Solubility Index and Water Absorption." *J. Food Sci.* 42:454–6.

———. 1981. "Water and Fat Absorption." In *Protein Functionality in Foods*, ACS Symposium Series 147, ed. J. P. Cherry, 177–200. Washington, D.C.: American Chemical Society.

Khan, M. N., P. Wan, L. W. Rooney, and E. W. Lusas. 1980. "Sunflower Flour: A Potential Bread Ingredient." *Cereal Foods Today* 25:402–4.

McWatters, K. H., and J. P. Cherry. 1981. "Emulsification: Vegetable Proteins." In *Protein Functionality in Foods*, ACS Symposium Series 147, ed. J. P. Cherry, 217–242. Washington, D.C.: American Chemical Society.

Paul, P. C., and M. H. Palmer. 1972. *Food Theory and Applications*. New York: John Wiley.

Pour-El, A. 1979. *Functionality and Protein Structure*, ACS Symposium Series 92. Washington, D.C.: American Chemical Society.

———. 1981. "Protein Functionality: Classification, Definition and Methodology." In *Protein Functionality in Foods*, ACS Symposium Series 147, ed. J. P. Cherry, 1–19. Washington, D.C.: American Chemical Society.

Puski, G., B. F. Szuhaj, and V. V. Kadane. 1974. "Emulgatoren: Sojaeiweiss and Sojalezithin." *Die Fleischwirtschaft* 12:1967–75.

Quinn, J. R., and D. Paton. 1979. "A Practical Measurement of Water Hydration Capacity of Protein Materials." *Cereal Chem.* 56:38–9.

Schmidt, R. H., 1981. "Gelation and Coagulation." In *Protein Functionality in Foods*, ACS Symposium Series 147, ed. J. P. Cherry, 131–147. Washington, D.C.: American Chemical Society.

Schultz, H. W., and A. F. Anglemier. 1964. *Symposium on Foods: Proteins and Their Reactions*. Westport, Conn.: AVI Publishing.

Smith, A. K., and S. J. Circle. 1938. "Peptization of Soybean Proteins. Extraction of Nitrogenous Constituents From Oil-Free Meal by Acids and Bases With and Without Added Salts." *Ind. Eng. Chem.* 30:1414–18.

Whitaker, J. R., and S. R. Tannenbaum. 1977. *Food Proteins*. Westport, Conn.: AVI Publishing.

Wolf, W. J., and J. C. Cowan. 1971. "Soybeans as a Food Source." *CRC—Crit. Rev. in Food Tech.* (Apr.):81–158.

CHAPTER 5
Bakery Products

Bread is probably one of the oldest known convenience foods. When bakeries came into existence is unclear. According to Shellenberger (1974), we do know that the Egyptians and Babylonians had knowledge of baking and brewing more than 1,000 years before the Christian era and that their knowledge of both baking and fermentation was given to the Greeks and Romans.

We can imagine that as cities grew in size, the need for bakeries also grew, not only in numbers but also in size. It was during the Middle Ages that Baker's guilds were formed because numerous bakeries were built to serve the needs of the large cities.

As time went on, as in all food-processing operations, ways and means were found to make things easier; today there is little in a large, modern bakery that resembles its predecessors. Most are completely mechanized.

In our consideration of protein additives in bakery applications, we have no intention of getting into baking in depth except to the extent that that knowledge will help us in utilizing protein additives effectively.

Three types of protein additives will be considered in this chapter: dried milk products, wheat gluten, and oilseed proteins (soy). Understanding the use of these products will give us a sufficient background on the subject, allowing us to adapt that knowledge in the utilization of other proteins in baking applications.

WHY MODIFY A BAKING RECIPE?

There are many reasons why a person would want to modify a baking recipe. The following are a few examples:

- Improve taste
- Improve texture
- Increase eye appeal
- Lengthen shelf life
- Lower cost
- Replace scarce ingredients
- Increase protein content and quality
- Improve nutrient profile
- Increase or lower calories
- Improve toasting properties
- Increase loaf volume
- Decrease fat pickup
- Strengthen bun hinge
- Produce a new product

When confining our attention to protein additives, we need to look at the functional properties of these additives that will be useful. Dubois (1982) listed some major functional properties of protein ingredients that contribute to the solution of some possible problems encountered in baking: structure building, water absorption/holding, toughening, tenderizing, emulsifying, film forming, stabilizing, whipping/aeration, and gelling.

Dubois pointed out that the most important protein, in both yeast-raised and chemically leavened products, is that found in wheat flour. "Without the structure forming ability of wheat flour when made into a dough or batter, bakery foods as we know them would not exist" (Dubois 1982).

The most common and widely accepted baked product is bread. When looking at the standards for bread, we will see a host of optional ingredients that can be used, permitting much leeway in altering a formula without destroying the basic character of a bread, roll, or bun. We are not restricted even to these guidelines as long as proper labeling is used.

FEDERAL STANDARDS

There are a limited number of FDA standards for bakery products, which may be found in Title 21 of the *Code of Federal Regulations (CFR)* under part 136.

The standards, which cover bread, rolls, buns, and their variations, are contained in the following sections of the regulations:

136.110   Bread, rolls, and buns
136.115   Enriched bread, rolls, and buns
136.130   Milk bread, rolls, and buns
136.160   Raisin bread, rolls, and buns

According to FDA definition (sec. 136.3), the only difference between a bread and a roll or bun is weight. Bread is a product that weighs one-half pound or more, whereas anything lighter than one-half pound is considered a roll or a bun.

In their simplest form, as stated in sec. 136.110, breads, rolls, and buns are foods produced by baking a mixed, yeast-leavened dough prepared from a wheat flour, yeast, and water. A variation of this preparation is using a moisturizing material that may be one or more combinations of water, a milk product, or an egg product. In any case, the minimum total solids content is 62 percent, or, to put it another way, the moisture content may be 38 percent maximum.

In the alternate water source of this part of the regulation, a milk protein or an egg protein additive may be used in bread, rolls, and buns [paragraphs (c) (2), (6), and (7)]. There are two other paragraphs in the regulation that cover protein additives: paragraphs (c) (11) and (18). In (c) (11), the regulation reads, "Nonwheat flours, nonwheat meals, nonwheat grits, wheat and nonwheat starches, any of which may be wholly or in part dextrinized, dextrinized wheat flour, or any combination of 2 or more of these, if the total quantity is not more than 3 parts for each 100 parts by weight of flour used" (21 *CFR* 1984, parts 100–169).

In paragraph (c) (12), regulations permit the use of whole ground soybeans or defatted soy products for their enzyme activity. The enzyme of interest is lipoxygenase. The baker is limited to a maximum of 0.5 part for each 100 parts by weight of wheat flour.

At one time, wheat gluten was limited to 2 parts for each 100 parts of wheat flour in bread, and 4 parts in rolls and buns. These limitations were in effect because the FDA was concerned about unwarranted nutritional claims for bread containing vital wheat gluten. It was decided that a limit is no longer necessary because present regulations require that any nutritional claim be accompanied by full nutritional labeling.

The remaining sections of part 136 of the bread, rolls, and bun standards are essentially the same except for the characterizing ingredient in each of the bakery items. In "enriched" products, the flour contains the added nutrients thiamine, riboflavin, niacin, and iron. In some cases, calcium also is added.

In milk bread, rolls, and buns, milk is the moisturizing ingredient. As an alternative, the equivalent may be used by incorporating milk solids and water; however, there is a restriction on the amount of solids.

In raisin bread, rolls, and buns, the regulations state that a minimum of 50 parts by weight of seeded or seedless raisins are used for each 100 parts by weight of flour used. Water extract of raisins may be used, but not to replace raisins. The baked product also may bear icing or frosting.

As the name implies, a whole-wheat bread, roll, or bun utilizes whole-wheat flour. The regulations do not permit the use of a regular wheat flour in this type of product.

A combination, such as enriched raisin bread, rolls, and buns, is permitted if the product is labeled with that information.

MODIFICATION GUIDELINES

Obviously, wheat flour is the most important ingredient in baking, particularly in bread, because it gives products their character. Of all the cereal flours, wheat flour is unique because, when mixed with water, it forms an elastic mass that holds the cells that develop during the earlier stages of baking until the starch gelatinizes. If the dough has been leavened, it will also hold the gas cells in place until the oven heat changes the character of the mass by denaturing the protein into a semi-rigid structure known as a bread.

The second most important ingredient in baking is water. Wheat flour can absorb fairly large amounts of water. Since the ingredients in a baking formula are listed as percentages in relation to the wheat flour content, water is listed in this manner. In a typical bread formula, water might be listed as 63 percent. This means that for every 100 parts of flour used (by weight), 63 parts of water are called for. Experience has shown that water usage at this level is about right for the proper development of the dough in most bread-type formulations.

The use of the proper amount of water is important in bread, as it is in other bakery products. Less than the optimum amount of water will cause the bread crumb (texture) to be harder. Loaf volume will be less, and the bread will be less acceptable. On the other hand, more than the optimum amount will cause a sticky and excessively soft crumb. Although the loaf will expand more, the resulting bread will collapse and look unsightly. The proper amount of water in a bread dough will result in a dough that is easily handled and molded.

Absorption depends a great deal on the protein content of the flour. One may have two flour products with the same protein content but entirely different water absorption characteristics. The higher its protein content, the more water it will absorb. Also, the higher the protein quality of the wheat flour, the more water it will absorb. A certain amount of absorption is due to the starch content of wheat flour, but this is of lesser importance.

The need for the proper amount of water in a particular formulation can be determined by using an instrument called a *Farinograph*. A Farinograph test will make the differences in water absorption characteristics among various flours apparent to the baker (Fig. 5-1). The Farinograph contains a small mixing vessel into which are placed the test ingredients along with the flour. During the mixing

Figure 5-1. Farinograph.

action, water is added to produce a dough. The design of the instrument is such that, as resistance builds in the development of the dough, that resistance is registered on a dial-type scale. Since it is important for the baker to follow dough development with respect to time, a tracing, or *farinogram,* also is made during the whole operation (Fig. 5-2). When examining the tracing, the baker determines a number of things that will act as a guide in production runs. For example, Fig. 5-3 shows the various parts of the farinogram that have special significance. The x, or horizontal, axis represents time in minutes. The y, or vertical, axis is dough consistency. When the water and flour are introduced into the mixing vessel and mixing starts, it takes a certain amount of time for the dough to develop. This is called the arrival time, which is shown as a. Continued mixing causes further development to a peak time represented by b. As mixing continues, the consistency starts to drop off to a specific point, at the reference line, which is called the time to breakdown depicted by d. From the point the dough consistency reaches the reference line in the beginning until the end, c is dough stability.

The reference line is an important point in dough consistency. It is the relationship of the tracing to the line that determines the absorption characteristics of the dough ingredients. If too little water is used, the dough will be too stiff;

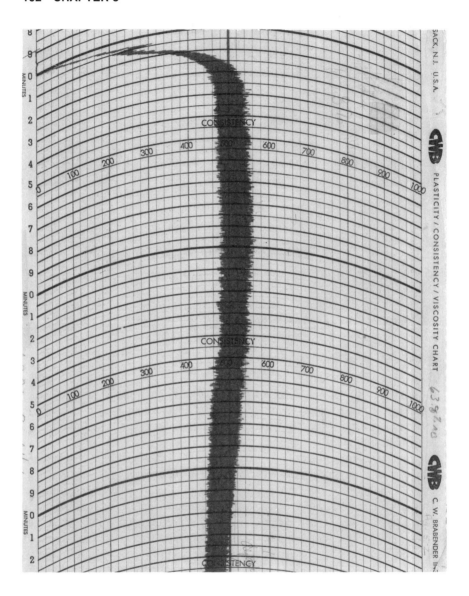

Figure 5-2. Typical farinogram tracing.

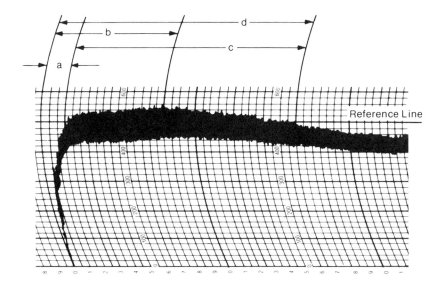

Figure 5-3. Important parts of a Farinograph tracing. (a = arrival time; b = peak time; c = stability; d = time to breakdown.)

if too much water is used, the dough will be thin and sticky. In both cases, the dough will be difficult to handle. Thus, the farinogram will tell the baker a great deal about the system in which he or she is working, how much water to use, and how long to mix the dough.

Wheat flour is made up of two types of protein that have different properties when hydrated separately. These proteins are called *gliadin* and *glutenin*. Hydrated gliadin is extensible and tacky, whereas hydrated glutenin is more elastic and tough. When hydrated together, which occurs when water is added to wheat flour, they form a cohesive, elastic network called *gluten*. It is the development of gluten that gives dough the desirable properties so important in baking. But all wheat flours are not alike in the development of the gluten. Some are relatively weak in this respect; others are relatively strong. It is important to know this when selecting a white flour for a particular use. If the product is relatively dense, such as bread, then a flour with a high, strong gluten-forming content is needed. A less dense product, such as cake, requires a flour with a lower, weaker gluten-forming content. These different flours have an influence on the volumes of the various bakery products produced. Flours are selected based on their protein content because the higher the protein content, the higher the gluten content. But it is also true that a high-protein flour is not necessarily a strong gluten flour.

Another important consideration in baking is proper mixing of the dough, which does a number of necessary things. First, mixing thoroughly blends all the ingredients. Second, it causes the water to wet all the ingredients thoroughly and uniformly, especially the protein. Third, it develops the dough. As the dough is developed, it is converted from a sticky mass to one that is relatively dry; it is transformed from a mass that has little if any elasticity to one that is elastic and stretchable. Such a dough will be machineable, have good gas-retention capabilities, and produce a loaf that has a large volume and very good texture. Fourth, mixing develops air cells, which act as nuclei for carbon dioxide produced by the yeast.

Improper mixing results in a number of problems. If the dough is undermixed, it will remain sticky and will be difficult to handle, and loaf volume will be less. Overmixing will cause a dough to become excessively slack and even "wet"; it will be hard to handle and will result in a product that has poor volume and texture.

During the development of a dough, the mixing action causes the hydrated protein fractions to be forced together, pulled, and stretched in a particular way to "develop" a protein with the needed properties. In overmixing, these bonds, and perhaps others as well, are pulled apart, thereby destroying some of the so-called needed properties.

Protein Additives for Bread-Type Products

As previously presented, there are many good reasons for using protein additives in bread-type products. However, the protein additives that do not have their origin in wheat flour, as a rule, do not possess gluten-forming properties. Therefore, they tend to dilute or weaken gluten structure. This may or may not be desirable. In most cases, as in breads, the weakening process must be reversed in some way. This may be done through the use of oxidants and/or emulsifiers, or even by the addition of vital wheat gluten. ("Vital" indicates that gluten is functional as opposed to being denatured.)

In this section, we will examine three types of protein additives that are used most often in bread-type products. There are others that are used to a lesser degree, but the information covered here will help the technologist to use some judgment when adapting other protein additives if he or she desires.

Nonfat Dry Milk (NFDM)

The use of fluid milk in baking has had a long history, even though it is not an essential ingredient in bread. Milk was used because it was felt that it yielded many benefits. However, as most homemakers know, best results are obtained when milk is "scalded" before using it in this application. As bakeries became larger, fluid milk use became a problem, especially because of storage. This led to the welcomed use of NFDM, but only after it was learned that the fluid skim milk needed to be heated to a temperature of 190°F for 30 minutes before spray drying. This heat-treating step, as well as the one mentioned about fluid milk, is necessary to denature the lactalbumin, which was found to have an adverse effect on the dough.

NFDM has a number of functional properties that make it attractive as an additive in bread; for example, it produces a softer crumb (texture), improves flavor, increases absorption, and improves both the nutritional profile and the browning property. (The browning property is aided by the presence of the naturally occurring reducing sugar lactose.) As to its nutritional benefits, Turro and Sipos (1968) reported that the use of 3 percent NFDM resulted in a PER of 0.75. According to Hoover (1979), NFDM-containing bread normally has a PER of 0.7.

The use of NFDM in bread declined rapidly in the late 1950s and early 1960s, when much of the bread production was converted to the continuous process. Recently, continuous mix bread sales have declined, and many bakers have converted to more traditional processes of bread production. However, they are not using the high levels of NFDM that were used before conversion. In many cases, NFDM has been eliminated from baker's formulas because the cost got to be too high (Lehmann and Dreese 1981). However, this does not mean that NFDM is not being used presently in breads. There are certain variety and specialty breads being produced that the consumer is willing to buy. In a project sponsored by Dairy Research, Inc., and undertaken by the American Institute of Baking, a study was made using NFDM at levels ranging from 0 percent to as high as 15 percent in breads made by different processes. Lehmann and Dreese (1981) looked at the use of NFDM in making white pan bread made by the sponge/dough process. They noted a number of benefits:

- Increased water absorption
- Slightly increased moisture content
- Decreased toasting time
- Increased tolerance to overoxidation
- Lengthened shelf life
- Retained flavor

Longer shelf life was considered to be the most significant benefit in the study. The extended shelf life was shown through the use of the Instrom Texture Press and taste panel studies. Bread containing 8.2 percent NFDM was as soft after 7 days as bread containing no milk at 5 days. Taste panelists preferred bread containing 8.2 percent NFDM over bread without NFDM when the bread was produced by a short-time straight dough process. Also, using 8.2 percent NFDM in breads made from a 40-percent-flour brew process, the formula improved

Table 5-1   White Pan Bread Formula

Ingredient	Percent
Flour	100.00
Yeast	2.50
Shortening	2.50
Yeast food	0.50
Water	64.00
Sugar	8.00
Salt	2.00
Nonfat dry milk/milk replacer	2.00
Mono- and diglycerides (hydrate)	0.50
Sodium stearoyl-2-lactylate	0.25
Protease enzyme	0.25
Calcium propionate	0.18
Soy flour (enzyme active)	0.50

Note: Percent based on flour as 100 percent.
Source: Dubois 1982.

break and shred, grain, and flavor characteristics. Table 5-1 shows a white pan bread formulation in which NFDM is an ingredient.

Vital Wheat Gluten

Since it is the gluten of wheat flour that is responsible for its dough-making properties, vital wheat gluten can be added to a formulation to strengthen flours that may be somewhat deficient or to provide structural support for bread varieties that carry a fair amount of nonflour ingredients. Gluten suppliers have found a number of benefits when using vital wheat gluten in bakery formulations. These are summarized in the following list.

Strengthens dough
Improves loaf volume (betters gas retention)
Makes batches uniform
Increases absorption
Strengthens sidewalls of expanded bread
Improves handling properties
Eliminates need for inventories of special strong flour for variety baked goods
Improves mixing tolerance
Lengthens shelf life due to moisture retention
Strengthens hinges of hot-dog and hamburger buns
Increases yield
Increases protein level of specialty breads

A number of the benefits overlap somewhat because they are due to similar

Table 5-2 Hamburger and Hot-Dog Bun Formula

Ingredient	Percent
Flour, bread	100.00
Yeast	3.50
Water	62.00
Sugar	12.00
Salt	2.00
Shortening	5.00
Yeast food	0.50
Calcium stearoyl-2-lactylate	0.25
Mono- and diglycerides (hydrate)	0.75
Vital wheat gluten	2.00
Calcium propionate	0.20
Protease enzyme	0.40

Note: Percent based on flour weight.
Source: Dubois 1982.

properties. For example, consider the entry, "strengthens dough." We can thus see the following benefits: improves handling properties; improves gas retention, thereby resulting in greater loaf volume; strengthens bread sidewalls; strengthens hinges for hot-dog and hamburger buns; and eliminates need for special strong flour for variety baked goods. In the latter case, this would apply to breads that contain a large amount of raisins, nuts, or any other nonflour products that add stress. The same is true of rye breads, especially when larger amounts of rye flour are desired in the dough. Gluten added to rye flour improves gas retention, which is needed.

Absorption is increased because more protein is added to the formulation. A good rule of thumb to follow is to add approximately 2 pounds of water to every pound of gluten. Since gluten has an affinity for water, it will tend to hold on to it, even during the baking process. Obviously, this increases yield. Although staling is a complex phenomenon, water retention is a contributing factor. For this reason, gluten tends to retard staling, thereby prolonging shelf life.

Gluten will reduce the occurrence of cripples (rejects) by providing increased dough stability; the dough will be stronger and do a better job of holding in gas. Gluten also will assure the baker of uniformity from batch to batch by increasing the mixing tolerance and will allow the baker to make formulation adjustments as needed. Of a similar nature is the development of a more resilient crumb in hearth breads such as French, Italian, and Vienna.

The normal usage of gluten in baked items does not require a special label declaration if the gluten is added for functional reasons. However, if a reference is made to anything that resembles a nutritional claim, the FDA requires special labeling, which places a greater burden on the baker to assure the consumer of the truthfulness of the required label. Use of the phrase "increased protein content" could trigger the Nutritional Labeling requirement. This means not only must full nutritional labeling be displayed but also the company is required to keep certain records, maintain good controls, and have laboratory results to substantiate all nutritional data listed.

Soy Protein Products

Although this section is on soy protein products, what will be discussed can be applied to other vegetable proteins, especially to oilseed proteins. Discussing these protein additives is a little more difficult than discussing NFDM and vital wheat gluten because there are so many different types available, each with its own special functional characteristic.

Based on protein content, there are three basic soy products: soy flour and grits, soy protein concentrate, and soy protein isolate. By definition and by the FDA Common or Usual Name guidelines, a product must contain at least 70 percent protein on a moisture-free basis to have the word *protein* in its name. Since the respective dry-basis protein levels of these two products are 70 percent and 90 percent, they are called soy protein concentrate and soy protein isolate, respectively. Any product with less protein is called by its name of origin together with its physical description; soy flour, soy grit, cottonseed flour, rapeseed flour, and so on. There can be full-fat soy flours and grits and there can be refatted or lecithinated products.

The largest commercial use of soy flour in the United States is in baking (Hoover 1979). Standard bakery soy flour has a PDI ranging from 50 to 70 percent (Cole 1976). As Hoover pointed out, the market for soy flour in baking has developed rather slowly but steadily since World War II, when soy flour was used as a substitute for milk powder in bread. Today, most of it is used as an NFDM replacer in combination with cheese whey. The combination is such that the protein and sugar contents closely approximate that of NFDM. According to Hoover, bakers do not find appreciable change in absorption, mix, and oxidant requirements when present-day soy flours are used at the 3-percent substitute level. In addition, soy flour provides better functional and water absorption characteristics than NFMS (nonfat milk solids), and at least equal tenderizing effect, body, and resilience. The degree of color reaction can be controlled by partial substitution of dextrose or liquid reducing sugars in place of the sucrose in the formula. Because soy flours have a high lysine content, this, together with the reducing sugar, results in the browning (Maillard reaction). Hence, soy flours may be used to improve browning. From this aspect, soy flour and cheese whey make a good combination because the whey is rich in the reducing sugar lactose.

Some bakeries use a blend of soy flour and cheese whey; others prefer to use these products separately because they feel that they have better control in formula adjustments. In the latter case, soy flour is used at a level of 1.5 to 2.0 pounds per 100 pounds of wheat flour. Because the maximum permitted level for the combination may be 3 percent in a standard bread, roll, or bun, the difference can be made up with dried whey if desired.

It is generally recognized that when soy flour is added to a bread formulation, a water adjustment must be made. French (1981) suggests increasing absorption 1.5 to 1.75 percent for each percent of soy flour added in an existing bread formulation. If the soy flour is used to replace NFDM, it is usually necessary to add an additional pound of water for each pound of replacement. If the formulation is adjusted by taking out a portion of the wheat flour and replacing it with soy flour, then the necessary water adjustment should be to add 0.4 pounds of water for every pound of replacement, according to French (1983). Hoover (1979) says that if water is added to reach the "feel of dough," the baker will automatically use the right amount of water.

As we learned earlier, the need for water can be shown by use of the Farinograph. A number of years ago, an experimental soy flour designed to replace NFDM in baking applications was tested. This particular product had a protein content of 60 percent. Initial studies involved the use of a Farinograph. Three of the tracings obtained in this study will serve to show how the instrument can help when adjusting for water.

A control tracing was obtained using 3 percent NFDM with an absorption of 64.6 percent (water content). When this tracing was compared with that obtained on a dough made with 3 percent soy flour and 64.6 percent absorption, the second tracing indicated a stiff dough—the peak was markedly higher. In order to obtain a tracing similar to the control, it was necessary to increase the absorption to 67.7 percent. In this case, when NFDM was replaced with soy flour, it was necessary to add an amount of water about equal to the amount of soy flour added, because of the water demand of the protein. This can be readily seen if we realize that NFDM with its 35 percent protein content was about half that contained in the soy flour. There is a definite protein-to-water relationship.

In specialty breads, the level of soy flour can go higher than 3 percent. When using greater amounts, however, it is necessary to make some formula adjustments in addition to water adjustments. Higher levels of soy flour usage will usually necessitate using an increased amount of oxidant, such as potassium bromate, potassium iodate, or azodicarbonamide. For example, if the level of soy flour usage is 5 percent, the bromate should be increased 10 parts per million, whereas if the soy is used at 12 percent, the bromate should be increased 30 parts per million.

Kulp et al. (1980) looked at the preparation of soy breads in which low-protein wheat flours were used. They found that the quality of the bread can be greatly improved if a combination of oxidants is used, such as 250 parts per million of ascorbic acid and 60 parts per million of potassium bromate.

At one time it was felt that in the sponge-and-dough method of making bread, it was best not to put the soy flour in the sponge. However, French (1983) found that there is a benefit in adding soy flour to the sponge because it shortens the fermentation time from about 4.5 hours to about 4 hours. He attributes this to the stimulating effect of certain yeast nutrients that are contributed by the soy product. When soy flour was first used as a bread additive, it could only be used in limited amounts. With the discovery and subsequent use of sodium stearoyl-2-lactylate (SSL), more soy flour could be added without adverse effects.

As previously mentioned, there is a special soy flour called enzyme-active. The enzyme of interest is lipoxygenase, which is inactivated with moist heat. Thus, when producing a soy flour that has lipoxygenase activity, it is necessary to use as little moist heat as possible to produce a product that will have a PDI of about 80 percent. Enzyme-active soy flour comes in two types—one made from whole soybeans, usually referred to as the natural full-fat product, and one that is a defatted product. In the latter case, it is important to be especially careful when removing the residual solvent with heat. The solvent usually is removed in processing through the use of dry heat or a vacuum.

Lipoxygenase has the ability to oxidize fats and to bleach carotenoid pigments, thereby giving the crumb a lighter color. Lipoxygenase also will produce peroxides when acting on certain fats. Since peroxides are oxidants, they will contribute to strengthening gluten (French 1981). The active flour is used in some bakery applications to impart a slightly tangy flavor. Regulations permit the use of enzyme-active soy flour to be used at a maximum level of 0.5 percent in a standard bread, bun, or roll. A higher level of usage of this type of soy flour is not desirable because of the flavor and the adverse effect it has on loaf volume. See Table 5-1 for a formulation in which an enzyme-active soy flour is used.

VARIETY BREADS

Although variety or specialty breads were discussed in some detail in the previous section, further comment on this subject is warranted. Variety breads are those that contain special ingredients to impart a particular flavor, texture, or general appearance to the finished bakery foods (Dubois 1982). More often than not, these breads contain nonflour ingredients present at levels that tend to reduce the effectiveness of the gluten. Consequently, it is often necessary to strengthen the dough by using oxidants, using a stronger wheat flour, or adding vital wheat gluten to the formulation (see Table 5-2).

Some of the variety breads are covered in the standard of identity, for example, milk bread, egg bread, raisin bread, and whole-wheat bread; others are not. Those that do not have a standard of identity must be labeled so the consumer

Table 5-3   Basic 12 Percent Soy-Flour Bread Formula

Ingredient	Percent
Wheat flour	100
Soy flour	12
Yeast	3
Sugar	5
Salt	2
Water	71
Stearoyl-2-lactylate	0.5
Bromate	40–60 parts per million

Source: Tsen and Tang 1971.

will know what he or she is buying. In addition, an ingredient declaration is required.

Regulations permit a maximum of 3 percent inclusion of nonwheat flours in a regular white bread, including NFDM and soy flours. When this level is exceeded, the product can no longer be called "bread" or "white bread"; it must be given a name that either alerts or informs the consumer as to what is being purchased. In this case, it is also necessary to include all ingredients used in the ingredient statement. If attention is brought to the fact that nutrition is improved in any way, the nutritional labeling regulation is triggered.

Whenever the desire is simply to increase the protein content of a bread, it is more likely that soy products will be used because of their high protein levels and attractive costs. NFDM is usually not considered because of cost and the presence of a high level of lactose. However, this does not preclude using specialty milk products, such as lactose-reduced products, or even those that may be combined with other protein products.

A fair amount of work has been reported in literature concerning protein fortification in bread through the use of soy flour. One of the earliest publications came out of Kansas State University. Tsen et al. (1971) were successful in producing a bread that contained 12 percent soy flour. Up to that time, experimental bakers were experiencing all types of problems using soy flour at high levels. Apparently, the secret to the successful use of soy flour rests in the proper utilization of the right emulsifier. As was reported by Tsen et al., good volume was obtained when they used sodium stearoyl-2-lactylate (SSL), calcium stearoyl-2-lactylate (CSL), or ethoxylated monoglycerides. The Kansas State Process for making soy bread or other high-protein breads led to the basic formula shown in Table 5-3.

Hoover (1979) said that prior to this development, the addition of high levels

Table 5-4   Producing Soy-Fortified Bread by a
            Straight Dough Formula

Ingredient	Percent
Soy-fortified flour	100.
Water	70
Yeast	3
Yeast food	0.25
Lard	2.0
Salt	2.25
Sugar	4.5

Mix 2 minutes at No. 1 speed, plus 6 minutes at No. 2 speed in Hobart A-200 mixer with McDuffee bowl. Dough temperature 83°F.; fermentation time, 45 minutes; scale 19 ounces; 10 minutes intermediate proof, mold, and pan at 107°F. and 85 percent relative humidity; bake 20 minutes at 435°F.

Source: Marnett et al. 1973.

of soy flour to wheat flour–based breads resulted in greatly reduced volumes; coarse, open texture; off-white or yellowish color; and a somewhat "beany" flavor. Besides improvements in each of these factors, there was also the improvement in the nutritional profile, particularly in the protein quality. The PER has been reported to increase from 0.7 in a regular white bread to 1.95 for the 12 percent soy flour–fortified bread.

Marnett et al. (1973) studied the use of a soy-fortified flour mix that also contained the required SSL emulsifier. This mix was composed of 100 parts of bread wheat flour, 12 parts of soy flour, defatted (lightly toasted), and 0.5 part of sodium stearoyl-2-lactylate.

Their studies consisted of using this soy-fortified mix in breads made by three conventional methods: 70 percent sponge dough, straight dough, and 100 percent sponge. They found that best results were obtained by the 100 percent sponge procedure. Tables 5-4 and 5-5 show the formulations for the 100 percent sponge and straight dough methods.

When referring to the use of high levels of soy in bread, Cotton (1974) stated that sodium stearoyl-2-lactylate (SSL) and ethoxylated monoglycerides are of greater benefit than oxidants. Although he was not referring to low-protein wheat flours specifically, this might also apply to them.

As was shown earlier, it is necessary to use more water with soy flour additions.

Table 5-5   Producing Bread by a 100 Percent Sponge Formula

Ingredient	Percent
Soy-fortified flour	100
Water	69
Yeast	2.75
Yeast food	0.5
Lard	2.0

Mix 3 minutes at No. 1 speed in Hobart A-200 mixer with McDuffee bowl, at 83°F.

Ferment 1 hour at 83°F.

Remix with 2.25 percent salt and 4.5 percent sugar.

Mix 2 minutes at No. 1 speed, plus 5 minutes at No. 2 speed. Dough temperature, 83°F.; floor time, 45 minutes; scale 19 ounces; 10 minutes intermediate proof, mold, and pan; panary proof to 0.5 inches above top of pan at 107°F. and 85 percent relative humidity; bake 20 minutes at 435°F.

Source: Marnett et al. 1973.

Hoover stated that "on a 100 part 12 percent soy fortified flour formula, 9–12 parts more water would be required for optimum dough development and workability" (1975, p. 268A). If water is added to obtain the "feel of dough," the right amount of water will be used. Hoover sees two additional advantages to the baker in making a 12 percent soy flour bread—the dough mixing time and the fermentation time are reduced.

Another approach in fortifying bread is to use soy grits, textured soy flours and/or other grains. These can be incorporated into the dough, giving the crumb a special nutlike characteristic that many people find pleasing to chew. Typical formulations are shown in Tables 5-6 and 5-7.

Work was undertaken at the American Institute of Baking to develop a special bread that would be suitable for individuals who are intolerant (allergic) to gluten. This work was reported by Ranhotra et al. (1975). These workers developed a gluten-free bread using unmodified wheat starch and soy protein isolate. Ranhotra et al. reported that the products they produced had good volume and appearance, exhibited excellent internal characteristics, compared very favorably with wheat bread in taste and flavor and were inexpensive to produce. These breads were appreciably higher in moisture content than regular breads. They also reported that the PER was greatly improved. Their findings were that regular bread had

Table 5-6   Multigrain Bread Formula No. 1

Ingredient	Percent
Flour, bread	100.00
Water	95.00
Yeast	4.50
Yeast food	1.00
Cracked wheat	14.00
Bran	4.00
Baby oats	2.50
Rye meal	4.00
Vital wheat gluten	5.00
Caramel color	0.25
Shortening	4.00
Whole-wheat flour	11.00
Wheat germ	5.00
Molasses	2.75
Honey	2.75
Brown sugar	10.00

Note: Percent based on bread flour as 100.00 percent.
Source: Dubois 1982.

a corrected PER of 0.7, while the product containing 40 percent soy protein isolate had a PER of 1.09.

CAKES

Cakes differ from yeast-raised products because flour is not the sole or primary structure-forming ingredient. Its structure can be the result of a number of ingredients that are capable of making a rigid framework on baking. Although most of these structure-forming products are proteins, we should not overlook the fact that starches also may play a role when the gelatinizing property is utilized. But even here, the batter emulsion needs to be stabilized during the time it is subjected to the oven heat to allow the starch to gelatinize. The most common structure-forming proteins are those that have certain properties, such as film-forming, toughening, gelation, emulsification, and stabilization. The protein found in wheat flour is considered to have the toughening property. In some cases, tenderizing agents are also important. Although tenderizers usually are such ingredients as sugar and fat, proteins also may have this property. These products need to be soluble but because they do not have a structure-building property, they do just the opposite; they tend to weaken or dilute protein structure. This is not entirely bad; it can be good because it can result in a more tender, desirable structure.

Table 5-7   Multigrain Bread Formula No. 2

Ingredient	Percent
Flour, bread	100.00
Yeast	4.50
Yeast food	0.75
Shortening	4.00
Sodium stearoyl-2-lactylate	0.50
Multigrain mix	22.00
Vital wheat gluten	6.00
Water	85.00
Salt	3.00
Sugar	13.50
Milk replacer	3.75
Mold inhibitor	0.20
Molasses	0.70
Honey	2.75
Corn syrup	3.50

Note: Percent based on bread flour as 100.00 percent.
Source: Dubois 1982.

Another general characteristic of cakes is that the mixture of ingredients usually results in a batter rather than a dough. By definition, a batter is a mixture of flour, water, and other ingredients that is thin enough to be "pour-dropped" from a spoon. Another general characteristic of a cake is that its batter is usually sweetened. Last, the batter is either fried or baked.

The traditional protein additives in cake batters have been eggs, either whole and/or their separate parts, and fluid milk. In commercial production, these products were replaced by whole egg solids, egg yolk solids, powdered or flaked egg white, and/or nonfat dry milk. As baking technology developed, understanding of these products grew; their functional properties were recognized and utilized in a more scientific manner. Turro and Sipos stated that the use of NFDM makes several interesting contributions, ". . . of which the enhancement of crust color is of primary importance. Since NFDM contains approximately 50 percent of the reducing sugar lactose and the cake batter is normally on the alkaline side (pH above 7.0), the Maillard reaction or browning takes place in the presence of proteins and heat" (1970, p. 58). They commented further that NFDM also has the property of blending homogeneously with the other batter ingredients; it neither interferes with nor suppresses the general flavor profile. Last, NFDM absorbs 0.75 percent of its own weight in water.

Over the years, the price of NFDM increased to a point that forced bakers to seek a substitute. Because bakers had some experience with soy flour as an

NFDM replacer in bread, they considered its use in cake. Turro and Sipos (1970) reported on the work they did on a number of types, such as pound, sponge, devil's food, and yellow layer cakes. In this study, they replaced NFDM with a special soy flour that had a protein content of 60 percent on an as-is basis. The replacements ranged from 25 percent to 100 percent. They found that substitution could be made in all cases with little change in the formulation, but it was necessary to add 1.5 percent extra water for every percent of soy flour. For the 25 percent and 50 percent substitutions, this was the only adjustment needed. Since the lactose of the NFDM had a function in the cake, it was necessary to add dextrose for the 75 percent and 100 percent replacements. They found that 4 percent was needed in the 75 percent replacement, whereas 8.8 percent was needed for the 100 percent replacement, based on the total sugar requirement in pound cake. Although dextrose was needed for the cakes studied, it was not needed for devil's food cake. It was necessary in every instance to increase leavening a little to maintain consistent cake volume. The baking powder was increased about 50 percent for the 100 percent NFDM replacement. Last, Turro and Sipos reported that soy flour overcame one problem noted when NFDM was used in a devil's food cake: It was necessary to add more chocolate because the milk product had a color-lightening effect. When the soy flour was used, the reverse effect took place; namely, it made the cocoa look darker. Many devil's food cake formulations now have soy flour as one of their ingredients.

Although it was not specifically pointed to by Turro and Sipos, soy flour does have the property of holding water not only in the initial stages of cake making but also in the finished product. This propensity for holding water tends to give the product a longer shelf life.

In a review paper on functional proteins in baking, Dubois (1982) reported an advantage of milk protein over soy flour in white layer cake. In this type of cake, the whipping of egg whites forms the cellular structure. Both whole egg and NFDM contribute to cellular structure. The casein of milk is the functional material in the milk contributing to structure, and is the reason why most soy/whey milk replacers are not too successful in this application. The defatted soy flour does not have the structure-building characteristics of the milk casein. Dubois acknowledges that, recently, soy concentrates and isolates have shown promise in this type of production. Along this line, there are some soy protein isolates and soy protein concentrates with a gelling property, which has a place in systems where viscosity and viscosity control are important.

Cole (1976) reported on the use of full-fat soy flours and on lecithinated soy flours. He stated that they often are used in sponge goods and pound cakes because of the increased richness and emulsification function they provide. He said that 5 percent or more of full-fat soy flour based on the wheat flour weight may be used. Not only is it necessary to increase the water by 1.5 to 2.0 percent for every percent of soy flour, but also additional sugar should be used in an

Table 5-8 Typical Cake Doughnut Mix Formulations

Ingredient	Average (%)	Minimum (%)	Maximum (%)
Wheat flour	100.0	100.0	100.0
Sugar (Baker's Special)	34.2	27.8	37.5
Dextrose	3.3	0.8	3.3
Salt (fine)	1.6	—	—
Shortening	4.9	3.3	4.9
Nonfat dry milk	6.2	4.1	8.2
Egg yolk solids	3.3	1.6	4.9
Lecithinated soy flour	6.5	3.3	6.5
Soda	1.5	1.5	1.5
Soda acid pyrophosphate	2.0	2.0	2.0

Batter temperature: 75 to 80°F.
Floor time: 15 to 20 minutes.
Frying temperature: 375 to 380°F.

Note: All percentages are based on the wheat flour at 100 percent.
Source: Doughnut Primer 1964.

amount equal to the soy plus the added water. Cole also reported that soy flour reduces the average air-bubble diameter in sponge cake batters, thereby increasing batter stability and improving cake volume. Last, he stated that full-fat and lecithinated soy flours permit reduction in the use of eggs and shortening.

In this regard, egg yolk solids are an important ingredient in cake doughnuts. Rakosky (1972) stated that, for one reason or another—economic, dietary, and so forth—it may be more desirable to cut back on this ingredient. Laboratory work has shown that approximately half the egg yolk solids can be pulled out of the formulation and replaced with a lecithinated soy flour. Not only are the original properties of the cake retained, but also a few additional advantages are noted in the modification. There are improvements in browning and texture. When the doughnut batter or dough enters the hot fat during the frying step, an apparent seal is formed at the surface, so that the moisture is sealed in and the fat pickup from the frying operation is lessened. This sealing phenomenon increases the shelf life of the doughnuts because it retains the moisture; also, the doughnuts have more consumer appeal because they are not heavy and greasy. A few additional advantages were pointed out, such as cost savings, better star formation (hole in the doughnut), and fewer cripples. Although Rakosky referred to laboratory work at that time, these benefits were realized in actual practice in the following years.

Table 5-8 shows how lecithinated soy flour–containing cake doughnut formulations can vary from the standpoint of maximums and minimums for the various ingredients.

Table 5-9 Cake Doughnut Formula

Ingredient	Percent
Cake doughnut flour	100.00
Granulated sugar (sucrose)	40.00
Dextrose (corn) sugar	3.50
Shortening	6.00
Defatted soy flour	7.00
Nonfat dry milk	2.50
Powdered egg yolk	2.50
Double-acting baking soda	3.80
Salt	1.70
Mono- and diglyceride	1.00
Lecithin	1.00
Water	73.00

Note: Percent based on flour weight.
Source: Dubois 1982.

It is not necessary to use lecithinated soy flour per se; it is possible to use soy flour and lecithin separately. As to which is used by a baker is determined by the equipment he or she has. The lecithinated soy flour is easier to handle since it is a powder. In many instances, the baker does not have the equipment to handle lecithin, which has a plastic consistency. Table 5-9 shows a doughnut formulation that utilizes the soy flour and lecithin as two separate ingredients.

Rakosky (1972) described the advantages lecithinated soy flour had in pancake mixes. As little as a 3-percent addition to the mix results in a pancake that has a golden-brown color and a light, fluffy texture that does not stick to the griddle during frying.

Although most of the preceding comments concerned soy protein products, there are other protein products that have utility in cakes—products such as defatted cottonseed flour, peanut flour, torula yeast products, rapeseed protein concentrate, sunflower flour, and pea flour. Of particular note, torula yeast products will partially replace eggs in cake doughnuts, chocolate cake, and cinnamon rolls. It was reported, according to Dubois (1982), that some rapeseed protein concentrate products have fat-holding, oil-emulsifying, and whipping characteristics.

Presently, there are several companies in the United States that are making specially prepared soy protein isolates that have whipping properties similar to egg white. When combined with certain other ingredients, these isolates may even simulate whipping cream. Usually, such soy products are of the low-viscosity type and/or are modified by either a chemical or an enzymatic hydrolysis.

COOKIES

The reasons for using protein additives in cookies can be placed in three broad categories: functional, nutritional, and economic. For example, one desirable functional property is the ability to hold moisture in a soft-type cookie. Another is a desirable change in the characteristics of the dough or batter. From the nutritional aspect, an obvious benefit is an increase in protein. Very often this will be accompanied by an improvement in the protein quality and, in some cases, a reduction in calories; the reduction in calories takes place because of the water-holding property of the protein. Last, there is an economic benefit because a less expensive product is substituted for a more expensive product. There is a less obvious benefit when the yield increases.

Tsen et al. stated that, "Cookies, though not a staple food like bread, have several attractive features, including long shelf life and good eating qualities. Long shelf life makes large scale production and distribution possible. Good eating quality makes cookies attractive for protein fortification and other nutritional improvement, particularly for child-feeding programs . . ." (1973, p. 34). There are any number of protein products that may be used in this application. They may be of either animal or vegetable types, such as single-celled protein, fish protein concentrate, cottonseed protein, soy protein, casein, or nonfat dry milk.

Tsen et al. (1973) studied the protein fortification of cookies using several soy protein products as a substitute for NFDM. In this work, they also looked at the use of certain surfactants to overcome some of the problems that arose when using soy. The problem they ran into was a lessening of cookie spread. They found that soy flour definitely influences the width and the thickness of the cookies. Depending on the amount of soy flour used, the diameter of the cookies was reduced and the thickness was increased. However, full-fat soy flour had less of an effect than the regular defatted soy flour, which they attributed to the fact that the full-fat product has less protein and more fat. They found that soy protein isolate also had the same effect found in the soy flour, but to a greater extent because of the increased amount of protein.

When the emulsifier sodium stearoyl-2-lactylate (SSL) was used along with the soy protein, the spread ratio was increased. Although additional shortening tends to help spreading, SSL seems to have a sparing action for the shortening. In their trials, Tsen et al. found that 0.5 percent SSL could substitute for 8 percent shortening for cookies made from one type of wheat flour and 4 percent for cookies made from another type of wheat flour; the former flour had a little lower protein content than the latter. When testing various emulsifiers, Tsen et al. found that SSL and SSF (sodium stearyl fumarate) worked best. They obtained spread ratios of 10.4 and 10.0, respectively, for SSL and SSF when used at a level of 0.5 percent and 28 percent shortening. In this work, Tsen et al. were able to raise the protein content of cookies from 60 to 100 percent by fortifying with 24 percent soy flour or soy protein isolate.

One cookie manufacturer had trouble removing the moisture of a soy flour–fortified cookie in baking. French (1980) suggested using one or more of the following for this particular baker:

1. Replace soy flour with soy grit.
2. Use a low-NSI product.
3. Use less water.
4. Cream soy in shortening.
5. Use more shortening.
6. Add soy near end of mix.

In another situation, a manufacturer in South America did not encounter the problem because they used a different method of depositing the batter/dough on the baking surface. This company used a wheat flour that had a protein content of 9 percent. The other ingredients used were 28 percent soy flour, 2 percent NFDM, and 8 percent shortening. Because the cookies were cut to shape with wire cutters, the dough had a moisture content of 30 percent. If roll molders were used, the moisture needed only to be 20 percent.

It can be seen from these examples that the results varied under different sets of conditions. In working with protein additives from various sources, or any other additives, one should not be too quick to decide that the additive is useless for that application. It is best to look critically at the conditions and make appropriate adjustments and try again. One might also contact the supplier of the additive and ask for suggestions in its use in the application of interest. Chances are that the supplier has encountered the problem previously. If he or she did, then it's to your advantage to try the suggested approach.

REFERENCES

Code of Federal Regulations. 1984. Title 21, Foods and Drugs. Part 100–169. Washington, D.C.: U.S. Government Printing Office.

Cole, M. S. 1976. "Bakery Applications for Soy Protein Products." In *Edible Soy Protein Seminar,* Moscow, U.S.S.R., Oct. 13–14 and Warsaw, Poland, Oct. 18–19. Decatur, Ill.: Archer Daniels Midland.

Cotton, R. H. 1974. "Soy Products in Bakery Goods." *J. Oil Chem. Soc.* 51:116A–19A.

Doughnut Primer (sales literature). 1964. Chicago: Central Soya.

DuBois, D. K. 1982. *Uses and Needs for Functional Proteins in the Baking Industry.* San Antonio, Tex.: American Assoc. Cereal Chem. Meeting.

French, F. 1980. Personal communication. Chicago.

———. 1981. *Bakery Uses of Soy Products.* Special ADM Foods Publication. Las Vegas: Bakery Expo 1980.

_____. 1983. Personal communication. Chicago.

Federal Register. 1976. "Bakery Products: A Revision of Standards of Identity." *Fed. Reg.* 41:6242–8.

Hoover, W. J. 1975. "Uses of Soy Proteins in Bakery Products." *J. Amer. Oil Chem. Soc.* 52:267A–9A.

_____. 1979. "Uses of Soy Proteins in Baked Goods." *J. Amer. Oil Chem. Soc.* 56:301–03.

Kulp, K., T. Volpe, F. F. Barrett, and K. Jonsson. 1980. "Low-Protein Wheat Flour Utilized in Soy-Fortified Bread." *Cereal Foods World* 25:609–12.

Lehmann, T. A., and P. Dreese. 1981. "Functions of Nonfat Dry Milk and Other Milk Products in Yeast-Raised Bakery Foods." *Tech. Bul.*, AIB III: Issue 10, Amer. Inst. of Baking (Oct.).

Marnett, L. F., R. J. Tenney, and V. D. Barry. 1973. "Methods of Producing Soy-Fortified Breads." *Cereal Sci. Today* 18:38–43, 50.

Rakosky, J. 1972. "Soy Protein Products as Functional Ingredients in Food Applications." Conf. on the Nutritional Improvement of Corn, Inst. of Nutr. of Cen. Amer. and Pan. (INCAP), Mar. 6–8.

Ranhotra, G. S., R. J. Loewe, and L. V. Puyat. 1975. "Preparation and Evaluation of Soy-Fortified Gluten-Free Bread." *J. Food Sci.* 40:62–4.

Shellenberger, J. A. 1974. "Baking Industry: Bread." In *Encyclopedia of Food Technology*, ed. A. H. Johnson and M. S. Peterson, 84–86. Westport, Conn.: AVI Publishing.

Tsen, C. C., W. J. Hoover, and D. Phillips. 1971. "High-Protein Breads: Use of Sodium Stearoyl-2 Lactylate and Calcium Stearoyl-2-Lactylate in Their Production." *Baker's Dig.* 45:20–4.

Tsen, C. C., and R. T. Tang. 1971. "K-State Process for Making High-Protein Breads. I. Soy Flour Bread." *Baker's Dig.* 45:26–32.

Tsen, C. C., E. M. Peters, T. Schaffer, and W. J. Hoover. 1973. "High-Protein Cookies. I. Effect of Soy Fortification and Surfactants." *Baker's Dig.* 47:34–9.

Turro, E. J., and E. Sipos. 1968. "Effects of Various Soy Protein Products on Bread Characteristics." *Baker's Dig.* 42:44–50.

_____. 1970. "Soy Protein Products in Commercial Cake Formulations." *Baker's Dig.* 44:58–64.

CHAPTER 6
Pasta Products

Wheat is utilized all over the world in various forms, the most popular of which are bread and pasta. Of the two forms of foods prepared from wheat, pasta products are the least variable. They are popular all over the world because they are easily stored and prepared, and are inexpensive. Boredom from eating pasta day after day can be offset somewhat because these products can be made into many different sizes and shapes (Fig. 6-1), and they can be prepared to conform to ethnic tastes.

Simple pastas, such as spaghetti and macaroni, are products made by extruding dough made with only flour and water and then drying. Although these pastas can be made in the home, most consumers buy commercially made products. Pastas may be made from various types of wheat flours; however, the better and more acceptable products are usually made from durum wheat.

Durum wheat is a very special wheat that has ideal properties for pasta products of the highest quality. Although durum has a protein level similar to the wheats used for breads, the protein is different. It is harder and flinty, whereas the protein for bread is more elastic. Durum is preferred by manufacturers of pasta products because of its protein characteristic and its natural pigment. The amber-colored kernel is ideally suited for milling into granular semolina because of its hard translucent endosperm (Banasik 1981).

Durum wheat is milled into three types of products that are used in pasta products: semolina, durum granulars, and durum flour. *Semolina* is a coarse-ground product that is especially uniform in particle size. It contains less than

3 percent flour. Semolina is preferred by pasta processors because it results in more uniform products than some of the other types.

Durum granular is very much like semolina except that it contains much more flour, about 20 percent. This product is used primarily in making macaroni. *Durum flour,* which is finely ground, is generally used in making noodles but sometimes to make macaroni. Although the macaroni has good color, it is less resistant to overcooking than products made from semolina or durum granular (Walsh and Giles 1974). To a lesser extent, farina and flour from common wheat also are used in pastas.

With the widespread use of pasta products, especially by many of the less affluent, pastas appear to be ideal vehicles to improve the diet of consumers. Unlike bread, which is also widely consumed, pasta lends itself to this means of nutrition improvement for several reasons. Generally, bread is more sensitive to modifications, especially since there are so many independent bakers. This is not true with pasta products because fewer manufacturers are involved. From the stability standpoint, bread has a relatively short shelf life. Pasta, a dry product, is relatively nonperishable. Pastas are consumed with a variety of well-flavored sauces and, as Seyam et al. (1976) pointed out, they are easily accepted by all age groups from small children to the elderly.

In a sense, protein fortification occurs in making pasta when milk or eggs are used as the moistening agent. In this case, eggs serve both as a moistening and a firming agent. In commercial operations, milk and eggs are regulated as to the amount incorporated and in the way the product is labeled.

As early as 1955, the FDA Standard of Identity for Macaroni and Noodle Products permitted the use of soy flour (*FR* 1955). However, when using soy flour in pasta products, the minimum amount required was 12.5 percent of the combined weight of wheat and soy ingredients. According to Hoskins (1961), the soy-fortified pastas had poor color, bitter taste, and poor mixing qualities when the soy was added to the durum semolina. It is not surprising that soy flour had an adverse effect on the pasta produced. At that early date, the production of soy flours was not the best and, in all likelihood, the wrong type of soy flours were used.

In 1967, the Agency for International Development (AID) sought help from the private sector to assist in providing new food products for developing countries. One product was brought out by General Foods called "Golden Elbow Macaroni," later renamed "Golden Elbow Enriched Corn-Soy-Wheat Macaroni." The product had a protein content of 20 percent with a protein value of 94.8 percent that of casein. In addition to improved protein quality, because the product was enriched with vitamins and minerals, it also had an improved nutritional profile over that of the regular macaroni. Its storage properties were similar to those of regular macaroni, and it cooked in 5 to 6 minutes, about half the time it took for regular macaroni. The company sales literature claimed the

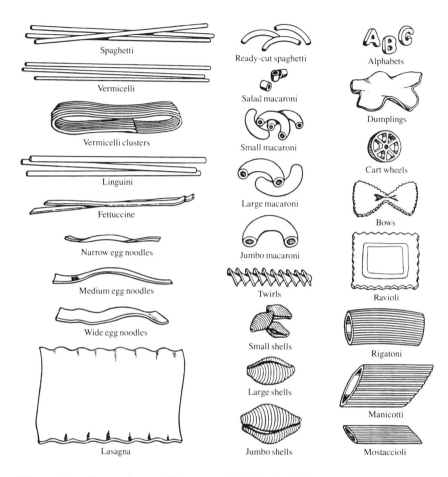

Figure 6-1. Pasta shapes. (Courtesy of the National Pasta Association.)

product to be less sticky than regular macaroni. The ingredient statement for the product read as follows: "corn flour, soy flour, wheat flour, calcium carbonate, calcium phosphate, niacin, iron, thiamin, and riboflavin" (General Foods Corporation, Post Division, White Plains, N.Y. [no date]).

According to Seyam et al. (1976), because the major ingredient was corn, the protein-fortified product found good consumer acceptance in Brazil, where it was first introduced. Some product tests were conducted in selected areas in the United States on an institutional basis in the early 1970s. An attempt was made to have the FDA change the standards for macaroni products. Since the product was quite a departure from the regular classical macaronis made for many years, both the durum wheat growers and the pasta manufacturers objected to it being called macaroni. They pointed out that the major ingredient was not wheat and that its quality did not come up to that of the classical macaroni products. The industry felt that there was no need for regulations permitting special fortified products because existing regulations already provided for them.

On February 22, 1971, the Food and Nutrition Service of the USDA issued *FNS* Notice 218 entitled, *Protein-Fortified, Enriched Macaroni-Type Products (B-2) to be Used in Combination with Meat or Cheese for Use in Lunches and Suppers Served Under Child Feeding Programs.* Although the notice did not specify the Golden Elbow product, the specifications were such that the product did comply.

Subsequently, a number of revisions have taken place in the Standard of Identity for Macaroni and Noodle Products. The last revision (*FR* 1984), as of this writing, became effective on April 19, 1984. In these revisions, several things took place. First, provisions were made for the use of enriched wheat flours, semolinas, and farinas with vitamins and minerals. Second, whole-wheat products were permitted. Third, provisions were made for the use of fortified proteins. In the latter case, a number of restrictions were included. The fortification could be made only in pasta products that included enriched wheat products. The protein content of the finished product had to be 20 percent on a 13-percent-moisture basis. In addition, the protein quality of the cooked food could not be less than 95 percent that of casein. The standard for wheat and soy macaroni products were essentially the same as previously written. Provisions were also made for vegetable macaroni products, that is, allowing the addition of certain vegetables to the pasta at levels of not less than 30 percent by weight of the finished product.

MACARONI AND NOODLE PRODUCT STANDARDS

The Standard of Identity for Macaroni and Noodle Products is covered in part 139 of Title 21 *CFR*. The following sections describe the various pasta products:

139.110	Macaroni products
139.115	Enriched macaroni products
139.117	Enriched macaroni products with fortified protein
139.120	Milk macaroni products
139.121	Nonfat milk macaroni products
139.122	Enriched nonfat milk macaroni products
139.125	Vegetable macaroni products
139.135	Enriched vegetable macaroni products
139.138	Whole-wheat macaroni products

When looking over the list, we can see that there are certain basic products, while the others are combinations of these products. For example, sec. 139.110 lists the permissible ingredients for macaroni, spaghetti, and vermicelli; sec. 139.115 lists the required vitamin and mineral content as well as some permissible ones; sec. 139.117 combines the two. In each of these sections, labeling requirements are also given.

FDA pasta standards that are of special interest to us will now be summarized. For more detail, obtain a copy of Title 9 *CFR*, which covers sec. 139.

As previously stated, macaroni, spaghetti, and vermicelli products all come under the heading of sec. 139.110, Macaroni products. The only difference in these products is their diameter: Macaroni may range from 0.11 inch to 0.27 inch, spaghetti may range from 0.06 inch to 0.11 inch, and vermicelli may not be more than 0.06 inch.

The composition of the various pasta products is as follows:

Sec. 139.110   Macaroni products. (a) Macaroni products are the class of food each of which is prepared by drying formed units of dough made from semolina, durum flour, farina, flour, or any combination of two or more of these, with water and with or without one or more of the optional ingredients specified in paragraphs (a)(1) to (6) inclusive of this section.

Optional ingredients. (Composition based on finished weight.)

(1)   Egg white—0.5 to 2.0% solids.
(2)   Disodium phosphate—0.5 to 1.0%.
(3)   Onions, celery, garlic, bay leaf, or any two or more of these. (Sufficient to season.)
(4)   Salt—sufficient to season.
(5)   Gum gluten—13% maximum protein of the wheat product combinations.
(6)   Concentrated glyceryl monostearate (not less than 90% monoester)—2% maximum.

Sec. 139.115   Enriched macaroni products. Products same as described in sec. 139.110, but in addition, each pound of finished product must contain certain vitamins and minerals, and may contain other specified nutrients. Regulations also permit the use of five percent partially defatted wheat germ. Another requirement is that iron and calcium may be added only in forms which are harmless and assimilable.

Sec. 139.117   Enriched macaroni products with fortified protein. (a)(1) Each of the foods for which a standard of identity is prescribed by this section is produced by drying formed units of dough made with one or more of the milled wheat ingredients designated in sections 139.110(a) and 139.138(a), and other ingredients to enable the finished food to meet the protein requirements set out in paragraph (a)(2)(i) of this section. *Edible protein sources, including good grade flours or meals made from nonwheat cereals or from oilseeds, may be used.* (Emphasis by author.) Vitamin and mineral enrichment nutrients are added to bring the food into conformity with the requirements of paragraph (b) of this section. . . .

(2)(i) The protein content (N $\times$ 6.25) is not less than 20% by weight (on a 13% moisture basis). . . . The protein quality is not less than 95% that of casein as determined on the cooked food. . . .

(ii) The total solids content is not less than 87%. . . .

(b)(1) Each food covered in this section contains in each pound:
Thiamin—5 mg
Riboflavin—2.2 mg
Niacin or niacinamide—34 mg
Iron—16.5 mg

(2) Each pound of such food may also contain 625 mg of calcium.

(3) Iron and calcium may be added in forms which are harmless and assimilable.

Sec. 139.120 Milk macaroni products. (a) These products conform to sec. 139.110 except that milk and/or reconstituted milks are permitted as a moisturizing ingredient provided that the solids content is not less than 3.8% of the weight of the finished macaroni product. In addition, one of the optional ingredients of Sec. 139.110(a)(1) and (2) are used (egg white and disodium phosphate). The protein content of the finished product cannot exceed 13%.

Sec. 139.121 Nonfat milk macaroni products. (a) These products conform to Sec. 139.110 except that:

(1)(i) In preparing the dough, nonfat dry milk or concentrated skim milk, or a mixture of these, is used in an amount such that the finished macaroni product made with nonfat milk contains by weight not less than 12 percent and not more than 25 percent of milk solids-not-fat. Carrageenan or salts of carrageenan conforming to requirements of Sec. 176.620 and Sec. 172.626 of this chapter may be used in a quantity not in excess of 0.833 percent by weight of the milk solids-not-fat used.

Sec. 139.122 Enriched nonfat milk macaroni products. (Products conform to the requirements listed in Sections 139.115 and 139.121.)

Sec. 139.138 Whole-wheat macaroni products. These products conform to Sec. 139.110 except that:

(a)(1) Whole wheat flour or whole durum wheat flour or both are used as the sole wheat ingredient; and

(2) None of the optional ingredients permitted by Sec. 139.110(a)(1), (2), and

(5) is used. (No egg white, disodium phosphate and gum gluten are permitted as additions.)

139.140 Wheat and soy macaroni products. (a) Wheat and soy macaroni products are the class of food each of which conforms to the definition and standard of identity, and is subject to the requirements for label statement of optional ingredients, prescribed for macaroni products by Sec. 139.110(a) and (f)(2) and (3), except that:

(1) Soy flour is added in a quantity not less than 12.5 percent of the combined weight of the wheat and soy ingredients used (the soy flour used is made from heat-processed, dehulled soybeans, with or without the removal of fat therefrom); and (2) None of the optional ingredients permitted by Sec. 139.110(a)(1) and (2) is used. When the optional ingredient gum gluten (Sec. 139.110(a)(5)) is added, the quantity is such that the protein derived therefrom, together with the protein derived from semolina, durum flour, farina, flour or any combination of these used, does not exceed 13 percent of the weight of the finished food.

As might be expected, these pastas must be labeled so that the consumer is well aware that the products are composed of wheat and soy. Examples given are: Wheat and Soy Macaroni, Wheat and Soybean Macaroni, Wheat and Soy Spaghetti, etc.

Noodle standards (Sec. 139.150, Noodle products) are very much like the macaroni standards with the additional requirement that these products must contain eggs in one or more forms as well as certain optional ingredients. Here too, wheat gluten may be used as long as the total protein content of the finished product does not exceed 13%.

Besides defining noodle products as containing egg, all the other pasta products containing 5.5 percent egg yolk solids are referred to as egg macaroni, egg spaghetti, and egg vermicelli.

Noodles also may be made with enriched wheat products, vegetable, and soy flour. These products are covered in those sections properly designated, but since they are similar to those described under macaroni products, they will not be covered here.

The purpose of the various quotations and summaries given under macaroni products was to familiarize us with the way these sections are handled. An additional purpose was to learn how protein additives can be used and what some of the restrictions are.

SCHOOL LUNCHES: PROTEIN-FORTIFIED, ENRICHED MACARONI-TYPE PRODUCTS

As was previously stated, on February 22, 1971, the Food and Nutrition Service of the U.S.D.A. issued FNS Notice 218 permitting the use of a *Protein-Fortified,*

Table 6-1   Chemical Composition Specification for
            Enriched Macaroni-Type Products for
            School Lunch

Composition	Minimum	Maximum
Protein, weight %	20.0	25.0
Moisture, weight %	—	13.0
Iron, mg/lb	13.0	16.5
Thiamine, mg/lb	4	5
Riboflavin, mg/lb	1.7	2.2
Niacin, mg/lb	27	34

Note: All values except moisture are on a dry basis.
[1] Nitrogen times 6.25.

Enriched Macaroni-Type Product to be Used in Combination with Meat or Cheese for Use in Lunches and Suppers Served Under Child Feeding Programs. The notice states that the attached specification for protein-fortified, enriched macaroni-type products—which, when prepared and served in combination with meat, poultry, fish, or cheese, may be used as a meat alternate—to meet part of the requirement for school lunch, that is, when served in combination with the above named animal products to meet one-half of the minimum requirement of two ounces (edible portion as served) of cooked meat as specified for the school lunch. It further states that

> One ounce of the dry macaroni product (which will measure one-half to three-fourths cup cooked) may be used as one ounce of meat alternate if served in combination with meat, poultry, fish, or cheese to meet the remaining requirement.
>
> The size of portion of the enriched macaroni-type product (manufactured according to the attached specification) when served in combination with meat, poultry, fish, or cheese may be adjusted to meet the meat and meat alternate requirement of the lunch and supper food patterns for other age groups served under the Department's Child Feeding Programs. The size of portion of this product shall not exceed 50 percent of the total meat or meat alternate portion (FNS Notice 218, 1971, pp. 1–2).

It was stated further that all ingredients shall conform with the requirements of the Federal Food, Drug and Cosmetic Act and regulations "pursuant to that Act as applicable."

The notice also published the chemical specifications for the protein-fortified and enriched macaroni-type product. These are shown in Table 6-1.

Another requirement was that the protein quality of the product shall have a PER that is not less than 95 percent of that for casein.

WHY MODIFY PASTA PRODUCTS?

When considering the question "Why modify pasta products?" we will undoubtedly hear that these products should never be modified. Some people believe
there is no need to modify because the product is good and highly acceptable.
Of course, this is assuming that everything is normal, that there is a ready supply
of ingredients, that the processing equipment is functioning properly, and that
the consumer is satisfied with available products. It is unrealistic always to expect
such ideal conditions. Ingredients are not always available, and since they are
biological materials, their composition and functionality are not consistent.
Equipment may break down when modifications must be made. Last, consumers
have their own ideas about what they want; they may want less expensive
products, more nutritional products, and a variety of products. There are many
valid reasons for modifying pasta products.

As we consider these reasons in some detail in the following sections, we will
see that a number of them overlap and that there are additional reasons within
those listed.

Achieving Variety

As we saw in the section covering standards, four basic types of products are
described, based on size and shape: macaroni, spaghetti, vermicelli, and noodles.
Variety is also achieved by making products that have different shapes, such as
twirls, shells, alphabets, cartwheels, and bows. Figure 6-1 shows these as well
as a number of other types of pasta products based solely on shape. Other pasta
products are different in less obvious ways. These include pastas that are made
with milk and eggs, those that are enriched, and those that are fortified. According
to the standards, noodles must include egg as an ingredient. Standards permit,
within narrow limits, the inclusion of other ingredients. Some of these modifications will cause color changes in the product. This may or may not be acceptable
to the consumer.

When achieving variety through the use of protein additives, a number of
things may take place that, in effect, overlap into some of the other reasons for
modifying pasta products with proteins. Additions can cause changes in textural
properties as well as changes in color, cooking loss, and even nutritional properties. Achieving variety by the addition of protein is not as practical as what
the standards call for, such as the availability of different shapes and sizes, and
the numerous methods of preparation, including the use of sauces. It is also
conceivable that if a more tender or softer product is desired after cooking
(softening often happens when protein additives are used), a practical approach
would be to use a softer wheat variety.

Variety may be achieved in the way a particular dish is prepared. This is under the control of the consumer or the food processor who makes preparations that include pasta as one of the ingredients. Typically, spaghetti can be prepared with tomato sauce, with or without certain meat products, and also with just butter and garlic. It is this versatility that makes pasta products so acceptable throughout the world and with so many ethnic groups.

Improving Quality

Consumers expect pasta to taste good, to have excellent and/or satisfying eating properties, and to have a pleasant feeling once it is consumed. The consumer also expects and assumes that the product is nutritious.

Improving Nutrition

As we saw when reviewing regulations, from the nutritional standpoint, provisions are made for the fortification of pasta products in sec. 139.117: "Edible protein sources, including food grade flours or meals made from nonwheat cereals or from oilseeds, may be used." Since there is a nutritional qualifier on the protein additive, many of the proteins obtained from cereals are excluded because of their deficiencies in lysine. However, this can be offset if steps are taken to make up for the deficiency by adding lysine or by including another protein that is rich in lysine, such as egg white, soy flour, or a dried milk product, which is allowed in present standards. Dried yeast preparations also may be added. In this instance, the yeast product will add to the vitamin and mineral content of the pasta along with a certain amount of protein.

Adjusting Product Variation

Product variation is another area where the macaroni standards provide a means for making proper adjustments. Of significant concern is the situation in which the protein content of the wheat product is below standard. In this case, the addition of gum gluten (vacuum-dried gluten) is permitted to bring the protein level up to 13 percent on an 87 percent solids basis in the finished product.

Using Available Ingredients

The concern here is about the availability of wheat products other than durum semolina. The expected quality can be obtained only by a formula adjustment. In such instances, egg white and gluten may be used to an advantage. Many people make pastas without using durum semolina. In fact, the usual home recipes use all-purpose flours along with egg. Obviously, not only are eggs moisturizers, but also they help build structure, making the pasta products firmer.

Beneficial combinations of wheat varieties are also included in the standards. Obviously, in such cases it is necessary to label the product properly for what it is, to show that it is not a standard product.

Accommodating Ethnic Tastes

When accommodating ethnic tastes, there is little that can be done with the pasta product per se. More likely, the accommodation will take place in the dish preparation. This is not to say that there cannot be a departure from the classical pasta product. One such product is Chinese noodles—a precooked, dried product that is not necessarily made from wheat.

Lowering Costs

There are several ways to look at the benefits of lowering costs. The first way is to improve production efficiency without lowering the quality. The second way is to lower production costs purposely through changes in the formulation, that is, to use less costly ingredients. This may or may not affect product quality. Nevertheless, if less expensive ingredients are used, the quality may suffer. This approach is often taken to make a product more attractive to less affluent consumers. As in all things, a tradeoff of costs and quality has a different appeal to different people. What the processor must do, if a product is being made available to the less affluent, is to conduct a market study to find out what product will have the best appeal.

An obvious way of lowering costs is to use less expensive ingredients, such as lower-cost wheat grades, to partially replace the more desirable durum semolina, which might be hard wheat flour (HWF) or soft wheat flour (SWF). Unfortunately, when this is done one or more of the desirable eating characteristics, such as firmness, will be affected. HWF has less of a deleterious effect on hardness than SWF. This was reported by Sipos and Young (1976). The reduction in eating quality can be lessened by the addition of other proteins. These additions will be discussed in the next section.

CONSIDERATIONS OF PROTEIN ADDITIVES

Breen et al. (1977) made a study of various protein additives that can be used in producing a high-protein spaghetti. They based their conclusions on color, uniform cooking tests, and taste panel evaluation. In all, they looked at 51 commercially prepared protein products. Because some of the proteins imparted poor color to the pasta product, 17 of the additives were eliminated from further study. They reasoned that color is the first thing a consumer notices. Evaluations showed that pasta products should have a golden amber color with a bright translucent appearance. The results of the study showed that when judging pasta products on color, cooking loss, cooked weight, and cooked firmness, that soy protein isolate, soy flour, vital wheat gluten, oat protein isolate, and egg albumin are good additives to use.

Gum Gluten

Regulations provide for the use of gum gluten as a means of bringing up the protein content of the finished product to 13 percent on an 87 percent solids basis. Such an addition will improve other properties as well.

According to the International Wheat Gluten Association (1981), less reliance is placed on durum wheat for pasta production today because many regionally available flours are strengthened through the use of wheat gluten. There are other benefits, such as improved product quality, improved breakage resistance, lessened cooking loss, increased heat tolerance, improved bite characteristics, and increased retorting stress tolerance when the product is canned.

There are two types of wheat gluten available—vital and devitalized. The former is essentially an undenatured product composed of two fractions, glutenin and gliadin, that interact to produce a viscoelastic material. This property is unique to wheat gluten because no other commercially available vegetable protein possesses this property (International Wheat Gluten Association 1981).

Devitalized gluten is a product that has been denatured in its production. Obviously, we cannot expect the product to exhibit much in the way of functionality. However, devitalized gluten still has value in raising the protein level when used as an additive.

From the nutritional aspect, the protein quality of wheat protein is low. The International Wheat Gluten Association states that the PER ranges from 0.7 to 1.0. As in most cereal products, the limiting amino acid is lysine. When it is combined with another lysine-rich protein product, a synergistic effect is achieved. The association publication reports that the optimum combination of wheat protein and soy protein is 30/70. This protein combination equates to 231.77 parts of wheat flour (13 percent protein) and 140 parts of soy flour (50 percent protein), or 62.35 percent wheat flour and 37.65 percent soy flour.

Nonfat Dry Milk

In 1966, the first guidelines were given on the use of nonfat dry milk (NFDM) in macaroni at levels from 12 to 15 percent. Glabe et al. (1967) studied the use of 15 percent NFDM in pastas produced on commercial equipment and found that it was improved in a number of ways. The product had a shorter cooking time and greater tolerance to overcooking than regular spaghetti, and the PER was 1.8 compared to 0.78 for regular macaroni.

As we saw earlier, sec. 139.121 of the FDA standards gives guidelines for producing nonfat milk macaroni. We saw that NFDM can be used in the range of 12 to 25 percent (milk solids-not-fat).

Soy Flour

Soy flour was first permitted in macaroni in 1955 (*FR* 20:9575) and has been permitted ever since. From the very beginning, regulations stipulated that soy flour must be used at a level of 12.5 percent based on the combined weight of the wheat flour and soy flour. The soy flour can be either the full-fat or the defatted type.

Matsuo et al. (1972) found that small additions of soy flour, up to 5 percent, had little effect on the cooking quality of spaghetti. Sipos and Young (1976) showed in their patent application that an acceptable spaghetti could be obtained when the product was made with 90 percent durum semolina and 10 percent soy flour. However, as they pointed out, this amount of soy flour somewhat darkens the spaghetti.

If soy flour can be added to pasta products, so can soy products that have higher protein levels. Usually, the proteins of greatest benefit in this application are those that have more functionality, that is, those products that are more soluble in water.

Egg White

FDA standards provide for the use of egg albumin in the form of "egg white, frozen egg white, dried egg white, or any two or all of these, in such quantity that the solids thereof are not less than 0.5% and not more than 2.0% of the weight of the finished product" (21 *CFR* 1984, part 139.110, sec. (1)).

Matsuo et al. (1972) studied the effects of various protein additives on spaghetti, including powdered egg albumin. They pointed out that powdered egg albumin is readily soluble in water and coagulates on heating. The coagulation of the albumin within the spaghetti increases firmness and elasticity in the cooked product. However, Matsuo et al. also noted that in achieving firmness, the spaghetti products were less compressible.

Whole Egg

As was reported in the FDA standards, noodle products are a class of food that contain whole eggs and/or egg yolk in some form. These products must contain not less than 5.5 percent egg solids and/or egg yolk solids.

It is common knowledge that pasta products prepared in the home make use of whole eggs both as a source of water to develop the dough and as an aid to produce a firmer product. Obviously, in these instances all-purpose flour is generally used. Whole eggs also are used to contribute to color (Walsh and Gilles 1974).

Both egg white and whole eggs may be used in pasta products to improve the protein quality by improving the amino acid profile. Particularly, they add to the lysine content, which is limiting in wheat protein.

Enriched Macaroni Products with Fortified Protein

Regulations permit the addition of "edible protein sources, including food grade flours or meals made from nonwheat cereals or from oilseeds . . . " (21 *CFR* 1984, part 139.117, sec. (a)(1)). However, regulations also require that these products must meet certain vitamin and mineral minimums (see sec. 139.117, Macaroni and Noodle Product Standards). To meet these minimums, the processor can add those nutrients that are lacking.

As the regulations stand at this time, any number of edible protein products can be added to pasta to meet the standards set out in sec. 139.117. This includes products that are mentioned in the previous section of this chapter as well as those that are not mentioned, as long as the FDA considers the protein product to be safe and edible.

It is also possible to produce products that are considered nonstandard, that is, products that do not conform to any of the standard products as defined by the FDA. In such cases, the products can be marketed as nonstandard, but they must be labeled properly. A complete ingredient declaration is necessary.

Many studies were made using protein products along with combinations of durum semolina and with a hard or soft wheat flour, with the expectation that the additive could overcome some of the shortcomings of the wheat flour addition. Usually, such studies were made to lower costs and/or to increase the protein level. One such study was made by Seyam et al. (1976).

These authors considered the production of a high-protein durum wheat pasta, as having a high nutrition value with good consumer acceptance at a minimum cost. Their nutritional goal was to have a PER of at least 95 percent of casein. Formulations were arrived at through linear programming. They had 14 constraints in their program, of which 9 were nutritional, 3 were quality factors, and 2 were taste panel evaluation and lot size. Of the nutritional constraints, they specified a minimum protein level of 20 percent and lower limits of essential amino acids. The amino acid requirements were specified to obtain a formula with an estimated PER of at least 2.4, based on the amino acid score of casein. Their quality-constraint tests included spaghetti color score, cooking loss, and spaghetti firmness.

Fifteen computer formulations were developed, resulting in the most promising

Table 6-2   Essential Amino Acid Composition of MCF-2 and Semolina Compared with the FAO Pattern

	MCF-2	Control	FAO Pattern	Chemical Score MCF-2	Control
Lysine	5.15	2.70	5.44	94.7	49.6
Threonine	3.80	2.38	4.00	95.0	59.5
Half-cystine and Methionine	2.89	2.42	3.52	81.4	68.8
Valine	4.14	5.00	4.96	83.5	100.8
Isoleucine	3.87	4.33	4.00	96.6	108.3
Leucine	7.98	7.93	7.04	113.4	112.6
Tyrosine and phenylalanine	9.12	8.30	6.08	150.0	136.5
Tryptophane	0.87	0.87	0.96	90.6	90.6

Source: Taken in part from Seyam et al. 1976.

formulation, referred to as MCF-2. This formulation consisted of the following percentages of ingredients:

Semolina	71.9%
Soy flour (white)	24.3
Vital wheat gluten	2.9
Modified whey protein	0.9
Dry basis protein	26.5

Formula MCF-2 was tested extensively in the school lunch system of Fargo, North Dakota. Commenting on this study, Banasik and Dick stated that, generally, they reached their objectives, "but the color of the finished product of all the formulations appeared to be one of the most degrading features" (1982, p. 555).

Of special interest is a comparison of the essential amino acid compositions of MCF-2 and the control with the FAO amino acid pattern. This is shown in Table 6-2.

Using the chemical score, we can see that there were both increases and decreases in essential amino acids of MCF-2 over the semolina control. However, the overall nutritional improvements revealed a corrected PER of 2.93 as was reported by Seyam et al. (1976).

Tsen (1978) claimed that pasta products prepared from durum semolina supplemented with soy flour or protein can be highly acceptable. Soy addition not

Table 6-3   Quality Characteristics of Cooked Spaghettis

Run	Description	Cooked Weight	Cooking Loss	Color	Firmness
1	100% DS	34.7	4.3	5.5	12.4
4	90% DS/10% ISP	32.1	6.7	5.5	14.1
2	100% HWF	35.9	6.7	4.5	11.8
5	90% HWF/10% ISP	33.2	5.6	4.5	12.6
3	100% SWF	35.4	7.7	4.0	9.4
6	90% SWF/10% ISP	33.8	5.5	4.5	11.4
1	100% DS	34.7	4.3	5.5	12.4
9	50% DS/50% HWF	35.3	7.6	5.0	11.8
11	45% DS/45% HWF/10% ISP	32.5	6.4	5.0	14.4
10	50% DS/50% SWF	36.1	9.4	5.0	10.3
12	45% DS/45% SWF/10% ISP	32.4	7.4	5.0	12.8
1	100% DS	34.7	4.3	5.5	12.4
11	45% DS/45% HWF/10% ISP	32.5	6.4	5.0	14.4
14	47.37% DS/47.37% HWF/ 5.26% ISP	33.6	5.6	6.0	12.3
1	100% DS	34.7	4.3	5.5	12.4
4	90% DS/10% ISP	32.1	6.7	5.5	14.1
7	90% DS/10% SF	32.6	6.6	5.5	13.6
5	90% HWF/10% ISP	33.20	5.6	4.5	12.6
13	90% HWF/10% ISP and natural color	31.95	7.4	7.5	12.9
15	90% HWF/10% ISP and heat-treated[1]	33.55	6.4	4.5	12.3

Key: DS, durum semolina; HWF, hard wheat flour; SWF, soft wheat flour; ISP, isolated soy protein; SF, soy flour.
[1] Autoclaved before extrusion.
Source: Sipos and Young 1976.

only improves the nutritive value but also increases brownness, firmness after cooking, and canning stability. Fortification of regular spaghetti with 10 percent soy flour or soy protein isolate greatly enhances its PER. The point that soy flour increases brownness is not necessarily an attribute, as we learned from the Seyam et al. (1976) study.

In their patent application, Sipos and Young (1976) reported on the benefits that soy protein isolate had in imparting desirable characteristics to a spaghetti product (see Table 6-3). In every case, the addition of 10 percent soy protein isolate to the wheat product increased the cooked firmness of the pasta. However,

Table 6-4   Protein Efficiency Ratio and Digestibility of Spaghetti Samples
Estimated by Rat-Feeding Test

Sample	PER	Digestibility (%)
Casein	2.50	93
100% DWS	1.00	88
Uncooked 75% DWS + 15% HWF + 10% SPI	1.92	89
Cooked 75% DWS + 15% HWF + 10% SPI	2.20	90
Uncooked 75% DWS + 15% HWF + 10% SF	1.47	84
Cooked 75% DWS + 15% HWF + 10% SF	1.92	89

Key: DWS, durum wheat semolina; HWF, hard wheat flour; SPI, soy protein isolate; SF, soy flour.
Source: Courtesy of Tsen 1970.

they noted that ISP darkens all 100 percent cereal bases slightly, which is more noticeable when a soft wheat product is used. When 5.26 percent ISP is added to a 50/50 mixture of DS (durum semolina) and HWF (hard wheat flour), the color produced is similar to a 100 percent DS control. These authors also claim that "oleoresin or carrot may be used successfully to alter the color of spaghetti" (Sipos and Young 1976, p. 5), which exhibit good color stability on cooking.

Sipos and Young also considered retorted spaghetti products. Retorting softens pasta products significantly. With flour blends, the addition of 10 percent ISP to the flour mix improves firmness to a more acceptable level. However, these authors reported that 100 percent DS is superior to all the products tested. Product firmness ranged from 1.4 for hard wheat flour to 4.2 for durum semolina. Using combinations of 45 percent durum semolina, 45 percent hard wheat flour, and 10 percent isolated soy protein produced a firmness of 3.6.

Tsen (1978) also reported on the use of ISP, showing that the addition of 10 percent ISP significantly improved the PER in the uncooked product. There was even greater improvement in the PER when the products were cooked. These results are shown in Table 6-4.

REFERENCES

Banasik, O. J. 1981. "Pasta Processing." *Cereal Foods World* 26:166–9.

———, and J. W. Dick. 1982. "Extruded Products from Durum Wheat." *Cereal Foods World* 27:553–7.

Breen, M. D., O. J. Banasik, and D. E. Walsh. 1977. Cited in O. J. Banasik and J. W. Dick, "Extruded Products from Durum Wheat." *Cereal Foods World* 27:553–7.

Federal Register. 1955. "Macaroni and Noodle Product Standards." *Fed. Reg.* 20:9575.

———. 1984. "Macaroni and Noodle Products." *Fed. Reg.* 49:10099.

Glabe, E. F., P. W. Anderson, and P. F. Goldman. 1967. "Macaroni Made with Nonfat Milk." *Cereal Sci. Today* 17:510–32.

Hoskins, C. M. 1961. "Additives and New Products for the Macaroni Industry." *Macaroni J.* 43:35, 38.

International Wheat Gluten Association. 1981. *Wheat Gluten—A Natural Protein for the Future—Today*. Shawnee Mission, Kan.: Inter. Wheat Gluten Assoc.

Matsuo, R. R., J. W. Bradley, and G. N. Irvine. 1972. "Effect of Protein Content on the Cooking Quality of Spaghetti." *Cereal Chem.* 49:707–11.

Seyam, A. A., M. D. Breen, and O. J. Banasik. 1976. *Study of the Use of the Unique Functional Characteristics of Wheat in Product Development*. Agr. Exp. Sta. Bulletin No. 504. Fargo, Ind.: North Dakota State University.

Sipos, E. F., and L. L. Young. 1976. Pasta Products. U.S. Pat. 4,000,330 (Dec. 28).

Tsen, C. C. 1978. "Soy Flour and Protein Used in Bread and Pasta Products." Proc. Intern. Soy Protein Food Conf., Rep. of Singapore. (Jan. 25–27).

Walsh, D. E., and K. A. Gilles. 1974. "Macaroni Products." In *Encyclopedia of Food Technology*, ed. A. H. Johnson and M. S. Peterson, 556–570. Westport, Conn.: AVI Publishing.

CHAPTER 7

Processed Meats

From the foodservice standpoint, meat can be made available as specific cuts and/or as special processed products. In the former case, there is little, if any, work done on the meat other than trimming and cutting it into convenient, usable forms. Processed meats, on the other hand, are handled in a more complicated manner, involving comminuting (grinding or chopping), blending, adding non-meat ingredients, cooking, smoking, and so on. The comminuting process can result in sizes that range from chunks to colloidal particles. The two most familiar forms of comminuted meat products are sausages and ground beef, such as the familiar frankfurters and hamburgers.

WHY GRIND MEATS?

The question may be asked, "Why have meats in comminuted forms?" Meats are comminuted for a number of reasons that evolved over the centuries. Originally, humans attempted to preserve meats by one means or another, for example, by drying and adding preservatives such as salt and spices. Since the effectiveness of these ingredients depends on an intimate contact with all the meat, we can suppose that this led to chopping meat with various additives. When doing this, humans created new forms of meat that not only were quite tasty but also had an extended shelf life. We can suppose that when these ground meat products were stuffed into casings, such as intestine or stomach, a sausage product was produced. We have no knowledge of when sausage products were first produced, but we do know that they are probably the oldest processed meat product. Rust (1976) said that sausage antedates recorded history, and that it was a commonplace article of food some thousand years before Christ. Rust went on to say that the American Indian preserved meat for use as food by combining chopped dried meat with dried berries and fat and then pressing them into a cake called pemmican.

Because of our familiarity with hamburgers and sausages, it seems senseless to ask, "Why do we need reasons for comminuting meat?" But the question must be answered to give us a better understanding of what will be discussed later. At least seven reasons can be listed as to why a processor would want to comminute meats:

1. It allows the utilization of meat scraps or those forms of meat that are not suitable for regular meat preparations.
2. It puts less tender cuts into a more palatable form, making them easier to chew.
3. It is a means of producing new, flavorful products more conveniently through the use of various seasonings and/or nonmeat ingredients.
4. In the case of certain sausages, it allows the product to be stored without refrigeration over extended periods.
5. In certain forms, it allows the product to be consumed more conveniently in a bun or roll.
6. It permits the duplication of nature by mixing fat and lean homogeneously, thereby making the product more flavorful.
7. It is an excellent means of achieving portion control, in which each meat serving has the exact same composition, shape, size, and weight.

The sixth reason is of special interest. We know that a well-marbled steak is tastier than one that is not. When sausages and/or ground meat products are made, a tasty product is the result if fat is uniformly dispersed throughout the mixture. Hence, there are many meat formulations in which fat is added to the lean meat before it is comminuted. There is, however, a limit in the use of fat, from both the regulatory standpoint and the consumer standpoint of acceptance. In most cases, the fat limit is 30 percent. Because fat is important in both sausage and ground meats, we need to understand how fat relates to lean in a formulation.

MEAT COMPONENTS

The meats used most often in making processed products are the skeletal muscles of the animal. For our purpose, meat is composed of two parts: lean and fat. The lean is composed of protein and water. Fat is considered simply as fat, except for the presence of a small amount of collagen connective tissue that becomes significant under only certain stress conditions. These conditions will

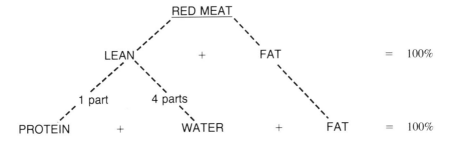

Figure 7-1. Red meat components from the sausage maker's standpoint.

be discussed later. From the functional and practical point of view, meat is composed of three parts. True, meat also contains various vitamins and minerals, but they do not enter into any formula calculations. With this breakdown of meat, it will be a simple matter to arrive at the level of two of the components when only one of the three is known (Fig. 7-1).

TYPES OF PROCESSED MEATS

There are a number of logical approaches to take when discussing the various processed meat categories. These meats can be classed by particle size, ranging from the very large to the extremely small: large intact pieces that are pumped and/or cured; chunks that are bound by one or more means to form larger pieces; coarse-ground meats such as loaves, patties, and certain sausages; medium-sized products that go into sausages and certain loaf-type products; and finely ground or emulsion-type sausages and/or loaves such as frankfurters, bologna, luncheon loaves, and spreads.

Sausages can be broken down into fresh, cooked, semi-dry, and dry. Ground-meat products can be in the form of patties, meat loaves, crumbles, and meats that are combined in special saucelike preparations such as chili con carne and sloppy joes.

This discussion of processed meats will be confined to ground meats, sausages, restructured meats, and pumped meats. Obviously, in each area emphasis will be placed on the beneficial use of protein additives.

This leads to the question, "Why use protein additives in processed meat products?" One practical answer is that protein additives perform certain functional tasks. However, there are other reasons, such as extending meats through partial replacement, improving and/or altering texture, giving meats certain properties, preventing shrink during cooking, and lowering cost. When considering these benefits we cannot forget quality, wholesomeness, and governmental regulations.

REGULATIONS GOVERNING THE USE OF ADDITIVES

Meat and poultry products, which include processed meats, are regulated by the U.S. Department of Agriculture under the Federal Meat and Poultry Program and are administered by the Food Safety and Inspection Service (FSIS). The FSIS inspects meat and poultry for wholesomeness, labeling accuracy, and safety. The agency's personnel monitor the food-distribution channels to prevent violations of laws and to test meat and poultry products for adulteration, including the presence of unsafe drugs and chemical residues (USDA/FSQS 1981). The program is designed to assure consumers that all meat and poultry products sold in the United States and shipped abroad are safe to eat and are truthfully labeled. It achieves its goals by having on-site inspectors who monitor processing operations from the time animals are delivered to the packing plant, through the various stages of processing, until the final products are shipped to local wholesale and retail outlets.

Foodservice operations, too, come under the provisions of the program if the meat products processed are offered for sale in outside channels; then, on-site inspection is required. On-site monitoring is not required if an establishment confines its activity to cutting, grinding, and so on for direct retail use. Also in this category are restaurants, catering companies, and some institutional operations where meats are prepared for internal use.

Some states conduct their own meat and poultry inspection programs. The 1967 Wholesome Meat Act and the 1968 Wholesome Poultry Products Act require state inspection programs to be at least "equal to" the federal inspection program. Only meat and poultry sold intrastate may be inspected in a state program. If states cannot maintain standards equal to federal inspection requirements, the Meat and Poultry Inspection Program must assume responsibility for intrastate inspection.

Much of the meat and poultry slaughtered in the United States today finds its way into products like ham, sausages, soups, frankfurters, frozen dinners, pizza, and pot pies. The Federal Meat and Poultry Inspection Program is responsible for the safety, content, and labeling accuracy of these products. FSIS reviews the procedures, recipes, and labels used by the manufacturers to assure that meat and poultry products will be safe to eat and accurately labeled. FSIS inspectors use these approved methods, recipes, and labels as yardsticks to measure whether the processing is done in a way to produce a safe and truthfully labeled product (USDA/ FSQS 1981, p. 2).

Standards of Identity or Composition

Many processed meat products come under a Standard of Identity regulation and, as such, must conform to those standards, particularly if certain product names are used. Because of this, we should know where these regulations can be found. Also, since we will refer to certain parts of the regulations, it is essential to understand how the various sections of the regulations are broken down.

As was stated in Chapter 1, the federal government publishes a *Code of Federal Regulations (CFR)*. These codes are published under various titles that are numbered like the volume numbers of a set of books: from 1 to 50 inclusive. However, they are not referred to as a particular volume number; they are called "Titles," such as Title 1. Meat regulations are covered under Title 9 of the *CFR,* or simply 9 *CFR* Animal and Animal Products. (All *CFR* books may be purchased from the Superintendent of Documents, Washington, D.C. 20402, or from any government bookstore.)

Title 9 *CFR* is broken down into four chapters. Chapter 3 covers Food Safety and Inspection Service. This chapter also is broken down into subchapters, with further divisions into parts and subparts. The important thing is not these breakdowns, but the numbers used. For example, Part 319 covers Definitions and Standards of Identity or Composition. The various regulations under part 319 are numbered using decimals. These are not decimals from the mathematical sense, but just a numbering system. For example, 319.5 is listed in the regulations before 319.104. This will become clearer when we start using the numbers to refer to the various sections.

Chapter III of 9 *CFR* has two subchapters that are of concern to us; Subchapter A—Mandatory Meat Inspection and Subchapter C—Mandatory Poultry Inspection. Although the regulations in both subchapters are similar, there are some minor differences that came about before the two inspection services became one under FSIS.

The important thing to note is that all section numbers referred to under part 319 will have 319 before the decimal point. To help the food technologist to locate particular regulations, subparts A through U of part 319 follow, with a brief description of each.

A: General
The areas covered are the labeling and preparation of standardized products, the use of nitrates and nitrites, and the mechanical separation of meats.

B: Meat Products
These products are miscellaneous beef and pork products. They cover chopped beef, ground beef, hamburger, beef patties, fabricated steak, and partially defatted beef and pork tissue.

C: Cooked Meats
These include barbecue meats and roast beef—parboiled and steam-roasted products.

D: Cured Meats, Unsmoked and Smoked

These items are corned beef preparations and cured and smoked products such as shoulders, loins, and hams of different types. This subpart also includes chopped hams and pumped meats.

E: Sausage Generally, Fresh Sausage

Included in this subpart are such products as fresh pork and beef sausages, breakfast sausage, whole hog sausage, and Italian sausage.

F: Uncooked, Smoked Sausage

The only product listed as of this writing is smoked pork sausage.

G: Cooked Sausage

Under this heading are such familiar products as frankfurters, frank, furter, hot dog, wiener, Vienna, bologna, garlic bologna, knockwurst, cheesefurters, braunschweiger, and liver sausage or liverwurst.

H: (Reserved)

I: Semi-Dry Fermented Sausage (Reserved)

J: Dry Fermented Sausage (Reserved)

The products of the above three subparts are not covered in the *CFR*. Approval for them is given on an individual basis because there are no set standards used in making such items, but this does not mean that there are not any standards set for such meats. In order to protect the consumer from unethical processors, the government provides for both standard and nonstandard foods. If a food product does not fit into a standard category, FSIS requests the formulation and the label. They then decide whether or not to approve the product.

K: Luncheon Meat, Loaves, and Jellied Products

Two types listed under this heading are luncheon meat and meat loaf. These products are essentially all-meat products. Other than the cure and some seasoning, water is limited to 3 percent of the total ingredients used.

L: Meat Specialties, Puddings, and Nonspecific Loaves

The products listed under this heading are scrapple and bockwurst. There are no specific regulations for nonspecific products except that all such meat preparations must have USDA approval and the ingredients incorporated are limited to "sufficient for purpose."

M: Canned, Frozen, or Dehydrated Meat Food Products

The items covered are chili con carne, chili con carne with beans, hash, corned beef hash, meat stews, tamales, spaghetti with meatballs and sauce, spaghetti with meat and sauce, tripe with milk, beans with frankfurters in sauce, sauerkraut with wieners and juice, lima beans with ham in sauce, beans with ham in sauce, beans with bacon in sauce, chow mein vegetables with meat, chop suey vegetables with meat, pork with barbecue sauce, beef with barbecue sauce, beef with gravy, and gravy with beef.

N: Meat Food Entree Products, Pies, and Turnovers
Only meat pies are listed.

O: Meat Snacks, Hors d'Oeuvres, Pizza, and Specialty Items
Several types of pizzas are listed.

P: Fats, Oils, and Shortenings
This subpart gives the standards for oleomargarine or margarine, mixed fat shortening, lard, and leaf lard.

Q: Meat Soups, Soup Mixes, Broths, Stocks, and Extracts
Beef extract and fluid extract of meat are the only products presently covered.

R: Meat Salads and Meat Spreads
The preparations listed are deviled ham, deviled tongue, potted meats, ham spreads, and tongue spreads.

S: Meat Baby Foods (Reserved)

T: Dietetic Meat Foods (Reserved)

U: Miscellaneous
This subpart lists only breaded products and liver meat food products. These latter types also go by the names of liver loaf, liver cheese, liver spread, liver mush, liver paste, and liver pudding.

Prior Approval of Additives

Because of our interest in the use of protein additives, it is important to know that all additives must be approved before they can be used. Written regulations refer to these ingredients as binders and extenders. Section 319.140 of the regulations on sausage typically list them as follows:

> Certain sausages provided for elsewhere in this part may contain binders and extenders; e.g., cereal, vegetable starch, starchy vegetable flour, soy flour, soy protein concentrate, isolated soy protein, nonfat dry milk, dry or dried whey, reduced lactose whey, reduced minerals whey, whey protein concentrate, calcium

reduced dried skim milk, enzyme (rennet) treated calcium reduced dried skim milk, and calcium lactate or dried milk. The finished product shall contain no more than 3.5 percent of these additives individually or collectively. Two percent of isolated soy protein shall be deemed equivalent to $3\frac{1}{2}$ percent of any one or more of these binders.

The additives listed may be used in certain Standard of Identity meat products in which binders and extenders are permitted. In nonstandard products, other protein products are listed in sec. 318.7. These include sodium caseinate, whey protein concentrate, and two specially treated products, sodium caseinate and dried skim milk. Isolated soy protein also is listed; it is shown to be permitted in two categories of products: in sausage, where it is limited to 2 percent, and in imitation sausage, nonspecific loaves, soups, and stews. In this latter category, sodium caseinate is permitted and, as with soy protein isolate, the amount permitted is "sufficient for purpose."

Because our consideration of protein additives in food systems is limited to those that contain a minimum protein level of 25 percent, the products permitted in processed red meat products are soy flour, soy protein concentrate, soy protein isolate, nonfat dried milk, reduced lactose whey (depending on how much lactose is taken out; the protein level must be 25 percent), whey protein concentrate, calcium reduced dried skim milk, enzyme-treated (rennet-treated) calcium reduced dried skim milk, and dried milk. In standard products, where such additives are permitted, these may be used up to 3.5 percent individually or collectively with the exception of soy protein isolate, because a 2 percent level is considered equal to 3.5 percent of the others. In nonspecific and/or imitation products, all are permitted in amounts "sufficient for purpose." Sodium caseinate is allowed in this type of nonstandard product.

So far, wheat gluten is not permitted in standard sausage products, but it is permitted in nonspecific products. Of the oilseeds, only soy protein products are approved for use in meats. In all likelihood, those products not yet approved should function in processed meat systems. Approval can be obtained if their use can be shown to be beneficial and/or functional. The FSIS also must be given a reliable and easily used analytical method for policing purposes.

Poultry Product Inspection

At one time, in-plant inspections of poultry processing plants were carried out by a different group within the USDA than the one that inspected red-meat processing plants. Today, both plants come under the inspection of the FSIS. Since they were administered by different groups originally, there are some minor differences in their regulations. For example, wheat gluten is permitted in poultry rolls. Section 381.159 (a) reads as follows:

Binding agents, including but not limited to gelatin and wheat gluten, may be added in quantities not in excess of a total of 3 percent for cooked rolls and 2 percent for raw rolls, based on the total ingredients used in the preparation of the product without affecting the name of the product. However, when such agents are added in excess of 3 percent or 2 percent, whichever is applicable, the common name of the agent or the term "Binders Added" shall be included in the name of the product; e.g., "Turkey Roll—Gelatin Added."

Product Labeling

Another aspect of the law is proper labeling of the finished meat product. Section 319.1 reads as follows:

Labels for products for which standards of identity or composition are prescribed in this part shall show the appropriate product name, an ingredient statement, and other label information in accordance with the special provisions, if any, in this part, and otherwise in accordance with the general labeling provisions in Part 317 of this subchapter, and such products shall be prepared in accordance with the special provisions, if any, in this part and otherwise in accordance with the general provisions in this subchapter. Any product for which there is a common or usual name must consist of ingredients and be prepared by the use of procedures common or usual to such products insofar as specific ingredients or procedures are not prescribed or prohibited by the provisions of this subchapter.

We will cover the legal requirements for specific products and their additives and labeling when they are discussed later in this chapter.

REASONS FOR USING PROTEIN ADDITIVES IN PROCESSED MEATS

It is a common practice of food technologists, homemakers, foodservice operators, and chefs to combine additives with ground or chopped meats. This is done for two reasons: to make the meats go further and to change the characteristic of the dish or product. When an ingredient such as bread is added, the meat often loses much of its binding power. To cause the product to hold together and to make it firmer, egg often is added. Many people use this method in their ground meat recipes. However, if hamburger is made this way commercially, it cannot be called "hamburger" from the legal standpoint; however, it can be called "meat pattie" or simply "pattie."

On a commercial scale, the processor does not normally use home recipes because they are usually too expensive. Instead, processors use protein additives to achieve benefits, that is, to alter texture; to change a characteristic; to alter a taste; to prevent shrinking on the grill; to provide a lacking function, such as binding; and to partially extend, either to lower costs or to hold them in line during times of rapidly increasing prices. The additive also may be used to increase the protein content of a product.

Protein/Fat Relationships

It takes protein to "utilize fat." As we know, fat is an important component in meat products because it is a factor in flavor, tenderness, juiciness, calories, and economics. Obviously, there are limits in the use of fat from a number of aspects: legal, dietary, and flavor acceptance. There are certain cuts of meat, such as beef plates (which cover the rib cage) that have fat contents as high as 50 to 60 percent. Products can be made from beef plates and protein additives that are acceptable from the legal, dietary, and economic standpoints. If such meat cuts are not used, their lack of use would add to the cost of other cuts of the carcass. These fatty meat cuts can be made acceptable through the use of lean cuts of meat, but lean cuts add significantly to the cost of the final product.

The preceding reasons will be covered in a little more depth when protein additives in specific meat products are discussed later.

ADDITIVE FORMS

Protein additives are available in three physical forms: powders, granules, and agglomerized or texturized products. Of the protein additives approved by USDA that fall into the 25 percent minimum protein level, we will look at only a limited number of "binders and extenders." As of this writing, such protein products include those that have their origin in milk or soy. Since it is possible that other proteins will be approved for use in meats at some later date, we need to keep in mind that what is said about milk and soy proteins can apply to similar-type products obtained from other sources.

Milk Proteins

Most of the forms of milk are powders that are obtained either by spraying or by some other type of drying process. The particle size of these products can be made to look like granules through an instantizing process. However, they usually do not retain this structure when hydrated. It is conceivable that milk products can be made into granular and textured forms, but this has not yet happened. The milk products most often used are nonfat dried milk (NFDM) and calcium-reduced dried skim milk. More recently, modifications of these two

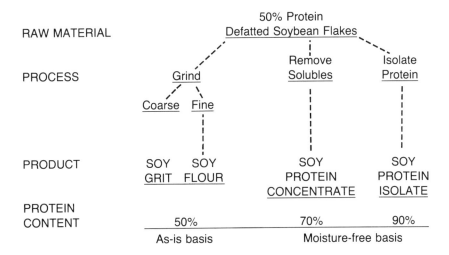

Figure 7-2. Basic soybean products.

products and whey protein concentrates have been approved for use in nonspecific products.

Soy Proteins

The soy proteins are usually derived from a defatted flake with a protein content of about 50 percent (Fig. 7-2). Soy flour and grit products are obtained by grinding defatted flakes. If the particle size is 100 mesh or finer, it is called a *soy flour*. Anything coarser is referred to as a *soy grit*.

If the soluble sugars are removed from the defatted soybean flake, the resulting product is a *soy protein concentrate*. It, too, can be in the form of a flour or a grit, but, for labeling purposes, both types are referred to simply as soy protein concentrate. Note: The grit form of soy protein concentrate is most often referred to as a granular product.

The *soy protein isolate* also is derived from the defatted soybean flake, but via an isolation or fractionation process. In most cases, it is available in a powdered form because it is usually spray dried. The other forms that seem to be gaining in popularity are granular and texturized types. The latter is available in the wet state.

In most cases, the various textured soy proteins can be colored and/or flavored. An exception is the isolate, which is attainable but not needed in these forms.

In all cases, soy protein products can be texturized to result in particles of various sizes, colors, and shapes that look very much like dried meat particles (both finely and coarsely chopped types). Textured products also are available in various flavors.

GROUND-MEAT PRODUCTS

Regulations

Ground or chopped meats are very popular forms in the United States, with hamburger the most popular. Included in the ground-meat category are meat patties, meat loaves, sloppy joe, chili con carne, taco filling, and similar products. From the regulatory standpoint, some of these products have a standard of identity, and thus a specific name. Products also may be nonspecific or nonstandard. Although we will talk mostly about ground- and chopped-beef products in this section, other specie forms, such as veal and pork, must conform to the same regulatory guidelines.

There are two types of standard of identity products: those that permit the use of protein additives and those that do not. In the types of products in which protein additives are permitted, certain restrictions are usually spelled out. The restrictions may be the amount of additive permitted or may require a minimum amount of meat in the formulation. In the latter restriction, the additive cannot be used to replace meat, but is permitted in addition to the other ingredients. In effect, this makes the formulation more expensive, and so its use less desirable. However, this may be offset by some other beneficial effects.

Other restrictions placed on standard products are the amounts of fat and water used. When there is a water restriction, the protein additive can be placed at a disadvantage because its own water needs may not be satisfied. When this happens, the additive cannot function properly, and the resulting product will be somewhat dry.

Fat and water restrictions also are placed on standard products where protein additives are not permitted. Hamburger is an example of this, as can be seen in Subpart B—Raw Meat Products, Sec. 319.15, Miscellaneous Beef Products of the 9 *CFR*. The regulation reads as follows:

> "Chopped beef" or "ground beef" shall consist of chopped fresh and/or frozen beef with or without seasoning and without the addition of beef fat as such, shall not contain more than 30 percent fat, and shall not contain added water, phosphates, binders, or extenders.

Standard products that have a minimum meat requirement are the following (the minimum meat requirement is shown in parentheses): chili con carne (40 percent), chili con carne with beans (25 percent), meatballs (65 percent), meat taco filling (40 percent), meat tacos (15 percent), salisbury steak (65 percent), sloppy joe (35 percent), stuffed cabbage (12 percent), stuffed peppers (12 percent), and tamales (25 percent). Two of these products, meatballs and salisbury steak, have a 12 percent limit on extenders.

Nonspecific processed meat products include beef patties, meat patties, or any name designation that is not deceptive. The product must not be mistaken for one of the standard products, intentionally or inferentially. "Beef pattie" regulations state that it "shall consist of chopped fresh and/or frozen beef with or without the addition of beef fat as such and/or seasonings. Binders or extenders, . . . may be used without added water or with added water only in amounts such that the product's characteristics are essentially that of a meat pattie" (9 *CFR*, part 319.15(a)).

Blending Meats

Any cut of meat can be ground and/or chopped and used as such in various meat preparations. Usually such products are available and labeled as "chopped sirloin," "ground round," and so forth. Since the grinding or chopping of meats makes them more tender than the original, comminuted products are usually made from less tender cuts, as well as from meats that may be of grades less than choice. Because economics is a prime factor in making processed meat products, particularly for foodservice use, meats are combined by blending to be as low as possible in cost for a particular quality level. When making such blends, the processor most often mixes to a particular fat level, which conforms to the law and also has the greatest consumer appeal. Especially helpful in making such blends is a simple calculation referred to as Pearson Square (Rust, 1976).

Pearson Square may be used to arrive at a specified level for a particular component when that component is present in at least one of the two products that will be mixed. In this method, one ingredient must have a concentration greater than the desired, or target, level while the other must have a lower concentration than the target level. In fact, it can be zero. For an example, we will use two beef cuts, chuck with a 15 percent fat content and the plates with a 50 percent fat content. Our goal is to mix the two cuts to arrive at a 30 percent fat level. The procedure is as follows. First, write the number "30" (the desired fat level). Using the "30" as a center point, draw a large *X*:

On the upper-left end of the *X*, write "15" (the fat content of the chuck) and label it "Chuck." On the lower-left end, write "50" (the fat content of the plates) and label it "Plates." Following the line from the 15 through the 30 to the opposite end, write the difference of the two numbers, which is 15. Do the same for the other line, which results in the number 20. Next, total the two numbers (35) on the right and enter that figure as shown here:

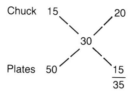

The two difference numbers represent parts of that particular meat cut; for chuck it is 20/35 and for the plates it is 15/35. These ratios times 100 will give the percentage of each cut needed in a mixture with a fat content of 30 percent. The complete form and calculations are as follows:

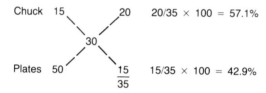

As proof that the method is dependable, it can be checked as follows: 57.1 pounds of chuck with a 15 percent fat content contain 8.56 pounds of fat, and 42.9 pounds of plates with a 50 percent fat content contain 21.45 pounds of fat. These add up to 30.0 pounds of fat in 100 pounds of the meat blend (rounding off to one decimal place in all calculations).

To use Pearson Square for three cuts of meat, it is necessary to make a preliminary blend for some particular fat level and then use that combination for one ingredient in the calculations. Of course, the third meat cut can then be considered to be the second ingredient.

It is interesting to note that the difference figure in the fat contents on the left of the X equals the added difference numbers on the right. Hence, this might be used as a double check of the first several calculations.

There are other ways to arrive at the proper blend of meats, but they go beyond the scope of this discussion. These methods consider other factors: costs of the various cuts, availability, binding properties, color-contributing factors, and so forth. With so many variables the computer is an invaluable aid. For the student who might be interested in pursuing this approach, the methods used involve mathematical procedures such as Matrices and Linear Equations.

Procedures in Utilizing Protein Additives

It is important to look first at ground-meat products without additives to understand certain principles. Since the ground-meat product used to the greatest extent in foodservice is hamburger or the meat pattie, we will concentrate on this product. Much of what is discussed here will apply to other ground-meat products.

Natural Binding Property of Meat

Hamburgers and patties are made from ground or chopped beef and are formed in pattie machines of one or more types. The ground meat usually is fed into a circular cavity in a steel plate that is over a temporary bottom plate, producing a pattie of a particular size, shape, thickness, and weight. The plate containing the meat slides out over a moving belt, and a hammerlike disc knocks the pattie onto the belt. Because every pattie is uniform in size, shape, and weight, this type of meat processing is referred to as portion control. It is important in this operation for the meat to hold together. The binding material responsible for this is found naturally in the lean portion of the meat and is called *myosin*. This type of protein is salt soluble and is "freed" during grinding and/or chopping, particularly when salt and water are present. During the grinding/chopping process, myosin coats the various particles of the mix and, because it has a sticky property, holds the mass together. When the product is cooked, the binding protein is denatured or is said to "set," locking all pieces in the shape of the pattie.

The binding property of myosin can be affected by a number of factors. It can be damaged or denatured by heating before the intended cooking period, and its effectiveness can be lessened by overextending it, that is, by dilution. This will happen if too much additive or fat is used, and/or if the lean meat is lacking.

Freezing and thawing tends to destroy myosin. Thus, if frozen meat is treated poorly in storage, the binding property can be adversely affected. This is especially true if the meat is allowed to thaw partially and refreeze several times. The more often this happens, the more the myosin's binding power lessens.

Bacterial spoilage also can affect the binding property of meat, as will certain chemicals, particularly if the pH is lowered.

Salt is a key ingredient and can be used to obtain the proper degree of bind. Usually, salt is used at levels of 2 to 3 percent. Judgment as to the proper amount of salt needed, other than for taste, usually is made by observing what happens during the pattie-forming operation. If the pattie does not stick together, more salt should be used. If the pattie tends to "hang up" or stick in the die, the salt level should be cut back.

There may be situations when salt is not the total answer, either because added salt is unwanted or because the myosin that is present is so dilute or denatured it cannot do the job. In this instance, certain protein additives can be used, including caseinate, soy protein isolate, or even the highly functional (high NSI) soy protein concentrate. When it is not necessary to follow USDA regulations, egg white or wheat gluten can be used to achieve a bind.

Flavor and Seasoning Needs

The flavor of a meat product depends on a number of things, such as the preparation, the specie of meat, the fat, and the lean. Whenever additives, binders, and extenders are used, the meat is diluted. The more additive used, the greater the dilution effect; the greater the dilution effect, the greater flavor reduction. This is especially apparent when the protein additive has a bland or neutral flavor.

There are certain trends regarding flavors in the use of soy protein products that should apply to other protein products. When ground meat is extended 10 percent, no adjustment is necessary in the formulation except for the addition of a little salt and pepper. With a 20 percent extension, it is beneficial to add other seasonings in addition to salt and pepper, including onion, garlic powder, monosodium glutamate (MSG), hydrolyzed vegetable protein (HVP), or soy sauce. At 30 percent and above, it is necessary to add meatlike flavor to make up for the dilution effect. This is one situation that favors the use of flavored textured products, giving them an advantage over some of the other protein additives.

Fat, too, is diluted when additives are used. Since fat plays an important role in texture and flavor, this factor must be taken into account. For example, if the original fat content of the meat blend is 25 percent and the blend is extended with 30 percent hydrated protein product, the fat content in the final mix will be 17.5 percent (25×0.7). This may make the product somewhat dry to taste. To overcome this, it will be necessary to add more fat. If it is desired to retain a 25 percent fat level in the finished product with the 30 percent protein extension, then the fat level of the starting meat should be about 36 percent.

Ground meats containing vegetable protein products should not be "charbroiled" because a burnt cereallike flavor can result. Many cooks feel that extended ground meat products take less time to cook.

Some soy products are limiting in their use because of flavor. Soy flour and grits can be used only at low levels because of their slight "beany" flavor; usually 3.0 to 3.5 percent is satisfactory on a nonhydrated basis (7.5 to 8.75 percent hydrated using 1:1.5 hydration ratio). With textured soy flour and soy protein concentrate, the hydration ratio can be much higher, as it can with soy protein isolate. However, as with all additives, there is a limit to additive use because of the dilution effect on meat flavor.

PROCESSING RECOMMENDATIONS

To use protein additives properly in ground-meat products, we need to consider a number of aspects. Since each aspect is important in the successful use of protein additives, improper use of any one may lead to failure. Improper use in number can be disastrous. The areas of concern are described in the following sections.

Additive Forms

The first thing to consider when using protein additives in ground meats is the additive's physical form. There is an obvious limit to how much of a flourlike product can be used because of texture incompatibility. The resulting product, if used to a great extent, may make the resulting ground-meat item a little mushy. Better results are usually noted with a granular or a textured product. As mentioned in a preceding section, certain additives can be used to help bind the meat mass. These additions may be flourlike in appearance and often may be used in combination with other protein additives. One product is used to obtain the proper texture, the other to get the proper bind. Examples of such combinations might be textured soy flour and soy protein isolate, textured soy protein isolate and regular soy protein isolate, textured soy flour and sodium caseinate, or textured soy protein concentrate and functional soy protein concentrate. Of course, other combinations of these may also be used.

Hydration Level

The next thing to consider is the proper hydration of the protein. As a starting point, we should take the supplier's recommendations into account. However, in their enthusiasm, certain salespeople get carried away on the amount of water their product can hold and do not take into account the type of product. It is best to hydrate an additive to a particular protein level, usually to a level that closely matches the system in which the product will be used.

As previously stated, we recommend hydrating soy flour with $1\frac{1}{2}$ times its weight of water, that is, one part of soy flour is hydrated with one and a half parts of water, making a total of two and a half parts. Because the soy has a protein level of 50 percent, the combination of the flour and water will result in 20 percent protein ($50/2.5 = 20$). This is an ideal protein level for meat applications; however, we can deviate from this level. Experience may show that slight adjustments one way or another perform better.

Again, the Pearson Square can be of value when researching the proper amount of water to hydrate a product to a particular protein level. Using the Pearson Square procedure for soy flour, we arrive at the following:

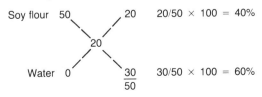

The ratio of 1:1.5 is the same as 40 percent soy flour and 60 percent water.

Caseinate and soy isolates both have about 90 percent protein. We can arrive at their hydration levels as follows:

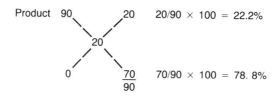

This equates to a ratio of 1:3.55 (78.8/22.2 = 3.549).

Hydration Time

The time needed to hydrate the product properly depends on the product type and the water temperature. Usually, it is best to rely on the supplier of the protein product to recommend the time needed. If this recommendation is lacking, then it is best to proceed as follows. Determine the proper ratio of water to additive using Pearson Square, then add that amount of water to the protein and observe the amount of time it takes to absorb all of it. Although the hydrating time can be shortened by the use of heated water, this is not recommended for bacteriological reasons, not because of what can occur during the time of hydration, but because of what can occur when the hydrated product is added to the meat, that is, bacterial growth.

Level of Extension

The next thing to consider is the level of extension. Here is a good case against the principle that "if a little is good, more is better." We discussed in the section on flavors and seasonings that when meat is extended, its flavor is diluted or lessened. For this reason, recommendations were made as to the necessity of adding seasoning and flavors.

With this thought in mind, at what level should we extend meat? The most apt answer would be similar to the phrase used by USDA, at a level "sufficient for purpose." However, we need to take this a little further. What is the technologist capable of doing when making a product that is acceptable to the consumer? It is possible to have two different people make similar extensions, and one will be acceptable while the other will not. The best approach is to start extending at low levels, 5 to 10 percent. After the technologist is satisfied with the results and has become familiar with handling the extenders, he or she can then gradually try for higher levels. At low levels, mistakes in processing are minimal; at higher levels, mistakes are greatly magnified. If a product is over-extended and not flavorful, the consumer can become prejudiced. Once that happens, it will be difficult to change that prejudice.

Processing Procedure

Experience has shown that it is best to add the hydrated protein product to the coarse ground meat and mix both in a blender. This should be followed by a second grinding step, at which time the additive should be intimately mixed. Very often, the first grind is made with a $\frac{1}{2}$-inch plate opening; the second grind is made with a $\frac{1}{4}$-inch plate. This procedure results in a uniform blend that usually does not show visible evidence of the addition.

There is another grinding process that is often used when making meat patties: a flaking operation. The idea here is to cut the meat into small disks that tend to lay flat and overlap one another, like a roll of coins when the wrapper is removed. This comminuting method is widely used in pattie operations. Textured soy protein products that are cut to size in similar cutting equipment also are available. Flaked meat can be made to simulate whole pieces of meat in appearance, in texture, and in bite. Such products can be made by using the pattie machine previously described, or by freezing, partially thawing, and then pressing into the desired shape with and without cutting of the final product. These products often are referred to as restructured meat.

Factors Affecting Shelf Life of Comminuted Meats

Fresh Meats

Fresh meats have few if any bacteria in the intact inner parts. Most microorganisms occur on the outer or exposed surfaces. When meat is comminuted by one means or another, exposed surfaces are greatly increased and the bacteria are introduced throughout. The degree of bacterial introduction depends on the original bacterial contamination of the meat before grinding, as well as on any further contamination in the process, especially if the equipment used has not been properly cleaned. The comminuting process provides not only more surfaces for bacterial growth but also readily utilizable nutrients that have been released from the muscle fibers as the individual cells are broken up. Ground meats not only have higher bacterial counts than intact muscle but also have a much shorter shelf life even when stored under refrigeration.

Knowing that bacterial growth is affected by temperature, pH, and the presence of certain chemicals, it is possible to retard bacterial growth, thereby increasing shelf life. Of utmost importance is the initial count of the prepared product; contamination of the product during processing must be controlled, which can be done by employing good sanitary practices. It is essential that processing equipment be kept clean and that the temperature of the meat be kept low, preferably 40°F or below. For hamburgers or patties, the use of salt as a seasoning also helps greatly in extending shelf life.

Protein-Extended Meats

It has been observed that many times, when using protein additives in ground meats, the shelf life is adversely affected because of bacterial growth. There are several reasons why this happens. First, there is increased manipulation or processing, such as the mixing of the hydrated protein material, thereby increasing the possibility of contamination and growth. Second, there is greater likelihood that there will be more free water, which will be more favorable to bacterial growth, especially if the protein is overhydrated. Third, and more probable, there is the buffering effect of the protein, that is, the pH trends toward neutrality, another favorable environment for bacterial growth. This pH shift was found by Harrison et al. (1983). By adding acetic acid to the water used to hydrate the protein, they suppressed microbial growth. In this case, the pH dropped to 5.8. They recommended using acetic acid solution as the hydrating water in the range of 0.001 to 0.006 M concentration, which would equate to using about 0.5 percent vinegar in the hydrating water. (The acetic acid content of vinegar is about 5 percent.) Using vinegar at this concentration in the hydrating water, together with 2 to 3 percent salt and following good sanitation practices, extends the shelf life of the ground meat product.

Nitrate in the Water Supply

There is another problem that came to light in a few instances when hydrated protein additives were used in ground-meat products: the cure effect. The cure effect comes about when the hydrating water contains nitrate in some form. If the water used has a nitrate level of 6 parts per million or more, the cure effect can take place.

When the naturally occurring bacterial flora in meat grow in the presence of nitrate, it is reduced to nitrite, which is the chemical used to cure meats. In the curing process, a chemical reaction takes place with the meat pigments and nitrite to cause the development of a pink color that is somewhat stable during usual cooking procedures. Depending on the number of bacteria present, the cure effect can take place in a relatively short time, in many cases in about 3 days; that is, in 3 days there will be enough nitrite present to "cure" the meat. Hence, when the meat product is used shortly after processing, all appears well. But in 3 days the cure effect shows up in cooked ground-meat products.

If the cure effect is noted, a check of the water supply should be made. Many municipalities are concerned about the potential hazard the water supply poses to infants via formulations, if the nitrate level approaches 10 parts per million.

If the water supply is free of nitrates and a cure effect is noticed, in all likelihood the "cure" is coming from another source, such as one or more of the ingredients. A key point to remember is that if the cure effect is noted immediately after the product is made and cooked, then the unwanted cure is probably present as a nitrite. If it takes several days for the effect to show up, then it is in the form of a nitrate.

See the following list for a summary of the points brought up when considering protein additives in ground meats.

1. Additive form
       For compatibility
2. Hydration level
       Aim for 20 percent protein content
3. Hydration time
       To achieve proper hydration
4. Level of extension
       For consumer acceptance
5. Processing procedure
       To achieve desired effect
6. Good manufacturing procedures
       For wholesome products
       To obtain good shelf life
7. Water supply
       To lessen undesirable effects

SCHOOL LUNCH PROGRAM

The School Lunch Program is a foodservice operation that is sponsored by the government and administered by the Food and Nutrition Service (FNS) of the U.S. Department of Agriculture (USDA). This program was the first to have such sponsorship in the area of foodservice. Much can be learned by examining the program from various aspects. Of special interest to us is its use of protein additives, particularly additives that are used to extend meat.

According to a pamphlet put out by the USDA/FNS (1968, p. 3):

> The first known school feeding operation in the United States began in 1853 and by the turn of the century several cities were operating "penny lunch programs" in elementary schools. It was not until the early 1930's that the Federal Government initiated a food assistance program to schools. This was the beginning of a chain of events which eventually led to the passage of the National School Lunch Act

in 1946 and thereby established school food service as an integral part of the U.S. educational system. Specifically, the Congress declared that the objective of the 1946 National School Lunch Act is "to safeguard the health and well-being of the Nation's children, and to encourage the domestic consumption of nutritious agricultural commodities and other food."

The program is essentially a community activity that must follow USDA guidelines if the schools are to benefit economically from funds allocated by the federal and state governments. Guidelines were established in a model meal that was referred to as a Type A lunch, which was designed to meet one-third or more of the daily dietary allowances recommended by the National Research Council for a 10- to 12-year-old child.

As originally specified, the Type A lunch must contain the following as a minimum:

1. One-half pint of fluid whole milk as a beverage.
2. Two ounces (edible portion as served) of lean meat, poultry, or fish; or one cup of cooked dry beans or peas; or four tablespoons of peanut butter; or an equivalent quantity of any combination of the above listed foods. To be counted in meeting this requirement, these foods must be served in a main dish or in a main dish and one other menu item.
3. A three-fourth-cup serving consisting of two or more vegetables or fruits, or both. Full-strength vegetable or fruit juice may be counted to meet not more than one-fourth cup of this requirement.
4. One slice of whole-grain or enriched bread; or a serving of corn bread, biscuits, rolls, muffins, etc., made of whole-grain or enriched meal or flour.
5. Two teaspoons of butter or fortified margarine (USDA PA-19, 1968, p. 5).

Since these guidelines were issued there have been several changes. The first major changes were spelled out in the *Federal Register* (*FR* 1970). Guidelines were given for meals in addition to lunch: breakfast, supper, and supplemental food served between such meals. They also gave guidelines for various age groups, breaking them down into 3 to 6, 6 to 12, and those over 12. The requirements for the 6- to 12-year olds were very much like the original Type A guidelines. As for those children over 12, provisions were made for them to receive adult-sized portions based on their greater food needs. This meant that additional food could be served to satisfy their appetites.

Also contained in this notice was a small paragraph that escaped the attention of many for a long time. The paragraph was in sec. 225.9 (g) of the regulations and read as follows. (Note: reference to the *CND* stands for "Child Nutrition Division.")

Table 7-1 Compositional Requirements of Textured
Vegetable Proteins

	Minimum	Maximum
Protein[1], weight %	50.0	—
Fat, weight %	—	30.0
Magnesium, mg/100 g	70.0	—
Iron, mg/100 g	10.0	—
Thiamine, mg/100 g	0.30	—
Riboflavin, mg/100 g	0.60	—
Niacin, mg/100 g	16.0	—
Vitamin B_6, mg/100 g	1.4	—
Vitamin B_{12}, mcg/100 g	5.7	—
Pantothenic acid, mg/100 g	2.0	—

Note: PER of protein shall not be less than 1.8 on corrected basis of 2.5 for casein.
[1] Nitrogen times 6.25
Source: FNS Notice 219.

The CND may approve variations in the food components of the meals on an experimental or a continuing basis in any service institution where there is evidence that such variations are nutritionally sound and are necessary to meet ethnic, religious, economic, or physical needs.

According to this paragraph, approval can be given, if requested, for any number of reasons. Thus, a school system could, if it desired, try any number of foods for the right reason. This opened the door to those schools that had vegetarians as pupils, and it even allowed schools to include textured vegetable proteins in their programs.

Almost a year later, in February 1971, *FNS Notice 219* was issued (USDA/FNS 1971). This notice allowed the use of textured vegetable proteins to be used as alternate proteins to extend meat products for economic reasons. These products were permitted as an alternate food to provide up to 30 percent (on an uncooked basis) of meat, poultry, or seafood used to satisfy the meat and meat-alternate requirements for the various child-nutrition programs. "The Department permitted the use of these products because they were nutritious, helped school food service directors to cope with the high cost of meats, and helped to provide more flexibility in menu planning" (USDA/FNS 1983, p. 775).

The department designed the nutrient specifications for textured vegetable protein products outlined in *FNS Notice 219* to be nutritionally equivalent to raw ground beef containing no more than 30 percent fat. The dry-textured vegetable protein was to contain at least 50 percent protein, and, when hydrated, to have a maximum moisture content of 65 percent (see Table 7-1). *FNS Notice*

219 was clearly designed around textured soy flour, which was the vegetable protein product available at that time. Other vegetable protein products were still in the initial stages of development.

On August 17, 1979, another notice was published in the *Federal Register* (*FR* 1979) listing some new changes. For one, the term "Type A" was stricken. The regulations charged the schools to have student, parent, and community involvement when setting up the local program and even when selecting the menu. It stated that, in addition to whole milk, the students were permitted to choose between whole milk and other forms of milk, such as lowfat, skimmed, and buttermilk. The department recommended that if schools did not offer children a choice of meat or meat alternates each day, they may serve no single form of meat (ground, sliced, pieces, and so on) or of meat alternate more than three times in a single week. Enriched macaroni product with fortified protein also could be used as a meat alternate or as a bread alternate, but not as both food components in the same meal.

Another change was announced in the January 7, 1983, edition of the *Federal Register* (*FR* 1983).

> Due to recent advances in food technology, several new types of vegetable products have been developed and made available—isolates and concentrates. On July 23, 1982, the Department issued a proposed rule which would allow wider choices than those described by FNS Notice 219 in the types of vegetable protein products used. The proposal, however, did not expand the amount of vegetable protein products allowed to substitute for meat, poultry, and seafood beyond what is currently allowed.

The guidelines for these vegetable products are spelled out in 7 *CFR,* part 210, appendix A, entitled "Alternate Foods for Meals."

Very briefly, these protein products may be used to extend the meat portion of the school lunch to a maximum of 30 percent with the hydrated product. Examples of items in which a vegetable protein product may be used include, but are not limited to, beef patties, beef crumbles, pizza topping, meat loaf, meat sauce, taco filling, burritos, and tuna salad. The product

> may be used in the dry form (nonhydrated), partially hydrated or fully hydrated form in combination with meat, poultry or seafood. The moisture content of the fully hydrated vegetable protein product shall be such that the mixture will have a minimum of 18 percent protein by weight or equivalent amount for the dry or partially hydrated form (based on the level that would be provided if the product were fully hydrated).

If the products are used for functional purposes—for example, as a substitute

Table 7-2 Nutrient-Level Requirement
for Vegetable Protein
Products Used in School
Lunch Program

Nutrient	Amount per Gram of Protein
Vitamin A (IU)	13
Thiamine (mg)	0.02
Riboflavin (mg)	.01
Niacin (mg)	.3
Pantothenic acid (mg)	.04
Vitamin B_6 (mg)	.02
Vitamin B_{12} (mcg)	.1
Iron (mg)	.15
Magnesium (mg)	1.15
Zinc (mg)	.5
Copper (mcg)	24
Potassium (mg)	17

Source: USDA/FNS, courtesy of the Soy Protein Council.

for starch or breading—they cannot be counted as alternate protein foods. They must be used in the meat product as partial replacements.

The protein quality, as measured by the Protein Efficiency Ratio method, must be at least 80 percent that of casein. In addition, the vegetable protein product must contain a minimum level of various vitamins and minerals (see Table 7-2). When comparing Tables 7-1 and 7-2, note that the first is based on 100 grams of product and the second is based on 1 gram of protein. The second important difference is the inclusion of four additional nutrients: Vitamin A, zinc, copper, and potassium. The regulations also spell out required and suggested labeling guidelines.

Economics of Meat Extensions

Since the USDA saw fit to allow the meat and/or meat alternate requirement to be extended, we should look at the economics of this action. This exercise will be of benefit to institutional feeding operations in other-than-school feeding programs.

The *Food Buying Guide* (n.d.) states that 17.2 pounds of 30 percent fat content ground beef are needed to feed 100 children 2-ounce cooked lean-meat portions. Normal cooking shrink is taken into account. Using $1.50 per pound for the price of the meat, the total cost is $25.80 for a per-serving cost of 25.8¢.

A 30 percent extension for 100 servings will require 12.04 pounds of meat and 5.16 pounds of hydrated textured product (HTP). Since the HTP will be composed of one part textured protein (TP) and one and one-half parts of water, we will need 2.064 pounds of TP at a cost of 83¢ (using 40¢ per pound price) and 3.096 pounds of water. The total cost for 17.2 pounds of the extended-meat product is $18.89, resulting in a per-serving cost of a little less than 19¢, which is about 73 percent of the cost of the all-meat product.

It is interesting to look at the economics from another standpoint: How many more servings can be made by extending the original amount of meat? In this case, we will need 7.37 pounds of HTP ($70/30 = 17/X$) or 2.95 pounds of TP ($7.37/2.5$). With the original cost of the meat $25.80 plus the cost of 2.95 pounds of TP at 40¢, this results in a total cost of $26.98. The total weight of the extended product is 24.57 pounds. This amount will feed 142.8 portions ($24.57/.172$). Thus, for an increased cost of $1.18 ($2.95 \times .40$) 42 more portions can be served.

As good as this sounds, we must keep in mind what was said earlier about the approach in making extensions—it is important to guard against overextensions.

Nutritional Considerations

Quite often when we talk about meat extensions, many people question the nutrition wisdom in doing this. The USDA's staff of nutritionists has studied this and, as a result, it made the recommendations for the fortification of textured product as shown in Table 7-2. Most nutritionists feel confident that extensions up to 30 percent with fortified textured-protein products should present no problems to children.

SAUSAGE PRODUCTS

Sausage is another area in which protein additives can be used for functional, nutritional, and economic reasons. In order to take full advantage of these benefits, it is necessary to cover a few basics in sausage making, which will make it easier for us to understand why certain things are done and will give us a foundation on which to make judgments. There are many types of sausage products, but for our purpose, the frankfurter will be used as a sausage model.

Frankfurter as a Model Sausage

In simple terms, the frankfurter is composed of lean meat, fat, water, salt, seasoning, sodium nitrite, and, in some instances, other additives in limited amounts. USDA regulations cover the frankfurter under Part 319, Subpart G— Cooked Sausage, sec. 319.180 for Frankfurters, frank, furter, hot dog, wiener,

Vienna, bologna, garlic bologna, knockwurst, and similar products. Essentially, all these products are the same, as far as major composition is concerned.

As spelled out in sec. 319.180(a), these products

> . . . and similar cooked sausages are comminuted, semi-solid sausages prepared from one or more kinds of raw skeletal muscle meat or raw skeletal muscle meat and raw or cooked poultry meat, and seasoned and cured, using one or more of the curing agents in accordance with s 318.7(c) of this chapter. They may or may not be smoked. The finished products shall not contain more than 30 percent fat. Water or ice, or both, may be used to facilitate chopping or mixing or to dissolve the curing ingredients but the sausage shall contain no more than 10 percent of added water. These sausage products may contain only phosphates approved under Part 318 of this chapter. Such products may contain raw or cooked poultry meat not in excess of 15 percent of the total ingredients, excluding water, in the sausage, and Mechanically Separated (Species) used in accordance with 319.6. Such poultry meat ingredients shall be designated in the ingredient statement on the label of such sausage in accordance with the provisions of 318.118 of this chapter.

The regulation continues by restating much of the above, but it describes products made with meat byproducts or variety meats.

As it relates to protein additives, sec. 319.180(e) also states the following:

> With appropriate labeling as required by s 317.8(a)(16) of this chapter, e.g., "Frankfurter, Calcium Reduced Dried Skim Milk Added," or "Bologna, with By-products (or Variety Meats), Soy Flour Added," one or more of the following binders may be used in cooked sausage otherwise complying with paragraph (a) or (b) of this section: dried milk, calcium reduced dried skim milk, enzyme (rennet) treated calcium reduced dried skim milk and calcium lactate, nonfat dry milk, dry or dried whey, reduced lactose whey, starchy vegetable flour, soy flour, soy protein concentrate and isolated soy protein, provided such ingredients, individually or collectively, do not exceed $3\frac{1}{2}$ percent of the finished product, except that 2 percent of isolated soy protein shall be deemed to be the equivalent of $3\frac{1}{2}$ percent of any one or more of the other binders.

With these regulations as background, we will now look at a model frankfurter formulation that does not include a protein additive. This frankfurter will be composed of 85 percent meat, 10 percent water, and 5 percent other, lesser ingredients consisting of salt, sugar, cure, spices, and seasonings. The cure, spices, and seasonings are present in minor amounts. With the exception of salt and sugar, their presence has little, if any, bearing on our discussion. We will think in terms of only the 5 percent consisting of 3 percent salt and 2 percent sugar.

When making a sausage product, it is necessary to distribute the fat and lean in a homogeneous manner by using a comminuting process such as a chopper or an emulsifying system of some type. In the case of a frankfurter, these meat components are in the form of a fine emulsion. In some other types of sausages, such as Polish sausage, the meat particles are much coarser.

In the comminuting process, there are four important functions: the meat particles are reduced in size, the salt-soluble protein (myosin) is extracted, the fat particles and other materials are coated with the extract, and the meat components are uniformly mixed.

The extracting process, as we discussed in the section on ground meat, is aided by the presence of salt and water, which solubilizes the myosin. Not only does the myosin coat the particles, but also it helps in the emulsification process. However, its chief function is binding the fat and other insoluble materials. When the product is cooked, the denatured myosin, which is in the continuous phase, locks all the material together.

The fat particles reduce in size and, as this happens, the surface area of the fat particles increases. If only a limited amount of the solubilized protein is available, there will not be enough of the protein to coat all the fat particles adequately.

This can best be appreciated if we look at two examples. The first is the simplest—a 1-inch cube that has 6 sides, each 1 inch square, resulting in a total surface area of 6 square inches. If the cube is cut in half, we expose 2 additional surfaces of 2 additional square inches. Every time the remaining sections are cut, the surface area increases (fig. 4-7). When 10 milliliters of oil are emulsified, the surface area of the oil reaches 300 square meters (3,261 square feet) when the droplet sizes reach 0.1 μ. Thus, we can see that the finer the emulsion is, the more surface area is exposed. This necessitates a need for more "solubilized" protein to coat the surfaces.

If the tiny fat particles are not sufficiently coated with myosin, the fat will melt in the cooking process and will not be held in place. This results in a "fatting out," or emulsion breakdown. In the standard frankfurter, this is not likely to happen if the sausage maker does not exceed the 30 percent fat level and if fairly good binding meats are used. Problems can arise if the protein is damaged and/or denatured in some way. This can happen if the meat is improperly handled, as in storage and even in improper freezing practices. Freezing usually reduces the binding property of the meat slightly even when properly done. The binding property also will be affected adversely if the meat is held under insanitary conditions.

Skeletal meats are the best binding meats, but they can differ somewhat from species to species. Usually, as the fat content goes up in the meat, the binding power drops because of the presence of connective tissue or collagen. Collagen protein has little, if any, binding property; hence, it usually adds to the stress of a sausage formulation. Because of this, only small amounts are tolerated. As to the binding properties of meats from various species, bull meat is considered

Table 7-3 Characteristics of Select Cuts of Meat for Use in Sausage

	Bind	Protein (%)	M/P Ratio[1]	Fat (%)
Beef				
Bull meat	1.00	20.8	3.4	8
Imported cow	1.00	19.0	3.65	10
Shank meat	.80	16.8	4.2	12
Trimmings (85/95)	.85	18.9	3.45	15
Boneless flanks	.50	9.9	3.54	55
Veal trimmings	.80	19.4	3.62	10
Boneless mutton	.85	18.1	3.70	15
Pork				
Blade meat	.95	19.2	3.76	8
95% trimmings	.90	18.9	3.73	10
Boneless ham	.80	16.9	3.80	19
50% trimmings	.55	9.7	3.64	55
Back fat, untrimmed	.30	4.2	3.83	80

[1] M/P = Moisture/protein.
Source: Anderson and Clifton 1967.

the best. Table 7-3 shows the relative binding properties of select meat cuts together with their protein contents, moisture/protein ratios, and fat contents. The table is quite general. Various meat cuts do have different binding capabilities that can vary from species to species and even within the same species.

Rust (1976) pointed out that, besides skeletal tissue and bull meat, there are other cuts that possess good binding properties, such as shank meat, chuck, and boneless cow. Just below these in binding power are head meat, cheek meat, and lean pork trimmings. Meats with inferior binding properties (low) usually contain a large proportion of fat or are nonskeletal or smooth muscle, including regular pork trimmings, jowls, ham fat, beef briskets, hearts, hanging tenders, weasand meat, giblets, and tongue trimmings.

In our basic description of a sausage emulsion, the chopper will be used as our comminuting device. The proper sequence of ingredient additions is important. Temperature control also is important because, during the chopping operation, the temperature rises due to the great amount of mechanical energy introduced. (Some sausage processors use soy protein isolates to help protect the myosin against the effect of mechanical heat during the chopping operation. They feel that they can chop to a slightly higher end temperature.) For protection against the excessive heat that can develop, ice is used instead of water.

The first components to be added to the chopper should be the lean meat, followed by ice, salt, sugar, cure, spices, and seasonings. At this time, the myosin is extracted. Shortly thereafter, the fat portions may be added. Chopping continues until the desired consistency is reached and/or a certain temperature is attained. At this stage, the emulsion is ready to be transferred to the stuffer, where it is forced into the casing. The stuffed casings are then tied into appropriate lengths, hung on racks, and then slowly cooked in the smokehouse.

The smokehouse operation is a fairly complicated procedure because the temperature must be taken up slowly in a controlled, moist atmosphere, with or without smoke. The smoke is essentially a flavor-producing operation, and in some cases the process helps to preserve the meat product. The beneficial properties of smoke may be obtained naturally from a smoldering hardwood fire or through artificial means, such as a smoke extract. The cooking that takes place in the smokehouse causes the protein to denature slowly and to lock in the fat before it has a chance to melt and break out of the emulsion. Usually, cooked sausages are heated to an internal temperature of 155°F (68°C).

Thus, the lean meat portion of a sausage formulation is an important component. As was stated previously, some cuts of meat have more myosin or binding protein than others. In any case, a certain amount of binding meat is necessary. If cooked meats or any other inert material (from the binding standpoint) are added, a greater demand is placed on the available myosin.

Let us now look at the meat formulation in another way. If we consider the 85 percent meat portion and accept the 30 percent maximum fat content, then the lean is 55 percent. The lean portion consists mainly of protein and water. For regulatory purposes, the government states that the lean consists of one part of protein and four parts of water. When policing the amount of water used in a frankfurter, the government analyzes for total protein. If there are any protein additives, they subtract that amount from the total, considering the difference to be meat protein only. Regulations state that the amount of water in a frankfurter can be only four times the protein plus ten. The 10 percent water addition is considered essential for processing. Although the government uses four times protein for the water content of lean meat, the average water content of lean meat is probably closer to 3.6, that is, 78 percent rather than 80 percent (3.6/4.6 versus 4/5).

Basically, the chemical composition of the model frankfurter is 12 percent protein; 58 percent water; 25 percent fat; 5 percent salt, cure, and so forth. With this as background, we can see that the lean content is controlled by the amount of fat used in the formulation. The more fat, the less lean, and vice versa. In all cases, the total fat and lean of the model frankfurter equals 85 percent. Since the lean portion of the formulation is the most expensive part, it stands to reason that the more fat that is used, the less costly the formulation. However, there is the legal limit of 30 percent. Water also will lower the cost, but this is limited. Costs can be lowered also by utilizing less expensive cuts of meat, which is somewhat limiting because, in all like-lihood, they will have lower binding properties. If organ meats are used in these formulations, there will be not only a lessened binding property but also a negative appeal to the consumer because of the way the product must be labeled.

Protein Additives in Model Sausage

This brings us up to the use of protein additives such as the milk and soy protein products. These products are used in sausages as binders and extenders. Even though they are called binders, protein additives do not have the binding prop-erties found in the lean meat. Such binding properties are approached in functional soy protein concentrates and soy protein isolates and will, to a limited extent, provide myosinlike properties to the meat emulsion. Wheat gluten also has this type of property, but, as of this writing, it is not permitted in regular sausage products. The same can be said for certain animal blood fractions, but some of these products are permitted in certain countries overseas.

Economic Considerations

When utilizing protein additives in a frankfurter emulsion from a simple extension standpoint, $3\frac{1}{2}$ percent milk proteins and/or soy protein products are permitted, with the exception that soy protein isolates are limited to 2 percent. Thus, when adding $3\frac{1}{2}$ pounds of protein product and taking out $3\frac{1}{2}$ pounds of lean meat, a savings is realized to the extent of the cost differences of the two. If the difference in cost between lean meat and the protein additive is 90¢, then a savings of \$3.15 for every 100 pounds of end-meat product produced is obtained. Based on this, it would seem that the lower the cost of the protein additive, the greater the savings. This is true, but only in part, because there are other factors that must be taken into consideration, such as flavor, texture, appearance of the final product, and even labeling. Using soy flour and soy protein concentrate as examples, soy flour has limited use because of flavor. Hence, at the $3\frac{1}{2}$ percent level, the product of choice is the concentrate that has a much better flavor. It is possible that, through technological advances, a flour may be produced that will be acceptable at this level of usage. In a sense, this has already been realized in the case of soy flour made from a textured product. Apparently, the texturizing operation removes much of the unacceptable flavor found in the regular flour. To use textured soy flour in sausage, the particle size cannot be larger than 40 mesh, according to regulations. This is required to avoid deception; the product may look like it has more meat than it actually does.

When using a soy flour and/or a soy grit in this application, a fully toasted product is the most desirable one to use. As the degree of cooking and/or toasting of the soy flour is increased, the more the so-called beany flavor is depressed.

What about using soy protein isolate in a standard cooked sausage product such as the frankfurter? Because of economics, it is not normally used, primarily because of return on investment. First, the cost difference between it and lean meat is less. Second, the amount that is used is less. Obviously, the savings will be less. If the cost difference is 50¢ at a 2-percent or 2-pound exchange, the savings will be $1.00 as opposed to $3.15 in the previous example.

If the sausage formulation is under stress—if there is not enough binding protein for the amount of fat that is being used—then the isolate can help supply some of the needed bind. One of the problems when utilizing the soy protein isolate in these standard items is that water is limited. To function properly, the protein needs more water. Used without the added water, the end product tends to be dry. In nonstandard or nonspecific sausages, more water can be used, and, under these circumstances, the isolates function quite well. More will be said about nonspecific sausages later.

Protein Additive Substitutions

There are situations when one protein product is needed to replace another, because of product unavailability, cost, and so on. Problems can arise if we are not aware of several facts. Each of the protein products functions in a slightly different manner; each may have accompanying components that are not common to those of another. Soy is a good example. Progressing from a soy flour to a concentrate and eventually to an isolate, not only does the protein content increase but also other component parts change in the reverse direction. Soy flour has some soluble sugars in addition to insoluble carbohydrates. Concentrate is practically devoid of soluble sugars, but has retained insoluble carbohydrates. Since the sugars are removed, both the protein level and the polysaccharide content rise (based on the weight of the final soy product). Soy protein isolate is practically devoid of all types of saccharides.

Half of the weight of nonfat dried milk consists of milk sugar (lactose). As a sugar, it is not very sweet, but its presence does contribute some sweetness to a sausage. Thus, if it is replaced with another protein product that does not have any sugar, there will be a difference in the "sweetness" of the sausage product. This problem can be corrected if a little sugar is added to the formulation. Obviously, the reverse is also true. For example, a formulation containing a sugarless protein additive as one of its components calls for some sugar added in the formulation. If that protein is substituted with nonfat dried milk, it also might be necessary to take out a little, if not all, of the added sugar and/or sweetener.

Sausage Types

Frankfurter and bologna are two products that are made from meat emulsions; they are finely chopped meat products. Similar sausages go by different names, such as franks, hot dogs, furter, and weiner, but all must conform to the same regulation. There are other products that are essentially the same except for the spicing used or the way they are packaged, such as Vienna and garlic bologna. Vienna is a small frankfurter that is packed in water and canned, and garlic bologna is a regular bologna that is heavily seasoned with garlic. Knockwurst, knackwurst, and knockblaugh are all essentially the same, but they differ from the frankfurter because the meat emulsion is a little finer and the sausage's size is both thicker and shorter.

Even though frankfurters and bologna are products similar in composition (but not in size), there is one difference that can be significant—the way the products are consumed. The frankfurter usually is eaten hot, while bologna usually is consumed cold in the form of slices. More often than not, bologna is used in sandwiches. Hence, the way the final product is to be used makes a difference in the use of a particular additive. In a number of cases, a particular formulation was acceptable for a bologna but not for a frankfurter. This occurred when a certain additive made the product somewhat soft for a frankfurter, but not for bologna. Since the formulation was the same for a frankfurter, the frank lost its firmness when cooked and served. This occurred when a soy protein isolate was used in a standard frankfurter formulation, which has a restriction on the use of water. Later, when sufficient water was used to satisfy the needs of the isolate, the softening effect was corrected. Because this is not permitted in a standard product, we have another reason why isolates normally are not used as the protein additives of choice.

Bologna-type formulations are used in luncheon rolls and nonspecific loaf products. Their emulsions may contain such things as pickles, pimento, cheese chunks, and olives. These products go by the popular names pickle and pimento loaf (PP loaf), cheese loaf, and olive loaf. We repeat, there are no regulatory restrictions on the use of the approved additive and water in such nonspecific products, other than the guideline "sufficient for purpose."

Other sausage products utilize coarser pieces of meat in the process, such as Polish sausage (kielbasa), Berliner, and salami (beef, beer, and cotto). There are times when such products are held together weakly because the binding protein is not extracted as efficiently as it should be. To obtain a better extraction, or a better bind, a two-step chopping process should be used. The first step is to make an emulsion and then introduce the coarse pieces of meat with a blending action. In this case, the emulsion needed is small in comparison to the amount of the coarse meat. This type of processing also is used when it is desired to bind large chunks of meats to make roll products.

Sausage Regulations

The following is a list of those regulations pertaining to the various sausage products that may contain protein additives. For the exact reading of the regulations, refer to Title 9 *CFR*, part 319. Protein additives are not permitted in the usual fresh sausage products, such as pork, beef, whole hog, and Italian, but are permitted in breakfast sausage and any other type that has a fanciful name.

Fresh Sausage
Sec. 319.143   Breakfast Sausage.

Cooked Sausage
Sec. 319.180   Frankfurter, frank, furter, hot dog, wiener, bologna, garlic bologna, knockwurst, and similar products.

Sec. 319.181   Cheesefurters and similar products.

Subpart L—Meat Specialties, Puddings, and Nonspecific Loaves
Sec. 319.280   Scrapple.

Sec. 319.281   Bockwurst.

Subpart M—Canned, Frozen, or Dehydrated Meat Food Products

Sec. 319.300   Chili con carne.

Sec. 319.301   Chili con carne with beans.

Sec. 319.305   Tamales.

Sec. 319.306   Spaghetti with meatballs and sauce, spaghetti with meat and sauce, and similar products.

Sec. 319.307   Spaghetti sauce with meat.

RESTRUCTURED MEAT PRODUCTS

Restructured meats are those products that have their form changed in some way. According to an article in *Meat Board Reports* ("Restructured Meat Products"), "restructured meat is meat from low value parts of a carcass that is sectioned, flaked or chunked into smaller pieces then pressed back together by mechanical means to form a new product—one that is much more versatile than conventional whole muscle cuts" (1981, p. 1). Generally, this is true, but there are instances in which this is done with a fairly expensive item and is made into a more expensive one. A good example is boned ham; after the bone is removed, the product is restructured into a particular shape and either is packaged in a special plastic wrapper or is canned. Obviously, this ham is more expensive than one containing the bone.

Sausages, loaves, and patties, then, are restructured products. It apparently becomes difficult, at times, to define restructured meats accurately. Generally, they are defined as in the *Meat Board Reports* article, but with an added qualification. The restructured product usually is made like a particular cut of meat in appearance, shape, and even texture. This was reported by Siedeman et al. (1982) when they gave three reasons for restructuring meat: (1) to upgrade the use of such carcass parts and provide more ready markets for their utilization, (2) to provide a higher profit margin for the meat industry, and (3) to provide the consumer with acceptable roasts, steaks, chops, and stew meats at significantly lower costs than their solid muscle counterparts.

Rolled Products

Among the oldest forms of restructured meats are those rolled and held together with string or clips. Eventually, it was learned that binding could be achieved by using the natural binding property of the meat. The approach is utilized in one of several ways. One is to use salt to extract the binding protein that binds the various pieces when formed and cooked. Another approach is to dust the meat pieces with a binding protein, such as wheat gluten or soy protein isolate, prior to the forming and cooking steps. Rolled products are made from all types of meats—beef, pork, and poultry.

Flaked and Formed Meats

Another early development took place in the pattie operation. Originally, the meat was comminuted in a chopper or a grinder. Some people felt that the texture of such products was unlike that of a piece of cooked, intact muscle. It was reasoned that better texture could be obtained if the comminuted meat particles were in the forms of plates or discs; they could overlap each other when formed into a pattie. Many processors adopted this type of comminution and, with some processing innovations, they obtained products that possess better bite characteristics. These portion-controlled items often are made to look like boneless steaks. This process is popular among many processors that make portion-controlled meats.

Chunking and Forming

Another approach used in restructuring meats is to produce large chunks that are either coated with dry binders or are mixed with binder-containing solutions. The entire mass is pressed into shape and cooked as such, in a way similar to that for rolled products. The product may be frozen either before or after cooking.

Pressed Frozen Meat

Frozen meat may be restructured if it is allowed to drop to a temperature several degrees below freezing, at which point it is somewhat plastic when subjected to a high pressure–forming operation. Usually, the form taken is that of a "log," which has a uniform shape throughout its length. After the log is cut into uniform thicknesses, all portions are essentially the same size, shape, and weight.

Sectioning and Forming

Another method of restructuring meat is called sectioning and forming (National Live Stock & Meat Board). "This procedure involves chopping meat into one- to six-inch sections and tumbling or massaging them to draw the protein to the surface. The pieces are then stuffed into a fibrous casing or a can. During cooking or curing, the sections are bound together, with the result being a product that closely resembles a whole muscle meat cut" (1981, p. 4). An important part of this process is the use of a tumbler or a massager. In both cases, the meat pieces are placed in a mixing vat together with a brine solution. Theno (1977) stated that if the production process is done correctly, several advantages are realized. First, the brine dispersion is accelerated in cured products, resulting in improved uniformity of cured color and texture and an enhanced release of the salt-soluble proteins. Second, from the economic standpoint, yields are increased during processing because of less weight loss during cooking. Last, a uniform high-quality and high-value product is realized. Theno points out that too much mechanical treatment will cause excessive muscle destruction.

Tumbling and Massaging

In both tumbling and massaging, mechanical action is used to break down the tissues to release the salt-soluble, binding protein. Tumblers are essentially horizontal, rotating cylinders containing baffle plates; they resemble a cement mixer. In fact, Theno said that early tumblers were cement mixers adapted to meat-

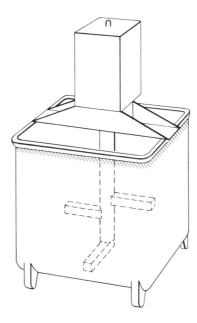

Figure 7-3. Pilot model meat massager. (*Source:* By permission of the *National Provisioner.*)

processing use. In tumbling meats with the brine, the meat is carried up one side of the mixer by the baffles and, as the meat nears the top, it drops to the bottom. This constant dropping action causes the cell structure to weaken, thereby simultaneously releasing the binding protein and incorporating the brine solution. Theno reported that the use of vacuum mixing with a programmable tumbling system was a further improvement in the process. Vacuuming is used to minimize the introduction of air into the exudate, to facilitate protein extraction, and to improve cure distribution.

The massager accomplishes a similar extraction, but through a milder mechanical action. The mixing container may be a stationary cylinder with baffles, or it may be a square tank (Fig. 7-3). Through the center is a vertical shaft containing a few armlike projections. As the shaft turns slowly, it causes the meats to rub against one another, causing the cellular structure to break down while releasing the salt-soluble protein. Massaging usually takes place on an intermittent schedule, perhaps for 10 to 20 minutes each hour for a period of 18 to 24 hours. The intermittent rest periods are considered essential for a properly massaged product.

We have been discussing the various methods of restructuring meats that take advantage of the natural salt-soluble, binding protein of meats. In the process, the brine solution often contains other materials in addition to the salt. Cure and phosphates quite often are used, and, in a number of cases, protein additives are included. During the tumbling and massaging action, the protein-containing brine is incorporated into the meat, thereby increasing the yield and giving a more tender, juicy product.

Dried Meats

Another early development in restructuring meat was described in two patents, Unilever (1965) and Coleman and Creswick (1966), for meat preparations that are used in dried soup mixes. The restructuring process was developed to solve a problem that faced the makers of these mixes. (The latter patent was assigned to Thomas J. Lipton, Inc.) No matter how much the makers tried, they could not predict the final degree of tenderness of meat that was reduced to small bits and then dried. More often than not, when the product was reconstituted in the soup mix, it became quite tough. The solution to the problem involved breaking the meat down into small muscle fibers and then rebuilding the structure through the use of a matrix binder, such as egg white and/or soy protein isolate. When egg white was used as a binder, the resulting product became quite tough; when soy protein isolate was used, the product became soft. However, when the two binders were used in combination, the degree of tenderness needed was obtained by adjusting the ratio. The best results were obtained when the ratio of 1:5 (egg white to soy protein isolate) was used.

The patent gave three examples of the procedure using beef, chicken, and shrimp. In the first example, 15 pounds of raw, frozen lean beef were cut into small squares, thawed, and cooked at 15 pounds steam pressure for 15 minutes. The meat was frozen once again to 10°F and mechanically reduced into small fibers in a Fitzpatrick Mill. A premix of the binder was made by combining six parts of soy protein isolate (sodium proteinate), one part of hydrogenated cottonseed oil, and one part of salt. One part of this mixture was blended with two parts of meat. Water then was added to the mixture in an amount sufficient to provide a dough or plastic mass having a moisture content of approximately 50 percent. After the dough was thoroughly mixed, the material was passed through a meat grinder to form cylindrical masses about $\frac{1}{4}$ inch in diameter, which caused the fibers to align themselves. The material then was simultaneously heat-coagulated and dried in a circulating air oven at a temperature of 175°F. Complete drying took place in about 2 hours, producing a final product moisture level of about 2 percent. The dried material then was ground to size. The patent stated that the dehydrated beef "bits," when placed in boiling water and cooked for 6 minutes, had an excellent flavor and were very tender.

In the second example, using chicken meat, the method was similar to that for beef, with the exception that the meat was cooked in the pressure cooker for 45 minutes at 15 pounds pressure. The chicken meat was deboned and formed into a frozen block at 10°F. Another exception was that egg white was used in addition to the soy protein isolate. In this instance, one part of dehydrated egg albumin, five parts of soy protein isolate (sodium proteinate), one part of hydrogenated cottonseed oil, and one part of salt were combined and added to the meat, as in the beef preparation. The final moisture content of the dried preparations was 4 percent. When the chicken "bits" were boiled in water for 7 minutes, they were similar to freshly cooked chicken meat with respect to flavor, chewability, and tenderness.

In the final example, fresh uncooked shrimp was frozen at a temperature of about 10°F and then shredded in a Fitzpatrick Mill. This material was mixed with the same type of binder preparation used for the chicken. The only difference in its further preparation was that the material was dried in a circulating oven at a temperature of 160°F with air velocity being 250 feet per minute as opposed to 200 feet per minute for the beef and chicken preparations. The dried product had a moisture level of 4 percent. The oven treatment not only dried the material and denatured the binder but also cooked the shrimp fibers. In this case, rehydration took place in boiling water for 10 minutes. Again, the product had excellent flavor and chewability.

Restructured Meat in Theory

As stated earlier, a beef pattie resembles a formulated steak in some respects, at least in the early days of pattie making. (It is interesting to note that a pattie in gravy is called a Salisbury steak.) Such patties were often shaped like steaks. However, not until the flaked beef method was used did the textural properties of the pattie more closely resemble a steak. Food technologists soon learned the value of the use of salt in extracting myosin to do a better job of binding the meat mass. Further improvements were gained when the meat was formed into shape under pressure. The inclusion of sodium tripolyphosphate (STP) also helped produce a product that had an even better texture. The salt and STP combination usually used was 2 percent and one-fourth of 1 percent (0.25 percent), respectively.

In theory, the restructuring of meat is very much like making sausage. Meat particles of varying size obtained by one or more methods of comminution are exposed to some type of mechanical forming step directly, or there is a myosin-extracting step used prior to forming. Large pieces of meat may also be restructured under pressure when the meats are in the semifrozen stage. In some cases, the products are placed in special wraps, sealed, and formed under pressure. There are any number of ways of achieving restructured forms of meat.

Another way in which the binding protein is extracted from meats is by mechanical action, such as tumbling and massaging. In both cases, the mechanical action tends to rupture the muscle cells, which releases the protein, which, in turn, is used to bind the mass of meat together in a subsequent forming process. The use of a tumbling or massaging action together with the addition of salts is, perhaps, the most efficient way of releasing the binding protein.

An additional way of making structured-meat products is first to make a lean sausage emulsion, which is used to bind larger chunks of meats together in some type of forming process. This process often is used when making roll-type products.

Protein Binders

Protein binders in meat systems are of three types: binders of water, oil, and meat particles. The latter type is of concern in this discussion. Perhaps a more apt term for this type of property would be a matrix former. Of the various binders (matrix formers) that can be used in meat systems, none is as efficient as that found in meat. Nevertheless, nonmeat proteins have value to varying degrees in meat systems. There have been many studies made to evaluate protein binders under special conditions. Siegel et al. (1979) investigated the binding abilities of a number of nonmeat proteins and rated them in order from the highest to the lowest when they were used at a level of 13 percent in the presence of 8 percent salt and 2 percent STP. Measured amounts of a particular protein solution were applied between two squares of meat. The combination was heated to 75°C, cut into sections, and placed in an Instron Universal Testing Machine to determine the force needed to separate the two pieces at the "bound" surface. Based on the strength of the binders used, the investigators rated the proteins as follows: first was wheat gluten, followed by egg white, corn gluten, calcium-reduced dried skim milk, bovine blood plasma, isolated soy protein, and sodium caseinate.

Only one type of soy protein isolate was used in this evaluation. (The same can be said of the other proteins.) There are several types of soy protein isolates, so even those that gel may differ somewhat. Because the gel strength of isolates increases with concentration, it is entirely possible that their binding strengths would be greater. When using a soy protein isolate or a similar binder in a meat system, sufficient water should be added to the protein to achieve a level of the combination of about 20 percent. This water should be considered apart from that normally used in processing. As we mentioned in the Lipton patent (Coleman and Creswick 1966), the isolate performed adequately in the preparation of dried beef "bits."

When looking at the various binders that can be used in holding meat particles together, we should not lose sight of the fact that combinations of binders may play an important role.

PUMPED MEATS

Pickling brine solutions were used to cover meat in order to both cure and preserve the product. Because brine penetration was slow, it took time for the entire piece of meat to be adequately treated. The larger the piece of meat, the longer it took to cure. In some cases, bacterial spoilage took place before the cure reached some of the inner parts of the meat chunks. Because of this problem, meat processors resorted to pumping or injecting the meats to speed up the curing action. Two types of pumping procedures were tried: arterial pumping and stitch pumping. Both methods are still being used. In many cases, pumping is followed by the tumbling or massaging process to assure the meat processor of a uniform distribution of the cure. In those instances when meat does not hold all the cure planned for it, the tumbling or massaging step causes the meat to take up additional cure if it is added to the loading of the container holding the meat.

Arterial Pumping

Arterial pumping consists of pressure injection of the brine into one or more blood vessels. Unfortunately, this type of pumping is not without problems. The process is time-consuming and requires skilled labor. All cutting operations, from slaughter to the time the particular meat cut is pumped, require careful work to keep the arteries intact (Holland 1983). Also, it is necessary to hold the product under refrigeration for a minimum of 24 hours to permit equilibration of the cure, which must diffuse through the blood vessel walls.

Stitch Pumping

Stitch pumping involves the use of a number of needles that inject the meat in many locations at once. Each needle has several openings that allow the brine to come into contact with many local sites within the muscle being injected. Originally, this operation was done by hand. Today it is performed by machines. Because of the multiple contact areas, less needle pressure is needed, which in turn lessens damage to the meat. Because of its ease of operation, the pumping procedure is used most.

Two popular meat items that are pumped are corned beef and water-added ham. Regulations governing these products may be found in Part 319, Subpart D—Cured Meat, Unsmoked and Smoked. For our reference, the various section headings will be cited. For regulation details, refer to Title 9 *CFR*, part 319.)

Subpart D—Cured Meat, Unsmoked and Smoked
Sec. 319.100   Corned beef.
Sec. 319.101   Corned beef brisket.
Sec. 319.102   Corned beef round and other corned beef cuts.

Sec. 319.103   Cured beef tongue.
Sec. 319.104   Cured pork products, unsmoked and smoked.
Sec. 319.105   Chopped ham.

Note that in several places in the regulations, the following reference is made. When a cured item is cooked, the weight of the finished product cannot be more than that of the fresh, uncooked product. When it is realized that significant shrink occurs in cooking, this regulatory requirement is not as restrictive as it may seem to the uninitiated. Normally, meat will shrink 20 to 30 percent on cooking. Thus, it can be said that the yield of the cooked product is 70 to 80 percent. However, in the cooked, cured, and/or pumped product, it is possible to obtain a cooked yield of 100 percent, a definite economic advantage. Besides the economic advantage, the product may be more flavorful and juicy.

The preceding discussion concerns cured products that conform to standards. There also are products that fall into the category of nonstandard cured products, which will be discussed next.

Nonstandard Pumped Meats

Before discussing these products, we should give a little background information. Under the heading "Cured, water added products" [Sec. 319.104(d)], water is permitted up to a maximum of 10 percent. However, when adding the water, the product must be properly labeled; the term "Water Added" must be part of the product name in prominent lettering. These items became popular because they were a little less expensive and more flavorful. It was not long before permission was sought from USDA to allow products to be made that were pumped to more than 10 percent, especially because this was being done in a number of European countries. The Europeans learned that the yield in pumped meats could be increased significantly if a protein were added to the cure before pumping. They also learned that more uniform distribution of the cure could be achieved if the pumped meats were subjected to a tumbling or massaging action. This procedure was especially useful in increasing the yield somewhat over that which could be achieved by pumping alone. The products produced by these procedures had wide market acceptance.

When the USDA was approached by processors in this country for their approval for a similarly processed product, permission was given provided that the product would be labeled as an imitation product. When "Imitation Hams" appeared in the marketplace, there was consumer acceptance. However, in a legal ruling involving a meat processor, a decision was reached that "the hind leg of a pig could not be labeled an imitation product just because it contained more water than normal. It was still the hind leg of a pig." Eventually the USDA released a proposal to call all nonstandard pumped products "Combination Products."

Hams would be labeled "Combination Ham Product" with a qualifier immediately below, such as "75% Ham." Although the proposal never was written into the regulations, USDA still gives approval for such products on a case-by-case basis. If the USDA feels that the product is properly processed with good controls built in, that there is no hint of fraud, and that the consumer is fully informed by the label, it will give label approval. The usual products that are made in this category are hams, beef roasts, and corned beef.

Although a number of protein additives may be used in the preparation of combination products, the one that has been used most is soy protein isolate. What can be said about this protein may be said of others as to the proper way to use them in the cure solution.

The biggest problem is to get the protein properly dispersed. Some proteins disperse faster than others, and various means are employed to do this, such as the use of Lightening Mixers and choppers. Usually, the protein level is in the range of 8 to 10 percent on a weight basis of the water used. Once the protein is in dispersion, other curing ingredients, such as salt, sugar, phosphate, nitrite, sodium erythorbate, and flavoring, are added. The usual method of incorporating most of the cure into the muscle tissue is by stitch pumping. If the desired amount of cure is not pumped into the meat, the additional amount needed may be placed in the tumbler or massager. After the tumbling/massaging operation, the product may be stuffed into casings, bags, or containers of various types and then cooked, or the product may be packaged and sold as such.

As we stated earlier, the USDA requires such products to be labeled properly; the label must state how much meat is contained in the product. This is always given in terms of the raw, uncooked product. For example, if a ham is pumped to a yield figure of 133 percent, the finished product will be 75 percent ham ($100/133 = 75$).

Duxbury (1986) reported on a development in which a protein-containing brine solution is incorporated into products that are too small for injection. Especially interesting is the treatment of scallops and shrimp. "Frozen seafood products often are shipped long distances and develop dehydration degradation over storage, and this process will add moistness and fresher texture even into cooked seafoods, such as shrimp" (Duxbury 1986, p. 30).

Essentially, the soy protein isolate/brine solution (which also contains tripolyphosphate, dextrose, and so on) is incorporated into the seafood by absorption. This is achieved by combining the products and the desired amount of protein/brine solution and tumbling slowly in a meat mixer or blender until most of the solution is absorbed.

For those readers who would like to have meat recipes, refer to S. L. Komarik,

D. K. Tressler, and L. Long, 1974. *Food Products Formulary. Volume 1. Meats, Poultry, Fish, Shellfish*. Westport, Conn.: AVI Publishing.

REFERENCES

Code of Federal Regulations. 1987. Title 9. *Animals and Animal Products*. Chap. III. Food Safety and Quality Service, Meat and Poultry Inspection, Department of Agriculture.

Coleman, R. J., and N. S. Creswick. 1966. Method of Dehydrating Meat and Product. U.S. Pat. 3,253,931 (May 31).

Duxbury, D. D. 1986. "Soy Protein Isolates in Restructured/Injected Meat Increase Cooking Yield 35%. Also Improves Raw and Cooked Seafoods." *Food Proc*. 47:(3)28–30.

Federal Register. 1970. "Special Food Service Program for Children. USDA/FNS." *Fed. Reg*. 35:6255.

———. 1979. "National School Lunch Program; Nutritional Requirements. USDA/FNS." *Fed. Reg*. 44:48149.

———. 1983. "Vegetable Protein Products; Used in Child Nutrition Program. USDA/FNS." *Fed. Reg*. 48:775.

Food Buying Guide for Type A School Lunches. USDA/FNS and USDC/NMFS. N.d. PA-270; 0100-1454. Washington, D.C.: U.S. Government Printing Office.

Harrison, M. A., F. A. Draughon, and C. C. Melton. 1983. "Inhibition of Spoilage Bacteria by Acidification of Soy-Extended Ground Beef." *J. Food Sci*. 48:825–8.

Holland, G. E. 1983. "Curing of Ham and Smoked Meats—The State of the Art." *Nat. Prov*. (Mar. 6):6.

National Live Stock & Meat Board. 1981. "Restructured Meat Products: Putting the Pieces Together." *Meat Board Reports* (Oct.).

Rust, R. E. 1976. *Sausage and Processed Meats Manufacturing*. Arlington, Va.: American Meat Institute.

Seideman, S. C., J. L. Secrist, and P. R. Durland. 1982. "Restructured Red Meat Products." *Nat. Prov*. (Oct. 30):21.

Siegel, D. G., K. E. Church, and G. R. Schmidt. 1979. "Gel Structure of Nonmeat Proteins as Related to Their Ability to Bind Meat Pieces." *J. Food Sci*. 44:1276.

Theno, D. M. 1977. "Update on Massaging, Tumbling for Sectioning and Formed Meats." *Nat. Prov*. (June 18):17.

Unilever Limited. 1965. Meat Products. Brit. Pat. 992,759 (May 19).

USDA/FNS. 1968. "National School Lunch Program." Pamphlet PA-19, GPO 19680L-289-128.

———. 1971. "Textured Vegetable Protein Products (B-1) To Be Used in Combination With Meat for Use in Lunches and Suppers Served Under Child-Feeding Program." *FNS Notice 219* (Feb. 22).

USDA/FNS. "Vegetable Protein Products in Child Nutrition Programs." Printed courtesy of the Soy Protein Council, with FNS and USDA.

USDA/FSQS. 1981. *FSQS Facts: Meat and Poultry Inspection*. USDA/FSQS, FSQS-18, GPO 877-18. (Updated FSQS to FSIS.)

CHAPTER 8
Dairy-Type Applications

The importance of dairy products is recognized for their value in both edible and inedible applications. In edible products, they are commonly used by almost everyone in developed countries, particularly in the form of fresh dairy products. This is not the case in the developing countries, where these products are practically unavailable and/or high priced.

Because of their nutritional value, nutritionists recommend that we consume dairy products in some form in our daily diet. Unfortunately, there are some negative aspects, as is the case with many foods, that concern many nutritionists and others in the medical field.

Andres (1981) reported that, although there are many consumers who do not want to give up dairy products, there are many others who do so because of self-imposed diet restrictions or at the request of a doctor. This caused many people to readily accept imitation and/or modified dairy products.

The trend toward greater utilization of imitation dairy products is of serious concern to the dairy industry. According to Graf (1985a), research findings of the United Dairy Industry Association (UDIA), reported by the chief executive officer at the group's 1982 annual meeting, quantified the U.S. dairy imitation volume as follows: 30 percent of the overall market for dairy products, 72 percent of the butter market, 50 percent of the cream market, 15 percent of the fluid milk market, 5 percent of the cheese market, and 1.7 percent of the ice cream market.

UDIA research indicated the following imitation vulnerability ranking of dairy

Table 8-1   Pounds of Whole Milk
Required to Make One
Pound of Dairy Product

Pounds of Whole Milk[1]	Product
24.3	Butter
10.6	Nonfat dry milk
	Cheeses
10.9	Parmesan (hard)
10.4	Cream
9.9	Cheddar
8.5	Swiss
6.5	Mozzarella

[1] Based on analytical data taken from *Handbook 8-1* (USDA/ARS 1976). Whole milk (3.29 percent protein, 3.34 percent fat).

products: (1) cheese, (2) cream, (3) fluid milk, (4) ice cream, (5) butter, (6) cottage cheese, and (7) yogurt.

Over the years, there has been a drastic change in the per-capita consumption of dairy products, particularly fluid milk. Because of consumer concern about fat consumption, the per-capita consumption of fluid whole milk dropped from 251 pounds in 1960 to 111 pounds in 1986, but on the other hand, the consumption of low-fat milk has risen almost 40-fold from 2.27 pounds to 88.79 pounds. The per-capita consumption of cheese, though, increased from 8.2 pounds in 1960 to 20.9 pounds in 1986 (Milk Industry Foundation 1987). Much of the increase in cheese consumption is attributed to the increasing popularity of pizza (Ahalt 1984).

In our consideration of the various dairy products, we need to have a full appreciation of the relationships between whole milk and specialty dairy products. In most cases, it takes a significant quantity of whole milk to produce each specialty product. The milk used for these products is unavailable for use at the consumer level. In addition, the prices of specialty products depend a great deal on the price of whole milk. Consequently, we should look at a few examples of the amount of milk it takes to produce 1 pound of dairy product. This can be seen in Table 8-1. The numbers obtained are calculations based on the analytical data given in Handbook 8-1 (USDA/ARS 1976).

Since dairy products are fairly well ingrained in our diets, we find their taste not only acceptable but also very pleasant. When substitutes are offered for a particular dairy product, they are at a disadvantage unless they are almost imperceptibly different from the real dairy products. However, this problem can also work in the reverse, as is the case with margarine.

Table 8-2 Per Capita Butter and Margarine Usage in Pounds from 1950 to 1980

	1950	1960	1970	1980
Butter[1]	10.8	7.5	5.3	4.5
Margarine[1]	6.1	9.4	11.0	11.3
Margarine/butter ratio	0.56	1.25	2.08	2.51

[1] Actual weight.
Sources: USDA/ESCS 1979a and 1979b.

Margarine was developed as a substitute for butter. Economic considerations were an overriding factor when it came to a taste difference between butter and the substitute, so many consumers switched to margarine. Over the years, many children grew up knowing the taste of only margarine. In later life, when they were offered butter in place of margarine, they often rejected it because of their developed taste for margarine. From 1950 to 1980, the ratio of the per-capita consumption of margarine, compared to butter, went from about half to more than twice as much (see Table 8-2). In 1981, the ratio increased again to 2.6, but in the following 2 years, the trend started to reverse. In 1982, the ratio was 2.47; in 1983, it was 2.02, which is a significant turn. Much of this is due to the fact that an increasing number of companies are now making margarine/butter blends that are receiving a favorable response.

Similar things have taken place in developing countries, where children rarely had the opportunity to drink fresh milk. When they did, they rejected it because of their acquired taste for reconstituted dried skim milk.

There is also the problem in which a "look-alike" is expected to function in the same manner in certain recipes as the original product. For a product analog to be successful, such problems must be offset by overriding advantages like economics, convenience, and dietary considerations. For these advantages, substitute products have been and will continue to be developed.

One of the earliest products produced that simulated a dairy product, either by design or by accident, probably took place when the Chinese produced a soymilk and a curdlike product from it called tofu. Tofu is much like cottage or farmer's cheese in appearance. As we have observed over the years, soymilk preparations were a godsend for many infants that were allergic to cow's milk.

REGULATORY ASPECTS

Before discussing existing regulations for dairy products, we should talk about some of the past difficulties that have a bearing on today's problems.

Filled Milk

Over the years, the price of milk has been based on its butterfat content. There were those unscrupulous operators who removed part or all of the butterfat and replaced it with another, such as vegetable oil, without letting the consumer know of the change. This led to the passage of the Filled Milk Act in 1923, making the practice illegal. According to the definition put forth in the act, filled milk is defined as follows:

> The term "filled milk" means any milk, cream, or skimmed milk, whether or not condensed, evaporated, concentrated, powdered, dried, or desiccated, to which has been added, or which has been blended or compounded with, any fat or oil other than milk fat, so that the resulting product is in imitation or semblance of milk, cream, or skimmed milk, whether or not condensed, evaporated, concentrated, powdered, dried, or desiccated. (United States Code Annotated 1972)

According to *Agriculture Handbook No. 51* (USDA/CMS 1968), only 29 states and the District of Columbia adopted the Filled Milk Act as written by Congress. Most of the remaining states permitted the production and sale of filled milk if the product was properly labeled. Federal regulations prohibited filled milk from passing from one state to another in interstate commerce. With an increased consumer demand for such products, a number of processors attempted to get around the law by calling their product "imitation milk." The National Dairy Council published an article entitled "Relative Nutritional Value of Filled and Imitation Milks," wherein it examined the problems of filled and imitation milks (National Dairy Council 1968). The chief concern was the use of coconut oil as the fat source. According to present information, the fat used in many products is based on hydrogenated coconut oil, which is notably high in saturated fatty acids (especially lauric acid) and low in essential fatty acids. They felt that the use of this fat for infants and children is questionable and is unsuitable for people on fat-modified diets. There was an additional concern about some filled milks because isolated proteins were used in addition to unspecified amounts of nonfat milk. These products were identified as imitation milk, and the Council felt that they were in no sense a nutritional replacement for milk in protein, minerals, and vitamins.

Imitation milk is a product that purports to be or resembles milk but contains no milk products as defined by federal regulations for milk products. Casein and caseinates, both of which are derived from milk, are considered to be nondairy products. This presents problems that will be discussed later.

The Dairy Council article recognized that, in contrast to filled milks, imitation milks do not fall under the provisions of the federal Filled Milk Act and, hence, can be shipped in interstate commerce.

The objections raised by the Dairy Council relative to the nutritional inadequacy of imitation milk can be corrected by using lightly hydrogenated soybean oil in place of coconut fat and by proper fortification.

Shortly after the Dairy Council article was published, the FDA published a proposed standard of identity for imitation milk and cream (*FR*-1968). In the opening paragraph of the proposed regulation, the following was said: "Notice is given that the Commissioner of Foods and Drugs, on his own initiative, proposes the establishment of standards of identity and standards of quality for imitation milk and creams" (1968, p. 7456). Imitation milks were then defined as

> . . . the foods that are not filled milks as defined in 21 U.S.C. 61(c) but which are made in semblance of and intended to be used in substitution for skim milk, low-fat milk, part-skimmed milk, milk, and high-fat milk in single strength liquid, concentrated, dried, or frozen form or half-and-half (milk and cream) in liquid form containing one or more of the optional ingredients listed in paragraph (b) of this section and having the edible oil or fat content specified in paragraph (d) of this section.

The proposal then listed what were considered optional permitted ingredients and explained how the products were to be processed and labeled. The imitation products were required to meet certain nutritional minimums. If they did not, this was to be clearly labeled on the package.

Food Processing ("Imitation Milk Battle" 1969) reported that the FDA's proposal for imitation milk standards has uncovered such intense disagreement among producers, processors, and consumers that it will be a long time before the FDA takes the next step. The disagreement between processors and milk producers turned to legal battles in various states.

In the January 26, 1970, issue of *Food Chemical News*, it was reported that the Carnation Company questioned the use of the term "imitation." The company felt that the definition was so vague that doubts were raised about its constitutionality. They believed that an attempt was being made to set up a standard for the "imitation product" when there was no standard for the "imitated product."

The unconstitutionality of the proposed regulation was finally settled in court 2 years later (*Milnot Co.* vs. *Richardson*. 1972. 350F supplement 221, Southern District of Illinois), when it was declared unconstitutional.

Casein and Caseinates

Over the years, skim milk was the raw material used in the manufacture of both nonfat dried milk (NFDM) and casein or caseinates. NFDM was price supported, which had quite a bearing on the price of casein. Before World War II, casein was produced in the United States, but imported casein cost less than domestically produced products. As a result, the amount imported became increasingly larger until its production in the United States eventually became practically non-existent.

Almost all casein produced until the later 1940s was for industrial application, such as glue and paper coating (Reed 1974). Most persons accepted casein as an industrial product rather than an edible dairy product; it was generally considered a chemical derivative. Later, as Reed (1974) pointed out, improved processing and developments changed this. Today, an estimated 60 to 70 percent of the casein produced is for edible use in the form of casein or caseinates.

Since caseinates were designated chemical products, formulations using caseinates were considered nondairy—hence, the appearance of "non-dairy creamers" and "non-dairy toppings." Many feel that this is misleading because many people want to know whether a milk protein is present for religious and/or medical reasons.

Present FDA policy still allows the use of caseinate in nondairy creamers, but they recommend that the ingredient statement show, in parentheses, that the caseinate is derived from milk (Sheeler 1985).

DAIRY PRODUCTS: MODIFIED AND/OR SIMULATED

Dairy products, like baked goods and meat products, are modified for basically the same reasons. The following list gives some of the reasons that have special appeal to certain population sectors. Those listed are not in any order of importance. Although we have many reasons for modification, the overriding factor is economic. All other reasons depend very heavily on product costs, that is, what is the consumer willing to pay for the new or modified product?

   Religious restrictions
   Health
     Intolerances
       Lactose
       Allergic
     Dietary restrictions
     Weight control
     Nutritional modification
   Storage stability
   New products
     Appearance
     Taste appeal
     Convenience
   Economics

Protein Ingredients

Many of the modern dairy-type products are made with ingredients that are exclusively, or at least partially, dairy byproducts, such as whey, casein, caseinate, and nonfat dry milk. From the economic and functional standpoints, these ingredients are still attractive. However, it appears that there will be a point in time when the cost of such ingredients will more than offset the functional advantages that they now have. On the other hand, nondairy ingredients are being made that no longer have the serious drawbacks they once had. They are becoming increasingly more attractive.

When selecting nondairy proteins for dairylike products, our own experience has been that the more desirable products, from a functional standpoint, are those that have a low viscosity. Products that form gels, such as certain soy protein isolates, are less desirable.

One of the problems in using protein products as ingredients in dairylike applications is getting the products to wet and disperse homogeneously. A number of methods have been tried with varying degrees of success:

1. Using an isoelectric product that will wet readily and adjusting the pH with constant stirring until a smooth, homogeneous dispersion is achieved.
2. Using a cutting action–type blender, such as a chopper, for dispersing a proteinate.
3. Mixing proteinate with other dry ingredients before dispersing in water.
4. Dispersing proteinate in melted fat and then introducing water slowly with stirring.

BEVERAGES

There are any number of approaches to be taken when making dairylike beverages, depending on what we want to accomplish or the reason for producing them. As we discussed in the previous section, one idea is to make a filled-milk product by emulsifying a nondairy fat with skimmed milk. The skimmed milk can be fortified with vitamins, minerals, and even with protein, such as nonfat dry milk or vegetable protein. Another way is to avoid using any dairy products. In each of the approaches, there are problems that need to be solved. Some of the problems and suggested solutions will be discussed as we cover the various preparations. When a company name, product, and/or formulation is used, we use it only as an example and as a starting place for the food technologist to begin his or her experimental work. No endorsements are being made.

Filled Milk

Although adding fat to a product is not in keeping with the title of this text, it does have a bearing on the production of acceptable-quality products. For this reason, we refer to a publication by Modler et al. (1970), in which the authors reported on their work studying the physical and chemical stability of filled milks made with various vegetable fats.

The authors made filled milks formulated from fresh skim milk, emulsifiers, and vegetable oils (safflower, corn, cottonseed, peanut, olive, and lightly hydrogenated soybean oil). They tried four commercial emulsifiers of the monoglyceride type, with iodine values ranging from 3 to 85, that were used at concentrations of 0.05, 0.1 and 0.2 percent (based on formula weight).

The filled-milk preparations were then pasteurized using high temperature, short time (HTST) at temperatures ranging from 200°F to 225°F with exposures of 8, 4, and 0.3 seconds. They rejected filled milks prepared with corn, cottonseed, peanut, olive, and safflower oils immediately after formulation because of objectionable oxidized off-flavors. Of the oils they evaluated, only the lightly hydrogenated soybean oil proved acceptable in a filled milk initially and throughout the first week of storage.

Only the monoglycerides worked best if the iodine levels were low (3–22) and if they were used at 0.1 percent concentration based on weight of product. They found it best to pasteurize before homogenization.

Soymilk

Soymilk probably is the oldest vegetable imitator of cow's milk. It was developed in China many centuries ago and was introduced "in the West in about 1897 by John Harvey Kellogg, M.D., a Seventh-Day Adventist and vegetarian of breakfast cereal fame" (Shurtleff and Aoyagi 1984, p. 197). The authors go on to say that it is interesting to note that Dr. Harry W. Miller, a student of Dr. Kellogg's, worked as a Seventh-Day Adventist medical missionary in China. He was responsible for starting the world's first soy dairy, which was built in Shanghai. Dr. Miller returned to the United States and patented a formulated infant soymilk that he called Soyalac. Soyalac is still being sold today by Loma Linda Foods. [An interesting account on Dr. Miller's life story is told in the book *China Doctor* by Moore (1961).] Formulated infant soymilk preparations also are sold by a number of other companies. One of the main reasons that soymilk baby formulations became so popular was because of a need to feed babies who were allergic to cow's milk.

Soymilk Preparations

The classical Oriental way of producing soymilk is to use whole soybeans as the starting ingredient. Essentially, the preparation involves soaking the beans overnight, discarding the water, adding fresh water, and then mashing the swollen beans into a milky white liquid. The preparation then is filtered through cheesecloth to remove the fibrous material. A small amount of salt and a larger quantity of sugar are stirred in. This is followed by a half-hour simmering step to debitter and to improve the nutritional properties. (Heating destroys the trypsin inhibitor, which is native to soybeans.)

The Oriental method of making soymilk can be done easily in the home. Using a modification of this method, we can make soymilk in our kitchens using typical home-handling techniques.

Instead of starting with the whole soybean, use cracked and dehulled "chips," which are taken from a processing stream leading to defatted soybean flakes for edible purposes.

Wash one pound of soybean chips in tap water until the water runs clear. Then soak the chips in excess water for approximately 20 hours at room temperature. Discard the soaking water and wash the chips until the water runs clear. Add 3 quarts of fresh tap water to the washed and drained chips. Blend approximately 1-pint amounts at high speed for about 30 seconds. After all of the material is blended, strain it through several layers of cheesecloth. Squeeze the residual mass (referred to as okara) to remove additional liquid.

At this stage, we would normally add a small amount of salt and sugar to taste, but do not do this. Bring the liquid to a boil and simmer for 15 minutes, then cool, bottle, and refrigerate. After overnight refrigeration, analyze the soymilk for total solids, protein, fat, bacteria, and fungi. The results of these analyses could be as follows:

Protein	2.83 percent
Fat	1.34 percent
Total solids	6.23 percent
Total plate count	100 per gram
Flat sour spores	<10 per 10 grams
Yeast and molds	<10 per gram
Coliforms	Neg. in 10 grams

Although this preparation has a fairly bland taste, there is still a small amount of beany flavor. A number of approaches were developed by various researchers to lessen this flavor, most of which involved the use of heat in some way to inactivate the enzyme lipoxygenase. Two such processes were worked out at Cornell University and the University of Illinois.

Early work at Cornell (during the 1960s) showed that grinding hydrated soybeans with hot water (above 80°C) and holding the slurry at this temperature for at least 10 minutes was very effective for reducing the beany flavor (Steinkraus 1976). Later, Bourne et al. (1976) looked at the effects not only of sodium bicarbonate but also of other alkalies and salts. They showed that the improvement came about because of the presence of the sodium ion rather than a pH effect. When making their soymilks, they started by soaking soybeans in cold water for 8 hours, followed by grinding them in hot water (minimum temperature of 180°F.), and then boiled the slurry for 10 minutes.

The Illinois process was described by Priepke et al. (1980), and it is summarized as follows:

1. Blanch dry dehulled soybeans in a boiling tap water solution of 0.25 percent sodium bicarbonate solution for 30 minutes. (Ratio of soybeans to solution is 1:5.)
2. Drain and add water to obtain a 12 percent solids content.
3. Grind soybeans and add water. (Use Fitzpatrick, Model D mill, first with 0.25-inch screen and second with 0.023-inch screen.)
4. Heat slurry to 82°C.
5. Homogenize with single-state Gaulin homogenizer at 3,500 psi. (Use Gaulin Model 15M 8TA homogenizer.)
6. Mix slurry with tap water to adjust solids to 6.0 percent (approximately 3.2 percent protein content).
7. Neutralize to pH 7.2 with 6 N HCl.
8. Formulate and/or flavor as desired.
9. Heat to 82°C.
10. Homogenize again as in step 3.
11. Bottle and cool. Store at 1°C.

A simple process was worked out in Mexico that can be duplicated in the home (Orellana 1980). As in the work reported by the universities, the key to the production of a bland product is heating at three stages in the process. The method is as follows, using tap water:

1. Wash soybeans until water runs off clear.
2. Add water and bring to a boil. Simmer for 5 minutes.
3. Pour off water, add fresh water, and allow to soak overnight.
4. Pour off water, add fresh water, and boil for 5 minutes.
5. Discard water and add required amount of fresh water.
6. Either mash soybeans in a blender or place soybeans in bag made of cheesecloth and squeeze by hand under liquid. (If done properly, this will take the place of the regular straining step.)
7. Bring soymilk to a boil and simmer for 10 minutes. Then cool.

8. If a blender is used to break up the soybeans, the soymilk must now be strained. (We have the option of straining or filtering before or after the final heat-treating step. From the bacteriological standpoint, it would be better to filter before the final heat treatment.)

Water Needs

Soaking.   There are several approaches to soaking the soybeans that may be used. If the method is simply adding water to the washed soybeans and allowing them to soak overnight, the weight ratio of water to soybeans should be three to one. Soybeans soaked in slowly running water are better from the bacteriological standpoint, but this adds to the expense of operation. In many cases, as was pointed out by Shurtleff and Aoyagi, 0.5 percent sodium bicarbonate is used as the soaking solution. This seems to decrease the beany flavor, "tenderize the soybeans to give a faster cook and better homogenization, reduce oligosaccharides, and help inactivate trypsin inhibitor" (1984, p. 210). The soaking time can be greatly reduced by increasing the temperature of the water being used.

Final Addition.   The amount of water added in the final addition depends on the type of soymilk desired. Shurtleff and Aoyagi (1984) refer to three types: rich soymilk, dairylike soymilk, and economy soymilk. In rich soymilk, the ratio of water to dry soybeans is 5.1 to 6.1, resulting in 7.0 to 8.7 cups of soymilk containing 10 to 11.5 total solids. In dairylike soymilk, the ratio is 8:1 to 8.5:1, yielding 12.5 to 14 cups of soymilk with a total solids content of 7.4 to 8 percent. The ratio of water to dry soybeans for the economy soymilk is 10:1, resulting in 17 to 18 cups of soymilk with total solids of 6 percent.

The soaked soybean will take up about 1.4 times its weight in water. This is approximate because water uptake depends on the starting moisture content of the soybean; the higher the moisture content, the less water it will take up.

For greater detail and background on the processing of soymilks, refer to Shurtleff and Aoyagi (1984).

COFFEE WHITENERS

Coffee whitener is a substitute for coffee cream. To have a better understanding of this product, we should know the various reasons for putting cream in coffee. Obviously, it is done to improve taste, to lessen harshness, or to give more body. Many people who have sensitive stomachs claim that cream makes coffee more tolerable. In all likelihood, this is because the protein in the cream complexes with the so-called caffetannic acids. These acids, which are not true tannins, impart an acrid flavor to coffee that some consumers find objectionable (Knightly 1969). People who use cream in their coffee usually judge the amount to use by the whiteness that develops. That is the real reason for calling such products "coffee whiteners."

The use of coffee dairy creams in foodservice poses problems in the areas of storage stability, inconvenience, and expense. In instances of improper storage and use, there is always the danger of spoilage, especially when small dispensers are allowed to remain on the dining-room table at room temperature. With the exception of small, packaged, sterilized portions, taking measures to prevent spoilage makes dispensing coffee cream inconvenient and adds to costs. Coffee cream per se is somewhat expensive. Because of these various objections and drawbacks, formulated substitute coffee whiteners are becoming increasingly attractive.

Coffee whiteners are of three types: liquid, frozen, and powdered. On a total solids basis, the products are commonly composed of fat, corn syrup solids (CSS) or sugar, protein, one or more emulsifiers, and buffering salt(s). Artificial flavors and colors also are added in many instances. In a powdered product, an anticaking agent may be included.

Coffee whiteners are not simple emulsions of water, fat, sugar, and protein because special demands are placed on them. Obviously, these products must be similar to coffee cream in appearance, taste, and effect. The emulsion must not break down, either in storage or in use. The acids in coffee, together with elevated temperatures, will have an adverse effect on the protein if certain preventative measures are not taken. The usual defect that occurs when the emulsion breaks down is an oiling one, and another phenomenon is known as feathering. Feathering is actually a curdling of the protein, which floats to the top, producing an unappealing white, grainy-type appearance much like that produced by cream that has soured.

Coffee whiteners that are stored frozen also must possess a freeze/thaw stability. If the liquid tends to separate, the effect is undesirable. This type of phenomenon is known as syneresis.

A powdered coffee whitener should readily wet and disperse in coffee, and it should not clump or cake in storage.

Although all three products are similar, they differ in some minor ways because special demands are placed on each.

One company that makes and distributes a frozen nondairy creamer (Rich Products) recommends diluting the thawed product with an equal part of water to obtain an equivalent of whole milk, and diluting one part to three parts water to obtain an equivalent to skim milk.

Sodium caseinate often is seen in ingredient declarations on packages of nondairy creamers. Those who are concerned about the presence of milk protein and/or any milk ingredient in the creamer should be aware of the fact that this ingredient is derived from milk.

Ingredients

Fat

In practically all cases, partially hydrogenated vegetable fats are used. Those most frequently seen on label declarations are soybean, coconut, palm, palm kernel, and cottonseed (not necessarily in order of prevalence).

According to USDA *Handbook No. 8-1* (USDA/ARS 1976), coffee or table cream contains about 19.31 percent butterfat, whereas half-and-half, which is more often used as coffee cream, contains about 11.5 percent butterfat. Most liquid coffee whiteners contain about 10 percent fat and most powdered whiteners contain about 35 percent fat.

Fat is considered to be the most important ingredient because it not only provides the whitening power to the creamer but also contributes to body and viscosity.

The fat that is used in coffee whiteners should have a proper melting range. If the fat does not melt entirely, the product will have an off-flavor. According to Knightly (1969), a fat with a melting point of 96–98°F and a high solids content index at the storage temperature of the emulsion is most satisfactory. When formulating the dried product, higher melting fats should be used, those that will retain a major portion of their triglycerides in the solid state at the maximum temperature encountered in transit or storage. These fats should have melting points in the range of 110 to 115°F.

Protein

The proteins currently used most often are sodium caseinate and soy protein isolate. When formulating coffee whiteners, we tend to duplicate coffee cream's composition; in the case of protein, that is about 3 percent. It is not always best to use this level with soy protein isolates because of problems that did not come up when lower amounts were employed. A stable emulsion can be achieved with less than 3 percent protein, and, in addition, there is less of a problem of feathering. A nongelling soy protein isolate is better than a gelling product.

Proteins are important in emulsion systems because they help not only to emulsify fats but also to stabilize the emulsion. Proteins contribute body and viscosity to the whitening product. As mentioned in the introduction to this section, whiteners, like cream, have a mellowing effect on taste, which is probably achieved by combining with the caffetannic acids.

In frozen coffee whiteners, certain proteins are better than others when lessening syneresis. Based on the label declarations seen on packages of current commercial products, both soy protein and caseinate are effective.

Although Knightly (1969) stated that good results can be obtained with protein levels ranging from 1.5 to 3.0 percent for sodium caseinate, *Handbook No. 8-1*

(USDA/ARS 1976) reported the levels for frozen liquid whiteners to be 1.0 percent for both soy protein and caseinate and the level for powdered products to be 4.79 percent.

Sugars

Dairy cream contains lactose, a sugar that is not very sweet. Care must be taken not to make a whitener too sweet, which would occur if a level of sugar were used to equal the level of lactose in cream. Although sugar is used to some extent, corn syrup solids (CSS) is used more often. CSS increases both the body and the viscosity of the creamer. Because CSS is hygroscopic, it is often necessary to include an anticaking agent in a powdered product.

Handbook No. 8-1 (USDA/ARS 1976) reported the carbohydrate level of liquid frozen whiteners to be 11.38 percent and 54.88 percent in the powdered product. This can be misleading because the general practice for reporting these analytical data is to add the numbers obtained for protein, fat, moisture, fiber, and ash, and to subtract that total from 100 to obtain the carbohydrate level.

Emulsifiers

The use of certain emulsifiers is governed by the FDA because only certain ones are permitted, at levels below a specified amount. A number of available commercial products are blends designed to work specifically in coffee whiteners. Some companies supplying these emulsifiers make use of a system referred to as *Hydrophile-Lipophile Balance (HLB)*. The HLB system is based on the fact that every surfactant molecule is partly hydrophilic (water-loving) and partly lipophilic (oil- or fat-loving). A certain definite balance between these two parts is necessary for various types of surfactant functions (Atlas Chemical Industries 1965). A number is assigned to a particular HLB combination. The lower the number, the more lipophilic the combination; conversely, the higher the number, the more hydrophilic the combination.

An emulsion chemist will soon become aware, after working with surfactants, that he or she must use water-soluble emulsifiers or blends to make an oil-in-water emulsion. On the other hand, to make a water-in-oil emulsion, he or she needs to select an oil-soluble emulsifier (relatively low HLB). Using the principles of the HLB System, it was determined that a surfactant or surfactant system having an HLB of 5 to 6 is required to prepare a stable emulsion (Atlas Chemical Industries 1965).

Buffering Salts

Buffering salts also are referred to as stabilizing salts. Most often they are disodium or dipotassium salts of phosphoric acid. Using a level of 0.10 to 0.15 percent of a disodium phosphate and adjusting the pH to 7.2 with citric acid results in a very effective buffer. Knightly (1969) pointed out that phosphate salts are desirable when the water used for manufacture is high in calcium or magnesium. However, if used to an excess, these salts can lead to problems by adversely affecting the protein.

Phosphate salts function in several ways:

1. Improve the colloidal solubility of the protein.
2. Act as buffers.
3. Act as chelating agents.

Stabilizers

Stabilizers act in two ways: They inhibit syneresis and add body and viscosity to creamers. When the formulator uses less than 10 percent fat or less than 1.5 percent protein, viscosity can be increased by adding CMC (carboxymethyl cellulose), locust bean gum, algin, or guar gum (Atlas Chemical Industries 1965). Carrageenan also may be used for this purpose. In this case, the colloid will react with the protein to increase viscosity.

Artificial Color and Flavor

These ingredients are optional. When examining label declarations of commercial creamers, we may note that these ingredients are not common to all brands. In only a few instances are both ingredients shown on the label. More often, one or the other is declared.

Artificial color often is beta carotene and riboflavin, whereas the flavoring material can be formulated flavors, such as imitation cream, butter, sweet cream, and, in some cases, diacetyl.

Processing Procedures

Initially, all three types of coffee whiteners are prepared in the same manner. In the powder preparation, only enough water is used to make the product fluid so that it can pass through the homogenizer and reach the spray drier. Obviously, this is to keep drying costs as low as possible. Another difference that takes place is blending in the sugar and the anticaking agent after spray drying.

When examining the recommended procedures by various suppliers of ingredients, we may note two approaches to obtain proper protein dispersions. One is to add a hydrophilic emulsifier to the heated water (160°F) and then introduce the protein, the dry ingredients, and the melted fat. Since this is normally done in a mixer or blender, agitation or stirring takes place from the start of the process.

The other approach is to melt the fat in the mixing tank and then add the emulsifier and the protein, which is dispersed evenly. Water, heated to 160°F and containing the remaining ingredients, is then introduced into the tank.

In both cases, the formed emulsion is pasteurized at 160°F for 30 minutes and homogenized in a two-step homogenizer at 2,500 and then 500 pounds per square inch. The preparation then is cooled and packaged. The regular liquid product is refrigerated; the other is stored in a freezer.

WHIPPED TOPPINGS

Whipped toppings are formulated to simulate whipped dairy cream. Their widespread use in foodservice began when certain benefits were realized: convenience, eye appeal, stable structure, good shelf life, wide acceptance, and low cost. There also is an appeal for those persons who prefer nondairy products for one reason or another.

The typical topping formulation is composed of fat, protein, sugar, sweetener, stabilizer, emulsifier, buffering salts, and, in some cases, artificial color and flavor. The formulation is very much like the formulation for a coffee whitener except that toppings have more fat. There are also minor differences in proportions of the other ingredients. As with coffee whiteners, each ingredient has a specific requirement placed on it.

Fat

Fat is the major ingredient. It gives a topping body, texture, and rich taste similar to that found in whipped cream. The fat needs to be more saturated than that used in coffee whiteners. Knightly (1968) pointed out that an unsaturated fat, such as cottonseed, does not allow efficient aeration and that the product is not stable.

From the flavor standpoint, lower melting fats are preferred over higher melting fats. Those with higher melting points, with a significant solids content melting above body temperature, were described as having a "greasy, waxy" aftertaste (Knightly 1968). Best results are obtained with fats that have a narrow plastic range and low melting point (96°F to 103°F) (Atlas Chemical Industries 1968). In the case of powdered topping concentrates, as with powdered coffee whiteners, the storage temperature is an important consideration. The maximum storage temperature cannot be higher than the melting point of the fat, according to Knightly (1968).

The level of fat usage ranges from about 30 to 35 percent, which gives ideal whipping characteristics and body similar to that found in whipped cream. A lower-fat-content topping will have less body, but the effect can be reversed by increasing the level of sugar, stabilizer, and emulsifier. However, a topping containing less than 25 percent fat is generally characterized by slack body and poor mouth feel, stability, and texture (Atlas Chemical Industries 1968).

Protein

Protein serves two emulsification functions in toppings: as an emulsifier of fat and as an emulsifier of air. As with coffee whiteners, protein also contributes to body and taste.

Any number of protein products can be used. In the early days of development, the two most used protein products were caseinates and nonfat dry milk (NFDM). According to Knightly (1968), when compared with other proteins, including caseinates, NFDM gave superior results. The topping aerated more quickly; it had a higher overrun (increased volume from the volume of air being whipped in); there was less, if any, syneresis; and the emulsion was more stable. Knightly feels that this may be attributed to the better colloidal dispersion of the undenatured milk protein and probably to the higher level of soluble protein and lipoprotein in the NFDM. Knightly believes the quality and quantity of protein is very important because protein determines the strength and resiliency of the film cell wall that surrounds entrapped gases.

As was previously pointed out, in the earlier developmental stages of whipped toppings, most commercial toppings contained a milk protein in preference to a vegetable protein for several reasons. The dairy protein functioned better, and its cost was insignificant because only low levels were needed. Since vegetable protein processors, particularly soy processors, learned how to obtain more desirable products for this use, they are now more competitive with dairy-derived additives. This is especially so as the price of dairy products rises. For this reason, more functional nondairy protein products are being produced and utilized in dairy simulated products.

Protein-containing toppings do not tolerate acid conditions. In such applications, it is best to use carboxymethylcellulose rather than a protein.

Sugar

Sugars are used for both sweetness and body. In most cases, combinations of sucrose and corn syrup solids (CSS) are used. Low dextrose equivalent (DE) CSS is preferred.

A typical liquid whipped topping requires 6 to 10 percent sucrose based on total weight. If too much CSS is used to replace sucrose, the product will have an unnatural sweetness and "gummy" body, and it will tend to be too viscous and difficult to aerate.

In toppings that contain less than 30 percent fat, a blend of sucrose and corn syrup in a ratio from 60/40 to 80/20 (depending on the DE of the corn syrup), will be more functional than sucrose alone (Atlas Chemical Industries 1968).

Stabilizers

Knightly (1968) reported that hydrophilic colloids may be used sparingly in high fat/normal solids toppings. This need increases as the fat and solid content decreases. Colloidal gums are needed to improve body and gas retention (strengthening of air cell structure). In frozen toppings, colloids are needed to improve the freeze/thaw stability of the product. The need is to offset the formation of ice crystals, particularly large ones, which will cause water separation. The colloidal gums work by reducing the amount of water that is available for freezing. The crystals that do form are quite small and not detrimental.

Proteins also improve the freeze/thaw stability of emulsions, based on observations involving soy proteins in various frozen food preparations. Apparently, proteins function in the same way colloidal gums do; they reduce the amount of water that is available for freezing.

Stabilizing Salts

The problems of syneresis and the effect divalent ions (calcium and magnesium) have in the water supply are similar to those noted for coffee whiteners. As with the whiteners, phosphate and citrate salts are effective in lessening these problems. The level of usage for the phosphate salts may range from 0.03 to 0.15 percent. Citric acid may be used to adjust the desired pH, which usually is 7.2.

Emulsifiers

Emulsifiers usually are surfactants that are required for stabilizing the emulsion and the amount of air that is whipped in. They also aid in increasing the efficiency in which air is whipped into the product.

Thalheimer (1968) stated that not all surfactants produce the aeration required in a topping. Those based on unsaturated fatty acids affect the protein, which, in turn, causes an unstable emulsion. Unsaturated surfactants, when used in minute quantities, can add a desired degree of dryness and stiffness to a whipped topping.

Knightly (1968) reported that, while good toppings can be formulated using only the lipophilic esters, such as glyceryl monostearate, better results are obtained using blends containing some hydrophilic surfactants. He stated that the most effective blends consist of a lipophilic surfactant—glyceryl monostearate (60 percent) or sorbitan monostearate (80 percent)—and a minor proportion (40 percent or 20 percent) of a hydrophilic material, such as polysorbate 60.

Flavors and Colors

Although flavors and colors are optional ingredients, it is recommended that a sweet cream–type flavor be used because this is what the consumer usually expects to taste.

Processing

The processing method used for toppings is similar to that used for coffee whiteners except for the first step, homogenizing pressure. The recommendation, according to Knightly (1968), is that a pressure no higher than 2,000 pounds per square inch be used. The second stage is the usual 500 pounds per square inch. Knightly reported that using 3,000 pounds per square inch in the first stage and 500 pounds per square inch in the second will result in excessively high viscosity, "perhaps due to the vastly increased number of fat globules with a concurrent increase in surface area per unit weight of fat" (1968, p. 85).

Following homogenization, the topping is pasteurized at 160°F for 30 minutes, cooled, packaged, and stored under refrigeration.

For a powdered topping, only that amount of water needed to produce fluidity for homogenization, pasteurization, and spray drying is used. Caking is a serious problem that can take place in high-fat powdered toppings. Anticaking agents will help, but so will the use of high levels of sugar, which can be added and mixed with the product after spray drying.

FROZEN DESSERTS

According to Cremers (1974), frozen desserts have been around for a long time. They were known to the Romans and were consumed by French and English royalty in the fifteenth century. The first ice cream enterprise was started by Jacob Fussell in Baltimore, Maryland, about 1851. Since then, ice cream has become a very popular dessert, not only in the United States but also throughout the world.

Basically, ice cream is a frozen-food product that is prepared from one or more dairy products, sweeteners, and a few other minor ingredients. The mix is pasteurized and frozen with constant stirring, during which time air is entrapped in the freezing product. As a result, the specific gravity of the product drops significantly. In the trade, this is referred to as overrun. Overrun usually is referred to as a percentage figure. It can run as high as 100 percent, which is a doubling of volume for a particular weight.

Imitation ice cream or alternative products were developed to satisfy consumer dietary and organoleptic desires. The dietary desires of certain consumers were for products with lower calorie content, no use of animal derivatives, and lower cost. To meet these consumer wants, a large number of products were developed and marketed. All of them, including ice cream, are classified as frozen desserts. As might be expected, after being confronted with certain marketing claims and a host of products, the consumer became confused. There was a need, in the eyes of the FDA, to set up standards. The FDA felt this was necessary to protect the consumer against fraud.

Federal Standards

The Food and Drug Administration's standards for frozen desserts are published in the *Code of Federal Regulations, 21 CFR,* part 135, under the heading "Frozen Desserts." The basic differences in these standards are summarized in Table 8-4. A few pertinent comments will be made about the various products.

Ice cream and French custard come under sec. 135.110. The only difference between the two is the amount of egg yolk solids in the product. Ice milk differs from these two products because it has less milk fat and less total milk solids. In the case of mellorine, the fat content can be as high as in ice cream. However, the fat can be of vegetable origin. The protein source also can be of vegetable origin, but the protein quality, as measured by PER, must be 108 percent of that of casein; that is, it must have a PER of 2.7. Sherbet is characterized by the fruit that it contains. It has a very low milk solids requirement. As can be seen in its weight per gallon of product, there is a very low overrun. The product also must have a titratable acidity of 0.35 percent calculated as lactic acid. It may also contain "distilled alcoholic beverage, including liqueurs or wine, in an amount not to exceed that required for flavoring the sherbet" (21 *CFR* 135.140(e)(4)). Last, the standard for water ices provides for a product that is like sherbet but with no milk derivatives or eggs except egg white.

Not listed are the "soft serves," ice creams or ice milks that are taken from a freezer without any additional hardening or tempering. These are drawn from the freezer at about 18 to 20°F. Soft serves usually have lower total sweetener solids than ice cream. This permits faster freezing to a stiff, dry consistency. The overrun ranges from 35 to 45 percent, depending on the mix solids, which is lower than for the solids of ice cream.

At one time, most soft serves were classified as ice milks. Now, depending on their composition, they may fall under that for ice cream, custard, ice milk, or mellorine. In any case, the labels of such products must inform the customer as to the type of product it is.

Ice cream and frozen desserts are described under paragraph (a) of sec. 135.110 as follows:

> **Description.** *Ice cream*—(1) Ice cream is a food produced by freezing, while stirring, a pasteurized mix consisting of one or more of the optional dairy ingredients specified in paragraph (b) of this section, and may contain one or more of the

Table 8-3 FDA Frozen-Dessert Standards

	Ice Cream	French Ice Cream French Custard Frozen Custard	Ice Milk	Mellorine	Sherbet	Water Ices
21 *CFR* Sec. No.	135.110	135.110	135.120	135.130	135.140	135.160
Total Milk solids	20% min.[3] 16% min.[1]	20% min.[3] 16% min.[1]	11% min.[3]		2% min. 5% max.	
Milk fat Solids	10% min. 8% min.[1]	10% min. 8% max.[1]	2% min. 7% max.	6% min. fat[4] 4.8% min.[1]	1% min. 2% max.	
Nonfat milk Solids	10% min.[2]	10% min.[2]	4% min.[2]		1.0% min.	
Protein				2.7% min.[5] 2.2% min.[1]		
Egg yolk Solids	1.4% max.	1.4% min. 1.12% min.[1]				
Solids/gal	1.6 lbs min.	1.6 lbs min.	1.3 lbs min.	1.6 lbs min.		
Weight/gal	4.5 lbs min.	4.5 lbs min.		4.5 lbs min.	6.0 lbs min.	
Other	Caseinates[3]	Caseinates[3]	Caseinates[3]	Vit. A 40 i.u. per gm of fat	May use alcoholic beverages for flavoring.	
Comments	May contain other safe and suitable nonmilk-derived ingredients.	Same as for ice cream except higher egg yolk solids.	Same as for ice cream except lower in milk fat and total milk solids.	Protein and fat may be animal and/or vegetable.	Characterized by fruit ingredients and titratable acidity as lactic acid of 0.35%.	Like sherbet except no milk derivatives and no egg except egg white. Not pasteurized.

[1] In presence of bulky flavoring ingredients.
[2] If milk fat solids are higher, nonfat milk solids may be reduced by equal amount. Milk fat solids + nonfat milk solids = Total milk solids.
[3] Caseinate cannot be included in total milk solids calculation.
[4] Fat may be milk fat and/or vegetable fat.
[5] PER 108 percent of casein or 2.7.

Table 8-4 Representative Frozen Dessert Formulas (By Percent)[1]

| | Ice Cream | | | | | |
	Premium[2]	Average	Ice Milk	Sherbet	Ice	Soft-Serve
Milk fat[3]	16.0	10.5	3.0	1.5	—	6.0
Milk solids not fat	9.0	11.0	12.0	3.5	—	12.0
Sucrose	16.0	12.5	12.0	19.0	23.0	9.0
Corn syrup solids	—	5.5	7.0	9.0	7.0	6.0
Stabilizer[4]	0.1	0.3	0.3	0.5	0.3	0.3
Emulsifier[4]	—	0.1	0.15	—	—	0.2
Total solids	41.1	39.9	34.45	33.5	30.3	33.5
Pounds/Gallon of mix	9.17	9.36	9.46	9.48	9.4	9.3
	Draw from Freezer					
Overrun (%)	65–70	95–100	90–95	50	10	40
Approx. lb/gal. finished product	5.4	4.6	4.8	6.25	8.5	6.5

[1] Frozen desserts containing vegetable fat (mellorine type) are permitted in some states. A wide variation of composition exists depending on individual State Standards.
[2] If classified as custard or French, it must contain not less than 1.4% egg yolk solids.
[3] Milk fat content regulated by individual State.
[4] Usage level as recommended by manufacturer of stabilizer and emulsifier.
Source: Cremers 1974.

of the optional caseinates specified in paragraph (c) of this section subject to the conditions hereinafter set forth, and other safe and suitable nonmilk-derived ingredients; and excluding other food fats, except such as are natural components of flavoring ingredients used or are added in incidental amounts to accomplish specific functions.

The optional dairy ingredients listed in paragraph (5) include various creams, butter, butter oil, skim milk, whole milk, evaporated, condensed, and even dried preparations of these products, as well as derivatives and/or fractions. This does not include casein or caseinate as such. In paragraph (c), the permitted caseinates are listed: "Casein prepared by precipitation with gums, ammonium caseinate, calcium caseinate, potassium caseinate, and sodium caseinate" (21 *CFR* 135.110(c)). As stated in Table 8-4, caseinate cannot be included in the total milk solid calculation, and it may only be added when the product contains 20 percent total milk solids.

In the preceding description of ice cream in paragraph (a), reference was made to "other safe and suitable nonmilk-derived ingredients." These include the sweeteners, emulsifiers, and stabilizers. At one time, the standards spelled out the permitted maximum amounts for these products. Now they are covered by several aspects of the law; the products must be safe, suitable, and used at a level sufficient to accomplish the desired results. This means, of the products that are permitted, only the minimum amount needed to perform a specific function will be permitted. Permitted products are listed in part 170 of 21 *CFR*, entitled "Food Additives."

Frozen Custard

The only difference between ice cream and frozen custard is the amount of egg yolk. Ice cream is permitted to have less than 1.4 percent egg yolk solids by weight, whereas, frozen custard must contain at least 1.4 percent egg yolk solids, except in the presence of bulky flavoring ingredients, when the minimum amount is 1.12 percent.

Ice Milk

Ice milk is very much like ice cream in preparation and in permitted ingredients, except that the milk fat content is less. Butterfat may range from a minimum of 2 percent to as much as 7 percent. The minimum solids content is 1.3 pounds per gallon as opposed to 1.6 pounds for ice cream. Also, the minimum milk solids content is 11 percent, which for ice cream and frozen custard is 20 percent.

Mellorine

Mellorine has the same solids content and weight per gallon as ice cream. It differs from ice cream because the fat and protein may be of animal or vegetable origin. The minimum fat content is 6 percent, except in the presence of bulky flavor ingredients, when the minimum can be 4.8 percent. As to the protein that is permitted, there is an additional nutritional requirement. It must have a PER 108 percent of that for casein, or a PER of 2.7. The product also must have a Vitamin A content of 40 international units per gram of fat.

Sherbet

This product is characterized by its fruity flavor and its titrable acidity of 0.35 calculated as lactic acid. The minimum milk-fat content is 1 percent and a milk solids content ranging from 2 to 5 percent. This product has a minimum weight per gallon of 6.0 pounds. The milk-fat content may range from 1 to 2 percent.

Water Ices

According to FDA standards, "Water ices are foods each of which is prepared from the same ingredients and in the same manner prescribed . . . for sherbets, except that the mix need not be pasteurized, and complies with all the provisions of sec. 135.140 (including the requirements for label statement of optional ingredients), except that no milk or milk-derived ingredient and no egg ingredient, other than egg white, is used" (21 *CFR* 135.160(a)).

Ingredients

The characteristics of a frozen dessert are influenced by all ingredients used and their interaction (Corn Products 1966). These include fat, protein, sugars, stabilizers, emulsifiers, and flavors. In ice cream and other dairy-type frozen desserts, for the most part, the fat, protein, and sugars come from milk. Although each of the basic ingredients in frozen desserts has a similar function, as in coffee whitener and whipped toppings, there are enough important differences to merit looking at each one under the current heading of frozen desserts.

Fat

In ice cream, fat is the most essential ingredient because it contributes to the creamy, mellow, and rich flavor for which it is known. Fat helps to produce a characteristic smooth, full-bodied texture.

The proper amount of fat is important in a frozen dessert. Too much may be objectionable to certain consumers, apart from dietary concern, because it makes the dessert "too rich." If the fat level is too low, the texture can become coarse and icy. A desirable fat content for commercial ice cream is 10 to 12 percent. In warm climates, the lower content is desirable for the greater cooling effect (Corn Products 1966).

In ice cream, a high fat content adds significantly to the cost and, from the dietary standpoint, adds significantly to the caloric content.

Protein

In dairy-type frozen desserts, the protein comes from milk. Its presence, along with the accompanying lactose and minerals, comes under the heading of "milk solids not fat" or "serum solids." Serum solids is a relatively inexpensive ingredient yet is high in food value. While adding little to flavor, it is important to prevent a weak body and coarse texture (Corn Products 1966).

Keeney (1972) believes that the functional effect of serum solids is due almost entirely to the milk protein. Protein is absorbed at the surface of fat globules when milk is homogenized. This improves emulsion stability, which carries through to the churning and freezing stage of ice-cream manufacture. The protein also seems to coat the air cells, making for a smooth texture. As in frozen toppings and coffee whiteners, the protein makes less water available for freezing.

Sugars

The serum solids or nonfat dry milk solids contain over 50 percent lactose, or milk sugar. To get the desired sweetness from lactose alone would lead to improper crystallization during the frozen state. Hence, sucrose is used because it contributes flavor, body, sweetness, and palatability. However, corn syrup solids also are used in combination with sucrose.

Sugars, along with other dissolved solids in the water of the mix, determine the ice-water equilibrium existing at any given temperature. The unique melting sensation and pliability of ice cream on the palate are greatly influenced by these dissolved salts. Without this, eating ice cream would be like biting into an ice cube (Keeney 1972).

Stabilizers

The chief function of ice cream stabilizers is to retard formation of large, coarse ice crystals during storage. They also help produce a smooth texture and impart a certain resistance to melting. Stabilizers are very important in sherbets and ices, but more so in ice cream because of the greater danger of sugar separation and body crumbliness, due in part to lower total solids (Corn Products 1966).

The 18 stabilizer ingredients listed in the federal standards are mostly polysaccharides from botanicals. Gelatin is an exception (Keeney 1972). Judging from what is written on frozen dessert stabilizers, polysaccharides are more effective and less costly than proteins.

Emulsifiers

Keeney (1972) said the principal reasons for using emulsifiers are to promote the extrusion of stiff ice cream from the freezer and to improve the air-retaining capacity of the mix (overrun). Emulsifiers are used to produce a certain amount of "dryness." However, this can lead to the problem of churning (fat agglomeration), especially if too much emulsifier is used. In soft serves, there is the compounded problem of obtaining a desired dryness without adversely affecting the overrun. Keeney reported that it is best to use combinations of emulsifiers to overcome these problems.

Both stabilizers and emulsifiers are listed in part 170 of Title 21 *CFR*. The listing includes the permitted additive and the amount that is permitted.

Processing

In processing, all frozen desserts seem to follow a similar pattern: mixing, pasteurizing, homogenizing, freezing, and incorporating air to obtain a desired overrun, packaging, and hardening. An exception to these steps is with the water ices; these mixes need not be pasteurized.

Proper storage is important because, during the fast-freezing step, very small, desirable ice crystals are formed. When the temperature of the product is allowed to fluctuate during storage, the small ice crystals grow and give the frozen dessert a coarse texture, thereby nullifying the advantages of rapid freezing (Corn Products 1966).

Standard Versus Nonstandard Frozen Desserts

The standards for frozen desserts as spelled out by the FDA take in a broad range of products. It is possible to make a product, for one reason or another, that does not fit into any of the listed products. It should also be noted that many states have their own standards for frozen desserts that do not necessarily conform to federal standards. When producing and marketing frozen desserts, we must be aware that differences might exist. In any case, if a nonstandard product is produced, all the regulatory agencies require that consumers be properly informed of what they are purchasing. If there is doubt as to the proper approach, it is recommended that the pertinent agency be contacted to obtain its opinion as to whether the product being produced conforms to the appropriate law.

CHEESE ANALOGS

According to Trauberman (1975), cheese making is a process in which most of the nutrients in milk are concentrated to produce a product that is less perishable than milk. Langhus (1974) claims that cheese has been used as a food for over 4,000 years. There are some 400 varieties of cheese, which can be grouped into four major types (Tauberman 1975): soft cheese (brie and camembert), semi-hard cheese (gouda and edam), hard cheese (cheddar and cheshire) and hard grating types (parmesan and romano). Cheeses within the four groups can be further classified according to moisture and fat content, texture, and ripening agent (if used).

Obviously, this classification is for *natural cheeses* that are made directly from milk. There also are *processed cheeses,* which are made from one or more natural cheeses with further processing, with and without additives, in a blending operation. The blending process usually involves melting the various cheeses and pasteurizing them.

With cheeselike products, reference is often made to imitation cheese, cheese analogs, cheese substitutes, as well as to a number of other names. According to the FDA definition, *imitation cheeses* are products that resemble natural cheese but are nutritionally inferior to the imitated product. *Cheese substitutes* are products that simulate the natural cheese product in appearance, flavor, and texture, and are nutritionally equivalent to the natural product. A *cheese analog* is a generic term for both the imitation and the substitute products.

In 1973, Anderson, Clayton and Co. became the first firm to produce and market a mozzarella cheese analog (Buss 1981). The following year, the school lunch program provided for the inclusion of cheese alternates along with natural cheese on a 50/50 basis (*FR* 1974).

Duxbury (1985) reported that cheese analogs are made primarily from dairy ingredients, vegetable fats, and processing aids (sorbic acid and its salts), together with water, flavorings, coloring, acidulants, and emulsifying salts. The latter two ingredients are used to adjust the body of the analog through pH control. Casein and/or caseinates are used almost exclusively in the production of cheese analogs. There is limited success, at time of this writing, using protein sources other than milk derivatives. More success has been achieved in combining other proteins, such as soy protein isolate, with casein. *Food Processing* (1981) published an article reporting on the successful use of a combination of four proteins to produce a mozzarella analog. The protein source consisted of equal parts each of casein, soy flour, wheat gluten, and leaf protein from alfalfa.

The first cheese analog was made centuries ago, which was completely vegetable in origin. That product is still being made today and is used extensively in many food preparations in the Orient. In recent years, it was introduced to the Western culture and is rapidly becoming popular, particularly with the growing number of vegetarians. This product is known as tofu, or bean curd, and is made from soybeans. Tofu has a cheeselike appearance, resembling cottage cheese in many respects. Unlike the process for most cheeses, tofu production is not a fermenting process. Tofu is made from soymilk using a divalent metal salt such as calcium or magnesium and/or an organic acid such as vinegar or lemon juice. The curding process takes place at an elevated temperature (below boiling). The resulting curd is pressed, washed, and usually packaged in water.

Markets

Cheese analogs can be used in large quantities to an advantage in three industrial segments that use large quantities of cheese and in which imitation cheeses can function adequately. These are in pizza, in the school lunch program, and in formulated foods containing cheese as one of the ingredients. In many of these usage applications, the analog can be combined with natural cheese to develop a desired flavor, texture, and functional characteristic, all at a reduced cost (*Food Processing* 1976b).

At this time, the food processor can choose from a host of cheese analogs (mozzarella, cheddar, American, provolone, romano, and parmesan). For the most part, the supplier can give the processor products to meet his or her specifications, ranging from flavor quality, melting point, stretchability, body, texture, and microbiological stability. These can all be given at a cost savings of up to 60 percent over that of the natural product (Duxbury 1985).

There are two distinct marketing segments for cheese—the as-is, or out-of-hand, segment and the food-processing and pizza segment (*Food Processing* 1976b). Economic forces, which cause an increase in production costs, plus consumer reluctance to pay higher prices for fabricated food containing cheese as one of the ingredients will widen the gap between the two marketing segments—imitation and natural.

Duxbury (1985) pointed out that the usage of cheese analogs in pizzas, lasagna, enchiladas, chili topping, and other ethnic foods is growing. Apparently, this is not true in the school lunch program. Duxbury feels that this is due to the availability of surplus government cheeses. As originally set up by Congress, the school lunch program is an important area that uses surplus agricultural products.

The motivating force that caused the increased usage of cheese analogs is cost. Natural cheese costs increase as milk prices increase. The cost differential between the natural product and the analog is significant, especially to foodservice operators. In 1976, the mozzarella and American cheese analogs cost about two-thirds as much as their natural counterparts.

Graf (1981) obtained wholesale prices for eight major types of cheese (cheddar, colby, mozzarella, provolone, processed cheese, processed cheese food, processed cheese spread, and cream cheese) from major manufacturers in 1980. He found that prices for imitation cheeses were from 8 to 57 percent less than those for their natural counterparts, with an average of $0.38 per pound, or 30 percent less. The smallest wholesale price differential between natural and imitation cheese was for cream cheese and colby, which were 8 percent and 11 percent, respectively. Imitation mozzarella and processed cheese had the highest savings compared to their natural counterparts, of 54 percent and 57 percent, respectively. The price savings per pound at wholesale for imitation cheeses compared to their natural counterparts were 7¢ for cream, 16¢ for colby, 25¢ for cheddar, 71¢ for processed cheese, 73¢ for provolone, and 78¢ for mozzarella.

Graf (1981) estimated that imitation mozzarella has captured about $\frac{1}{3}$ of the total mozzarella market because of the increased popularity of pizza, where most of these cheeses are used.

In general, cheese analogs have become popular because of advantages such as consistent quality and stable supply, coupled with some disadvantages of natural cheese such as limited shelf life, refrigeration requirements, and variations in flavor, texture, price and supply (Bozzi 1980). Bozzi reported that the cheese analog market reached $1 million in 1979. He projected a 40 percent average annual growth, which places the market well over $1 billion in 1985. According to Graf (1981), imitation cheese competition with natural cheese could have a substantial impact on U.S. dairy farmers and the entire dairy industry because natural cheese production utilizes about one-quarter of the U.S. milk supply.

Bozzi's projection for 1985 is overly optimistic. According to Graf (1981, 1985a), in 1980, 200 million pounds of imitation cheese were produced. In 1984, the estimated production was 300 million pounds. Even this was overly optimistic. Recently, Professor Graf said that there is no reliable data after 1985. In 1985, approximately 6 percent of the total cheese market was imitation cheese, 280 million pounds (about $275 million). In 1981, the imitation cheese market was 4 percent of the total, about 201 million pounds (Graf 1988).

We can expect the price spread between cheese analogs and natural cheese to widen because of probable increasing costs for raw milk needed for the natural product. It is believed that with improved technology, a higher percentage of milk will be graded "A," resulting in a higher price. Also, consumer demand for fluid milk, which brings higher prices than can support an extensive distribution system for hauling raw milk over long distances, will reduce milk available for cheese production; milk for cheese historically moves only short distances (*Food Processing*, 1976b).

In 1984, natural cheese production amounted to 4.6884 billion pounds. Of this amount, CCC (Commodity Credit Corporation) cheese purchases amounted to 468 million pounds. With the industry estimate for cheese analogs at 300 million pounds, this amounts to 64.1 percent of the CCC purchases, which exerts a significant impact on the cheese industry. As quoted by Graf (1985), the industry estimates that, of the 300 million pounds of cheese analog produced, one-third went into consumer sales, one-third into prepared foods such as pizza, and one-third into fast-food outlets. Industry estimates closely correlated with the increase in casein imports between 1981 and 1984.

The cheese industry is very concerned about the growing production of analog products. Imitation cheese is a threat to natural cheese, and its competitive challenge is increasing. Industry estimates suggest approximately 90 percent of imitation cheese is used by food processors, restaurants, and institutional feeding operations. Fast-food operations appear to be the fastest growing outlet for imitation cheese, with increasing use of imitation cheese in pizza, fondue, blended dips, and cheeseburgers (Graf 1985).

Regulatory Aspects

Any food product moving in interstate commerce is subject to FDA regulations, including cheese products of various kinds. Most cheese products are covered under sec. 133 of Title 21 *CFR*. As of 1987, standards for over 70 cheese foods were listed.

As pointed out by Graf (1981), producers of imitation cheeses also must operate within the regulations of the states where their plant is located or where they expect to conduct sales. There is general indecision with respect to regulations of imitation cheese at state levels, which has retarded development of clear-cut regulating policies for imitation cheese.

Graf (1981) contacted all 50 states, Puerto Rico, and the District of Columbia and obtained a wide diversity of regulations, which he summarized in his paper. He found that only 2 percent of the states specifically prohibit the sale of complete imitation cheese at wholesale and 4 percent at retail, while 60 percent specifically allowed its sale. The rest have no ruling on the sale of imitation cheese.

In a personal communication, Professor Graf (1985b) said that Wisconsin, which was one state that banned the retail sale of imitation cheese, lost a lawsuit and, as a result, must permit the retail sale of imitation cheese products. He claimed that regulations based on economics will never hold up in court (Graf 1988).

Much of the confusion that exists among the various states is due to a "wait and see" attitude as to what the FDA will do. Meanwhile, manufacturers of imitation cheeses continue to use a variety of names on packages of the product sold in commercial channels (Graf 1981). As of 1988, the FDA still has no final ruling.

Whenever a pizza contains 3 percent meat or more, the manufacture and distribution of these products come under USDA regulations. This includes those instances when the word *meat* appears on the label, or if the pizza "appears" to contain meat. "Pizza with Meat" must contain not less than 15 percent raw meat. "Pizza with Sausage" must contain not less than 12 percent cooked sausage or not less than 10 percent dry sausage.

Graf (1981) broke down state regulations on labeling imitation cheese into five groups, based on responses to his questionnaire. (He received responses from 49 of the 50 states, Puerto Rico, and the District of Columbia.)

1. "Imitation" required on the label regardless of the nutritional equivalency to natural cheese—39 percent. (Alabama, Alaska, California, Connecticut, Illinois, Iowa, Kentucky, Louisiana, Maryland, Mississippi, Missouri, New Hampshire, New York, Ohio, Oklahoma, South Carolina, Texas, Vermont, and Wyoming.)
2. "Imitation" required on the label if not the nutritional equivalent to the natural product, and a fanciful name permitted—35 percent. (Florida, Georgia, Hawaii, Idaho, Indiana, Kansas, Maine, Montana, New Jersey, New Mexico, North Carolina, North Dakota, Pennsylvania, Rhode Island, Tennessee, Vermont, and Virginia.)
3. Fanciful name permitted regardless of the nutritional equivalency—4 percent. (Colorado and Oregon.)
4. Labeling regulations determined on case-by-case basis as situation arises—8 percent.
5. No ruling on labeling regulations—14 percent.

In a further breakdown, Graf (1981) found that five states prohibit the production of imitation cheese (Colorado, Kentucky, Missouri, Montana, and North Dakota).

Of the ten major milk-producing states, five have imitation cheeses produced in their states. All permit the sale of imitation cheese at wholesale, but only one, Wisconsin, did not permit its sale at retail (at the time of the survey). It is interesting to note a comment made in the *Wall Street Journal* (Buss 1981) relative to prohibiting state laws. "The courts . . . have recently shown a tendency to strike down state laws prohibiting retail sales or commercial use of imitation cheese. Recently, for example, a federal judge in Madison, Wis. ruled that Wisconsin can't prevent the sale of frozen pizza containing fake *(sic)* cheese" (Buss 1981, p. 1).

Preparation

A typical cheese analog contains caseinate, vegetable oil, salt, emulsifiers/stabilizers, colors, and water. Many manufacturers of cheese analogs use caseinate rather than casein because of functional and flavor considerations. Caseinates usually are of sodium, potassium, and calcium types. Since the desire is to have a calcium level in the analog that duplicates that in natural cheese, calcium caseinate is the leading caseinate ingredient. Sodium or potassium caseinate normally are added to increase functionality and water absorption in the finished product. Flavor, functionality, and price are the determining factors when choosing which caseinate to use (*Food Processing* 1976b).

Example 1

A U.S. patent was granted to Middleton (1980) for a process he developed, wherein caseins of various types can be used in the cheese analog formulation. The key to the method is the conversion of an acid-precipitated casein into a calcium caseinate, to which calcium chloride is added and then the usual procedure is followed when making a cheese analog. Claims are made that a better, more consistent flavor is the result and that the final synthetic cheese product has a superior body and melting characteristic. The addition of calcium salts optimizes certain properties of the resultant synthetic cheese, which are the string, melt, and opacity characteristics. Calcium chloride provides the optimum string and melt to mozzarella or cooking-type cheese used on pizza. No calcium chloride is used when little or no string is required or desired, such as with imitation American cheese. The beneficial results of the calcium ion probably cause additional cross-linking of the protein (Middleton 1980).

The edible oils recommended in the patent are those that have a Wiley melting point in the range of 70 to 115°F. The edible oils or fats may be further defined as those that have a Solid Fat Index (SFI) of the following ranges at the temperatures indicated.

50°F	20–75
70°F	0–60
80°F	0–50
92°F	0–25
100°F	0–15
110°F	0

Middleton prefers vegetable oil or a blend of vegetable oils, such as soybean, cottonseed, and coconut oils. A 100 percent soybean oil (hydrogenated) may be used, as can hydrogenated cottonseed oil or corn oil. Animal fats or oils, such as butter, butter oil, or lard, also can be used.

In summary, the steps in the patent for the production of a "synthetic mozzarella" are as follows.

1. Heat 1 kilogram of water to between 95 and 97°F.
2. Add 0.85 grams of calcium hydroxide and 30 grams of acid casein.
3. Maintain the suspension at 95 to 97°F with stirring for 1 hour.
4. Add 1.9 grams of a 20 percent calcium chloride solution.
5. Adjust the pH to about 6.15 with phosphoric acid.
6. Add 0.4 milliliters of single-strength rennet.
7. Maintain the temperature and continue stirring for $\frac{1}{2}$ hour.
8. Dewater the curd formed.
9. Place 67 grams of dewatered curd (27 grams of calcium caseinate and 40 grams of water) in a jacketed laboratory blender/cooker and blend in 18.8 grams of emulsified vegetable oil (a blend of soybean, cottonseed, and coconut oils).
10. Add 1.5 grams of salt, 1.5 grams of sodium aluminum phosphate, and 5 grams of water (to allow for evaporation).
11. Heat the mixtures to 165 to 170°F with continued stirring.
12. When smooth, add 1.2 grams of adipic acid to adjust the pH to 5.2. Continue stirring for 2 minutes.
13. Place the hot product in containers and refrigerate.
14. Store under normal 45°F refrigeration.

At the end of Example 1, the claim was made that, after 3 months storage, random samples revealed no change or deterioration of the mozzarella analog on flavor, body, and texture. The patent included two commercial-size production examples for American cheese and mozzarella analogs.

Table 8-5   Preparation of a Semi-Hard Imitation Cheese

Ingredients	Percent
Rennet casein (30 mesh or finer)	14
Acid casein (30 mesh or finer)	14
Salt	1.0
Dipotassium hydrogen phosphate	1.0
Fat	30
Water	40
Coloring and flavoring	As needed

Procedure: Mix water, fat, salt, dipotassium hydrogen phosphate, coloring, and flavoring. Heat mixture in water bath to approximately 80°C. Dry-blend rennet and acid caseins and add this mixture to the liquid. Stir vigorously while maintaining the high temperature, until a homogeneous cheese mass is formed. Cool to room temperature.

Source: From a sales brochure, The New Zealand Dairy Board.

Example 2

It is of interest to look at another example of a cheese analog preparation as offered by the New Zealand Dairy Board (see Table 8-5). In this case, a blend of rennet and acid casein is suggested.

Kasik and Peterson (1977) obtained a U.S. patent on an instant cheese analog preparation. This is of special interest to foodservice operators because the product can be instantly reconstituted with water, without the need of specialized equipment or of following unduly restricted procedures.

Two advantages of the analog produced are its shelf stability and its convenience. The product is ideally suited as an ingredient in a cheese sauce.

Without getting into too much detail, we can summarize the preparation as follows. Acid casein is converted into a magnesium caseinate using a magnesium chloride solution at 200°F. The whey is drained off, and the curd is washed and then neutralized with magnesium oxide. In Example 1, the product was spray dried.

In this example, 51.5 parts of the neutralized casein are slurried in water (15 to 20 percent solids content), and 48 parts hydrogenated soybean oil (95°F melting point) are mixed in. As a flavoring ingredient, 0.5 parts of lipolyzed butter oil are added. The total solids in the slurry, including the fat, is about 30 percent by weight. The analog is heated to 150 to 160°F and spray dried. The powder is blended with 4.2 percent dry powder lactic acid (30 percent solids) and 2 percent sodium chloride. The blend is then packaged and sealed.

Example 3

One method of usage for the powdered product is to place 1 part of the dry powder produced in Example 2 in a mixer adjusted to a speed of 600 revolutions per minute. Slowly add 1 part of water heated to 160 to 170°F and mix until the mixture begins to string (in about 45 seconds). Stop mixing, take out the mixture, and shape it into a loaf. Cool at about 43°F in a refrigerator for $\frac{1}{2}$ hour, after which time the loaf will maintain its shape. The product can then be cut and shredded and used as a mozzarella cheese substitute. The taste, melt, and string are similar to mozzarella cheese.

Analogs Using Nondairy Protein

To fully appreciate the difficulties likely to be encountered when substituting a protein, particularly a vegetable protein, for casein and/or caseinate, we should consider the role casein or caseinates play in making natural cheese. We need to include those factors that have an influence in changing some of the properties of the milk protein and why we would even want to do this.

In most cases, casein and/or caseinates are the proteins of choice when making cheese analogs. Due to increasing prices and the threat of import restrictions on caseins and caseinates, there is a great deal of interest in utilizing protein products, particularly the vegetable types, which are considerably less costly.

An excellent article that covers many of the principles in which we are interested was published by Shimp (1985). We will paraphrase many of the points reported by Shimp.

Cheese is composed of an oil phase of fats and oil-soluble substances and a water phase of a solution of water-soluble proteins and minerals. The two incompatible phases are emulsified with surface-active proteins that have both lipophilic and hydrophilic sites on them. These proteins tend to collect at the interfaces between the two phases, in an oriented fashion. In most cases, one end of the casein protein contains calcium phosphate groups and carries essentially all the protein charge, while the other end is organic and nonpolar. The phosphate end is water-soluble, while the organic end is fat soluble (Fig. 8-1). The emulsifying properties can be modified by such things as the amount of calcium in the calcium phosphate end, the pH of the cheese, the age of the cheese, and the temperature to which the cheese is subjected during processing. Since calcium affects solubility, the more calcium that is present, the less soluble the water-compatible end of the protein and the less the emulsifying power. Protein configuration also is affected by the pH of the cheese.

Casein has certain characteristics that would be difficult to duplicate, so the likelihood of completely replacing milk protein is remote. It is more likely that

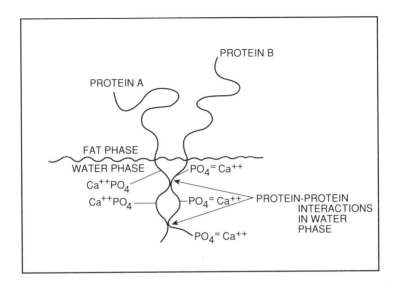

Figure 8-1. Schematic of emulsifying proteins. (*Source:* Reprinted from *Food Tech.* 39(5):63–70. Copyright © by The Institute of Food Technologists.)

other proteins will be modified to duplicate one or more properties of the milk protein in question, but not all the properties.

In the work done as of this writing, food technologists have been fairly successful in replacing about ½ of the casein/caseinate in a cheese analog formulation.

A thorough study was made by Chen et al. (1979) on replacing the dairy protein with peanut protein in a cheese analog. What was learned in this study should be of value to anyone interested in trying nondairy proteins as a partial replacer in a cheese analog. In this particular study, the peanut protein isolate used had the following chemical composition:

Moisture	6.30%
Protein (as is)	86.56%
Protein (dry basis)	92.38%
Ash	4.32%
Fat	0.14%

The basic cheese analog formulation used is shown in Table 8-6, and the processing scheme used is shown in Fig. 8-2.

Table 8-6 Cheese Analog Formula

Ingredients	Grams	Percent
Ca/Na caseinate (Savortone 491)	90.25	14.39
Peanut protein isolate	90.25	14.39
Oil (or fat)	126.50	20.17
Distilled water I	212.50	33.88
Distilled water II	27.50	4.31
Distilled water III	55.50	8.62
Sodium chloride	11.50	1.83
Sodium citrate	2.50	0.40
Sodium pyrophosphate	2.00	0.32
Lactic acid	8.65	1.38
Total	627.15	99.99

Source: Chen et al. 1979.

The researchers made cheese analogs with the following variables:

1. Protein ingredients: Portions of calcium/sodium caseinate (Savortone) were replaced with peanut protein isolate at levels of 0, 10, 20, 30, 40, 50, 60, 75, 85, and 100 percent.
2. Oil (or fat) ingredients:
    a. Types: butter, hydrogenated oil (Wiley melting point of about 35°C (95°F), and peanut oil; and
    b. Adjusted levels of peanut oil and moisture: 22.36 percent reduction of oil requiring 10 percent increase in moisture, 10 percent reduction of oil requiring 4.2 percent increase in moisture, normal oil and moisture levels, 10 percent increase of oil requiring 4.2 percent reduction of moisture, and 22.36 percent increase of oil requiring 10 percent reduction of moisture.
3. Emulsifying salts (Na citrate and Na pyrophosphate): These two salts were tested at several different levels.
    a. Na citrate: 0, 0.2 percent (half normal), 0.4 percent (normal), and 0.8 percent (double normal); and
    b. Na pyrophosphate: 0, 0.16 percent (half normal), 0.32 percent (normal), and 0.64 percent (double normal).

The following are some of the reported findings Chen et al. observed:

1. With decreasing Ca/Na caseinate content and increasing peanut protein isolate, cheese analogs become softer and less rubbery.

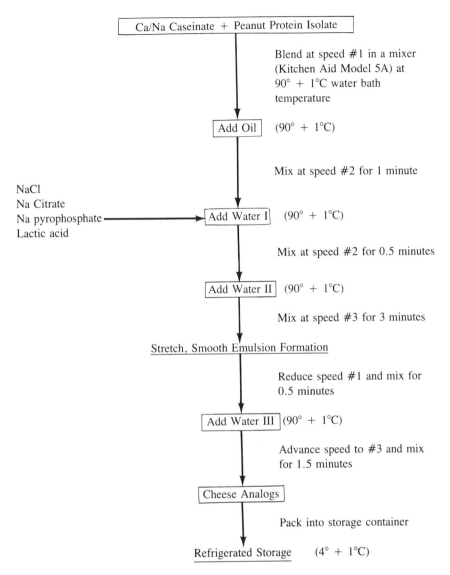

Figure 8-2. Flow diagram for manufacture of cheese analogs. (*Source:* Reprinted from *Food Tech.* 33(7):88–93. Copyright © by The Institute of Food Technology.)

2. At 40:60 replacement levels, the cheese analog texture had low adhesiveness force and desirable cheese analog characteristics, and it was easy to break.

3. The 50:50 (standard formulation) level resulted in the typical desirable characteristics of cheese products.

4. As peanut protein isolate levels increased from 60 to 85 percent, the texture became mushy and less elastic.

5. At 85 percent replacement level, cheese analogs exhibited smooth, spreadable textural properties almost identical to cream cheese.

6. The 95- to 100-percent peanut isolate cheese analogs had considerable amounts of free oil and no textural body.

7. Analogs containing hydrogenated oil with a Wiley melting point of about 35°C (95°F) had the toughest texture; peanut oil exhibited the softest texture.

8. Solid-type fat ingredients made cheese analogs less cohesive, less elastic, and highly adhesive.

9. Melting properties also were consistent with textural properties; peanut oil products showed higher melting temperatures than the other two.

10. Melting properties also were affected by the oil and moisture contents. Analogs with higher oil content showed higher emulsion viscosity than those with lower oil content.

11. Sodium citrate and sodium pyrophosphate were quite similar because they did not have any specific effects on peanut cheese analogs.

The authors reached the following conclusions:

1. Peanut protein isolate and oil can be successfully utilized when manufacturing cheese analogs.

2. Of the three ingredients (protein, fat, and emulsifying sodium salts) studied, protein is the most important, and it significantly affects both textural and melting properties.

3. Elasticity and melting behavior of cheese analogs are controlled by the unique characteristics of caseinate, but all-caseinate formulas do not necessarily produce desirable cheese analogs.

4. Peanut protein isolate can be used to produce and modify marketable cheese analogs.

5. Replacement levels of 40 to 50 percent appear optimum in producing analogs of cheddar, mozzarella, and process cheeses. However, an 85 percent replacement level produces other types of cheese suitable for use as cream cheese and cheese spread products.

6. Fats and salts also are important.

7. Peanut oil and hydrogenated vegetable oils were used successfully for replacing milk fats in the manufacture of cheese analogs.

As was stated earlier, there is no reason why other vegetable protein isolates cannot be used as peanut protein isolate was used in this particular study. The possible exception is wheat gluten, which can be expected to affect stretchability.

Another study, to which we referred earlier in this chapter, needs to be mentioned at this time (*Food Processing* 1981). In this particular study, it was reported that equal portions of casein, soy flour, wheat gluten, and leaf protein (alfalfa) were used as the protein portion of the cheese analog preparations. These protein products were selected for the following reasons: wheat gluten because it improves stretchability; soy flour because of its availability, its low cost, and its good amino acid profile; and leaf protein to show that other domestic sources of protein can be used. The results of the work indicate that the combination of protein sources gives a good amino acid profile, and the prototype product exhibited good mozzarella appearance, texture, and stretchability. However, "additional research is required to develop a final product with all desirable characteristics including flavor."

Yang and Taranto (1982) looked at the possibility of using soy protein when making a mozzarella cheese analog. They recognized that most mozzarella cheese analog is used in pizza, making that a good area at which to look. Before beginning their work, they listed a number of characteristics the analog should have:

1. It should possess moderate toughness and adequate stringiness.
2. It should shred, grind, and slice with a minimum of matting.
3. While in the oven, the shred should release enough oil to engulf the other ingredients in the pizza topping and still maintain its shape and right degree of stringiness.

They recognized that the protein should form a gel structure to act as a matrix to hold in moisture, fats, polysaccharides, and other ingredients. The soybean gel has a certain amount of this desired gel property. Preliminary work by the authors in another publication (Taranto and Yang 1981) tested the feasibility of using soy protein gels to imitate the textural properties of natural mozzarella, which solidifies at low temperatures and melts and stretches at high temperatures. They learned that additional ingredients are needed in the product formulation to duplicate the textural properties of natural mozzarella. In some preliminary work, it was learned that a combination of soy base, gelatin, and gum arabic in the ratio of 5:2:2 seemed to yield a gel with the desired properties.

Based on the results observed in their studies, Yang and Taranto concluded the following:

1. A mozzarella cheese analog prepared from soy protein, gelatin, and gum arabic can be made to exhibit both textural and stretching properties that are similar to natural mozzarella cheese.
2. The natural pH of the combined ingredients is adequate, and no pH adjustment is required.
3. A 10 percent fat content is suitable for a moderate hardness of the gel system with improved heat stability and meltability.
4. Stretchability of the product is related to the amount of soy protein.
5. Salts, such as calcium chloride, were found to improve the stretchability of the progel.

Analogs from Concentrated Skim Milk

A recent development was reported by Andres (1986). "Cheese substitute" is being made from concentrated skim milk, and it is claimed that it has twice the calcium of natural cheese, contains no lactose, and is shelf stable. Up to this development, most of the commercial cheese analogs were made (wholly or in part) by utilizing imported casein. Andres claims that the approach gives us the advantage of using domestic ingredients rather than imports. There are other advantages as well. One is that the development eliminates the problems associated with whey in the cheese-making process. Now whey protein can be included in the cheese products without the inclusion of lactose. This is especially good news to those who have an intolerance to lactose.

The skim milk concentrate is made by the ultrafiltration technique, which allows the processor to remove much of the water and, if desired, the lactose and soluble minerals. The report stated that the cost of the system makes it possible for the larger farms to make the concentrated product, and, since much of the water content is eliminated, shipping costs should be significantly less. This would go a long way in permitting less costly cheese products.

For the individuals who are concerned about consuming animal fat, vegetable fat can be used to produce a cheese analog.

Andres reported that, so far, four products have been developed in which the skim milk concentrate has been used. Four are being marketed: parmesan, feta cheese, American, and mozzarella analogs. Other cheese types are being explored.

Other Considerations

Those interested in working with cheese analogs on an experimental basis should become familiar with the article entitled "Process Cheese Principles" (Shimp 1985).

Another article of value is one that was written at a time when there was a

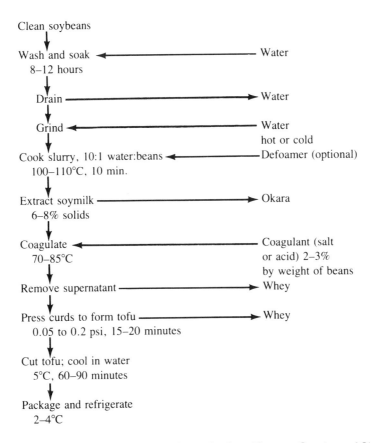

Figure 8-3. Flow chart for regular tofu production. (*Source:* Courtesy of Shurtleff and Aoyagi 1984.)

great deal of interest in producing filled dairy products. As was explained earlier in this chapter, filled-milk products are basically dairy products in which the butterfat is replaced with a nondairy fat. Ryberg (1968) discussed the economics of using vegetable fats over butterfats in imitation cheese. He also discussed the advantages and disadvantages of using vegetable fats.

When comparing analytical data of various fats with butterfat, Ryberg saw that vegetable fats have far fewer fatty acids, and these generally are composed of molecules from the longer-carbon-chain lengths. The lauric, or imported, fats, such as coconut oil, contain the shorter-chain fatty acids, and thus permit blending a fat system containing the desired makeup if the fatty acid profile is critical for the product being formulated.

In his discussion on vegetable fat cheese formulations, Ryberg pointed out

Table 8-7   Percentages by Weight of Various Coagulants Used in Preparing Various Types of Tofu

Type of Tofu	Coagulant	Percent by Weight of Dry Beans	Percent of Weight of Soymilk[1]	Coagulation Temperature
Regular or firm	Nigari-type[2]	3.0	0.3	78–85°C
	Calcium sulfate	2.2	0.27	70–75°C
	Lactone (GDL)	3.0	0.60	90°C
	Lemon juice	21.0	2.1	80–90°C
	Vinegar	16.3	1.6	80–90°C
Silken tofu	Nigari-type	3.1	0.8	65–68°C
	Calcium sulfate	2.7	0.6	70°C
Packaged silken	Lactone	1.1	0.27	85°C[3]
	Calcium sulfate	1.8	0.4	90°C[3]

[1] Soymilk from regular tofu contains 6 percent solids; for silken tofu, 11 percent solids.
[2] Includes natural nigari, magnesium chloride, and calcium chloride.
[3] Coagulant is added to cold soymilk, which is then heated to 85 or 90°C.

that the fat used should have a melting point close to body temperature and should possess good stability and a bland flavor. He also claimed that the fat should be selected with deference to the fatty acid composition. This depends on the type of cheese being made. Mozzarella cheese does not have a flavor resulting from lipase activity on the fat. Hence, short-chain fatty acids can and should be avoided. However, in a cheese where lipase activity is a part of the flavor development, as in provolone, a fat containing low levels of short-chain fatty acids should be used. Here is a case where the addition of lipolized butter oil would help contribute flavor similar to the conventional cheese.

Ryberg discussed a number of other factors pertaining to the use of vegetable fats/oils, and he included several basic formulations that should be of interest.

TOFU

A few more comments should be made about tofu, especially since this product is becoming increasingly popular, not only in Chinese/American restaurants but also in other channels. Many college cafeterias now offer vegetarian-type meals in which tofu is frequently included. Tofu often is found in the produce section of large supermarkets and is being used at home by many people. Undoubtedly, this is due to the growing popularity of stir-fried dishes that utilize the wok. Many Chinese recipes call for tofu in stir-fried preparations.

For those who are interested in learning more about tofu, its preparation and its use, two publications by Shurtleff and Aoyagi (1983, 1984) are excellent for the detail that is given on the subject. Not only do these publications cover the various ways to prepare tofu, but also they include recipes. The second reference (1984) gives the necessary information for setting up a processing plant.

To give a better idea of what is involved in making tofu, Fig. 8-3 shows a flow chart for regular tofu production taken from Shurtleff and Aoyagi (1984).

Broadly speaking, there are several types of tofus, based on the firmness of the product. Firmness usually is controlled by the amount and duration of pressure used to remove the whey after curd formation. Other variables that have a bearing on texture are the total solid content of the soymilk, that is, the amount of water used in relation to the soybeans; the variety of soybeans; the type of clotting material; and the conditions under which clotting takes place.

Table 8-7, taken from Shurtleff and Aoyagi (1984), shows the percentage weights of the various coagulants used to prepare different types of tofu.

REFERENCES

Ahalt, J. D. 1984. "The Economics of Dairy Products from Farmer to Food Processor." In *Dairy Products for the Cereal Processing Industry*, ed. J. L. Vetter, 181–202. St. Paul: American Association of Cereal Chemistry.

Andres, C. 1981. "Prototype Products Include Higher Protein/Lower Calorie/Lower Cost Frozen Desserts, Milk-Based Drinks." *Food Proc.* 42 (Nov.):60.

———. 1986. "Cheese Substitute from Concentrated Skim Milk." *Food Proc.* 47 (Mar.):24–5.

Atlas Chemical Industries. 1965. "Atlas Emulsifiers for Coffee Whiteners." Brochure LG-88-1-66-5C. Wilmington, Del.

———. 1968. "Product Information Bulletin—Guidelines to the Formulation of Whipped Toppings." Bulletin LG-103. Wilmington, Del.

Bourne, M. C., E. E. Escueta, and J. Banzon. 1976. "Effect of Sodium Alkalis and Salts on pH and Flavor of Soymilk." *J. Food Sci.* 41:62–6.

Bozzi, M. J. 1980. "Cheese Analog Advantages Range Beyond Economic Aspects." *Food Prod. Dev.* 41 (June):42.

Buss, D. O. 1981. "Fake Food—To Dairymen's Dismay, Imitation Cheeses Win Growing Market Share." *Wall St. J.* 61 (July 20):1.

Chen, S. L., P. J. Wan, E. W. Lusas, and K. C. Rhee. 1979. "Utilization of Peanut Protein and Oil in Cheese Analogs." *Food Tech.* 33 (7):88–93.

Code of Federal Regulations. 1987. Title 21. *Food and Drugs*. Part 133, Cheese and Related Products. Part 135, Frozen Desserts.

Corn Products Sales Co. 1966. "Means and Methods of Manufacturing Frozen Desserts," 1–15. Brochure SW-50-02.

Cremers, L. F. 1974. "Ice Cream and Related Frozen Desserts." In *Encyclopedia of Food Technology*, ed. A. H. Johnson and M. S. Peterson, 519–525. Westport, Conn.: AVI Publishing.

Duxbury, D. D. 1985. "Imitation Cheese Market Growth Based on Improved Quality, Variety, Custom Formulations." *Food Proc.* 46 (Sept.):58–60.

Federal Register. 1968. "Imitation Milks and Creams—Standards of Identity and Quality." *Fed. Reg.* 33:7456–7458.

_____. 1974. "National School Lunch Program and Special Food Service Program for Children." *Fed. Reg.* 39:12258–9.

Food Processing. 1969. "Imitation Milk Battle Shifts States and USDA." *Food Proc.* 30 (Mar.):86.

_____. 1976a. "Peanut Flakes—Duplicate Texture/Taste of Egg, Meat and Dairy Products." *Food Proc.* (Jan.):42.

_____. 1976b. "Imitation Cheeses Receive Excellent Reception." *Food Proc.* (Feb.):76.

_____. 1981. "Cheese Analog Contains Protein From Four Sources—Dairy, Oilseed, Cereal, Leaf." *Food Proc.* 42 (Oct.):28–9.

Graf, T. F. 1981. "Imitation Cheese—Economic Friend or Foe?" Staff Paper Series #201, Agricul. Econ., Coop. Exten. Prog. Madison, Wis.: University of Wisconsin.

_____. 1982. "Economic Impact of Imitation Cheese." Staff Paper Series #208, Agricul. Econ., Coop. Exten. Prog. Madison, Wis.: University of Wisconsin.

_____. 1985a. "Effect of Imitation or Filled Dairy Products." Staff Paper Series #239, Agricul. Econ., Coop. Exten. Prog. Madison, Wis.: University of Wisconsin.

_____. 1985b. Personal communication. Madison, Wis.

_____. 1988. Personal communication. Madison, Wis.

Kasik, R. L., and M. A. Peterson. 1977. Instant Cheese, Cheese Sauces and Related Compositions. U.S. Pat. 4,031,254 (June 21).

Keeney, P. G. 1972. "Commercial Ice Cream and Other Frozen Desserts." Circular 553. University Park, Pa.: Pennsylvania State University.

Knightly, W. H. 1968. "The Role of Ingredients in the Formulation of Whipped Toppings." *Food Tech.* 22 (6):73–86.

_____. 1969. "The Role of Ingredients in the Formulation of Coffee Whiteners." *Food Tech.* 23 (2):37–48.

Langhus, W. L. 1974. "Cheese." In *Encyclopedia of Food Technology,* ed. A. H. Johnson and M. S. Peterson, 178–183. Westport, Conn.: AVI Publishing.

Middleton, J. L. 1980. Process for Producing Synthetic Cheese. U.S. Pat. 4,197,322 (Apr. 8).

Milk Industry Foundation. 1987. "Milk Facts." 888 Sixteenth St., N.W. Washington, D.C. 20006.

Modler, H. W., A. L. Rippen, and C. M. Stine. 1970. "Physical and Chemical Stability of Soybean Oil–Filled Milk." *J. Food Sci.* 35:302–5.

Moore, R. S. 1961. *China Doctor. The Life Story of Harry Willis Miller.* New York: Harper & Bros.

National Dairy Council. 1968. "Relative Nutritive Value of Filled and Imitation Milks." *Dairy Coun. Dig.* 39 (Mar./Apr.):7–12.

Orellana, R. S. 1980. Personal communication. Mexico City.

Pripke, P. E., L. S. Wei, A. I. Nelson, and M. P. Steinberg. 1980. "Suspension Stability of Illinois Soybean Beverage." *J. Food Sci.* 45:242–5.

Reed, P. M. 1974. "Casein and Caseinate." In *Encyclopedia of Food Technology,* ed. A. H. Johnson and M. S. Peterson, 174–175. Westport, Conn.: AVI Publishing.

Ryberg, J. R. 1968. "Choosing a Fat System for a Filled or Imitation Dairy Cheese." *Food Prod. Dev.* 4 (Aug./Sept.):60–66.

Sheeles, P. 1985. Personal communication. Washington, D.C.

Shimp, L. A. 1985. "Process Cheese Principles." *Food Tech.* 39 (5):63–70.

Shurtleff, W., and A. Aoyagi. 1983. *The Book of Tofu*, 2d ed. New York: Ballantine.

_____. 1984. *Tofu and Soymilk Production*. Lafayette, Calif.: New-Age Foods Study Center.

Steinkraus, K. H. 1976. "Soybean Milk Processing and Technology." *Applied Nut.* 4:49–62.

Taranto, M. V., and C. S. T. Yang. 1981. Quoted in Yang and Taranto, 1982. *Scanning Electron Microsc.* 3:483.

Thalheimer, W. G. 1968. "Whipped Topping a Complex Emulsion." *Food Eng.* (Reprint LG-104 Atlas Chemical Industries, Inc., Wilmington, Del., May.)

Trauberman, L. 1975. "Cheesemakers Reap Dividends with Mechanical Systems." *Food Eng.* (June):59–63.

USDA/ARS. 1976. *Composition of Foods—Dairy and Egg Products. Raw—Processed—Prepared*. Ag. Handbook No. 8-1. Washington, D.C.: U.S. Government Printing Office.

USDA/CMS. 1968. *Federal and State Standards for the Composition of Milk Products (and Certain Non-Milkfat Products)*. Ag. Handbook No. 51. Washington, D.C.: U.S. Government Printing Office.

United States Code Annotated. 1972. Title 21, *Food and Drugs*. Chap. 3, Sec 61 (c), 20. West Publishing Co., Inc., St. Paul, MN.

USDA/ESCS. 1979a. *Fats and Oils Situation*. FOS296. U.S. Department of Agriculture, Washington, D.C. 20250.

USDA/ESCS. 1979b. *National Food Review*. NFR-8. U.S. Department of Agriculture, Washington, D.C. 20250.

Yang, C. S. T., and M. V. Taranto. 1982. "Textural Properties of Mozzarella Cheese Analogs Manufactured From Soybeans." *J. Food Sci.* 47:906–10.

CHAPTER 9

Dietary and Miscellaneous Uses

Protein additives are used to the greatest extent in baking, processed meats, dairylike products, and pastas. These areas were covered in the previous four chapters. In all cases, we saw that the use of protein additives resulted in functional, nutritional, and economic benefits. Although all three benefit categories are good reasons for using additives, we cannot overlook the fact that the economic benefit is a prime motivator. This is especially evident when vegetable proteins are used to replace, partially or completely, animal proteins in a formulation.

As we consider protein additives further in foodservice applications, we will see that many of the principles used in the four areas covered earlier also apply in dietary and miscellaneous use applications.

It is impractical to cover every dietary and miscellaneous use in detail. The principles mentioned as we discuss certain specific areas should serve to guide the food technologist to successful developments as he or she works in related areas.

When considering protein additives in dietary applications, we will cover two subdivisions: protein fortification and special dietary uses. Coverage of miscellaneous applications will go into only enough depth to get us started in our own developmental work. In most cases, formulations and suggestions given in this text or by a supplying company are given only to help the technologist develop his or her own formulations, serving only her or his needs and that of the organization sponsoring the work. Contact protein supplier companies for help in starting a particular project.

PROTEIN FORTIFICATION

Protein fortification is an important area to cover when setting the stage for dietary applications. We are interested in protein fortification for two reasons: to increase the protein level and/or to improve the protein quality, both of which are usually done for nutritional reasons.

If food products are promoted and claims are made relative to their protein content and/or quality, nutritional labeling is triggered, according to Title 21, sec. 101.9 (*CFR* 1984). As to our dietary needs for proteins, FDA regulations state that the U.S. RDA of the protein in a food product is 45 grams if the PER of the total protein in the product is equal to or greater than that of casein (2.5). If the protein quality is less than that of casein, then the U.S. RDA for the protein is 65 grams. However, if the PER is less than 20 percent of that of casein (0.5), a statement cannot be made on the label in terms of percentage U.S. RDA. Instead, the label must state, "not a significant source of protein" immediately adjacent to the protein-content statement, regardless of the actual amount of protein present.

Increasing Protein Level

The desire or need to increase protein may be to conform to a guaranteed or promised level in the food, as in special dietary products. The protein additives that are usable for this purpose can be any one of those mentioned previously. However, there are several limiting factors that apply to the protein under consideration. Obviously, the first factor is that the product must have a higher protein level than the target protein level. Second, the nonprotein components of the additive must be compatible and not cause a problem. For example, if the food being fortified has a protein level of 10 percent and the desire is to use nonfat dry milk (NFDM) as the fortifying product, will the accompanying lactose cause a problem or can it be tolerated? The lactose level in NFDM is 50 percent, while the protein level is about 35 percent. Thus, for every percent of NFDM protein added, 1.43 percent of lactose is also added. For other proteins, the accompanying factors to be taken into account may be color, oil content, fiber, and flavor. Last, the protein additive per se must be compatible with the system in which it will be used. An obvious example of an incompatibility is the use of an insoluble protein form in a system that needs to have a soluble one.

It is relatively easy to calculate the amount of protein needed to bring the total protein of a product up to a desired level. In Chapter 7 we discussed the

Pearson Square (PS) method of calculation and saw how the procedure is used to guide us when making meat combinations to attain a particular fat level. We also saw how it could be used to guide us in obtaining a specific hydration level by adding water to dry protein. PS also can help us to arrive at the proper amount of protein additive to use in fortifying various food products. An example of the procedure follows.

Example

Our purpose is to increase the protein content of a food preparation from 13 to 15 percent using a 90 percent protein product. Recall that we place the target percentage (15 percent) at the center of an X.

The protein level of the food product (13 percent) is placed at the upper left of the X and the protein fortifier level (90 percent) is placed at the lower left.

We now fill in the "difference" numbers between the figures on the left and the target figure. The resultant values are placed at the opposite ends of the cross lines.

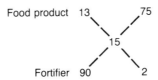

To complete our calculations, as shown in Chapter 7, the difference values are added and each is considered a fraction of the total. These values, times 100, tell us the percentage of each ingredient to be used in the combination to give us the target protein level in the mixture.

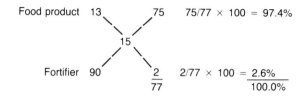

The calculations show that the proportion of the mix is 97.4 percent food product and 2.6 percent fortifier. If we want to know how much to add to 100 pounds of food product, we will find that we need to add 2.67 pounds of fortifier.

$$\frac{97.4}{2.6} = \frac{100}{X} \qquad X = \frac{2.6 \times 100}{97.4} = 2.67$$

If NFDM is the fortifier we see the following:

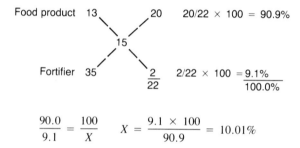

$$\frac{90.0}{9.1} = \frac{100}{X} \qquad X = \frac{9.1 \times 100}{90.9} = 10.01\%$$

As was pointed out earlier, 10 pounds of NFDM also include 5 pounds of lactose. This may or may not be a problem.

Improving Protein Quality

Protein quality is improved when the amino acid content more nearly matches that of the model protein and/or matches a specific standard. We discussed in Chapter 3 that there are several ways to measure protein quality. The easiest method for our purposes is the amino acid or the chemical score. Here is an example of the procedure.

Example 1

The model amino acid profile we will use is the Food and Nutrition Board pattern. The amino acid profile of a product under consideration is matched against the standard pattern. The chemical score is arrived at by dividing the limiting amino acid level of the food product by that shown in the standard pattern and multiplying by 100. Hence, if the food in question is limiting in lysine, the lysine content is 31 milligrams per gram of protein, and the standard has 51 milligrams, then the chemical or amino acid score is 60.8 percent (31/51 × 100).

Here, too, we find that PS will help us arrive at a combination of proteins to give an improved or a higher-quality protein combination. However, these calculations are a little more involved than those shown in previous examples. To help us understand the procedure, we will use PS to find the proper amount of soy flour to add in improving the protein quality of cornmeal. Before getting into the example, please note Table 9-1.

Table 9-1 lists a number of food products with their essential amino acid contents. The table also gives the standard FAO/WHO and the FNB amino acid patterns. The last two columns show the amino acid scores based on both patterns to show their differences. When going over examples, we will use the amino acid levels shown in this table.

Example 2

For this example, we will fortify cornmeal with soy flour. Cornmeal is limiting in both lysine and tryptophane. The amino acid scores (AASs) of these two amino acids are 56.9 percent and 54.5 percent, respectively. Thus, cornmeal is more limiting in tryptophane than in lysine. Looking at the lysine and tryptophane contents of soy flour, their respective AASs are 123.5 percent and 127.3 percent. Hence, soy flour can be used to fortify cornmeal in both instances. Because the AAS for lysine is less than the tryptophane in soy flour, we will base our calculations on lysine. When doing this, we also should take care of the tryptophane deficiency.

Using the lysine amino acid levels shown in Table 9-1, we will follow the PS procedure. In this case, the target level is that amount of lysine contained in the standard, which is 51 milligrams.

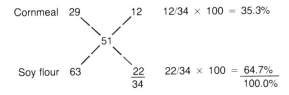

To achieve an ideal combination of cornmeal and soy flour, we need to combine 35.3 pounds of cornmeal protein with 64.7 pounds of soy flour protein. Since cornmeal has a protein level of 9.2 percent (USDA/ARS 1963) and soy flour has a protein level of 50 percent, we need to combine 383.7 pounds of cornmeal (35.3/0.092) with 129.4 pounds of defatted soy flour (64.7/0.5), giving us a rough proportion of 75 percent cornmeal and 25 percent defatted soy flour. This combination has a protein level of 19.4 percent [(75 × 0.092) + (25 × 0.5)].

Table 9-1 Essential Amino Acid Pattern of Selected Foods

	Mgm of AA Per Gram of Protein								Amino Acid Score	
Food Item	Ile	Leu	Lys	Met Cys	Phe Tyr	Thr	Trp	Val	FAO/WHO	FNB
FAO/WHO Std. AA Pattern	40	70	55	35	60	40	10	50	100	—
FNB Std. AA Pattern	42	70	51	26	73	35	11	48	—	100
Milk—human	46	93	66	42	72	43	17	55	100	99
Milk—cow	47	95	78	33	102	44	14	64	94	100
Egg	54	86	70	57	93	47	17	66	100	100
Casein	64	101	79	34	112	44	14	72	97	100
Beef muscle	53	82	86	38	75	44	12	55	100	100
Pork tenderloin	51	74	82	37	74	47	13	48	96	100
Fish	51	76	88	42	62	45	10	52	100	85
Oats	48	70	34	34	84	31	12	56	62	67
Rye	40	64	39	35	79	30	12	48	71	76
Rice	52	86	38	36	92	38	10	66	69	75
Cornmeal	47	132	29	32	107	40	6	52	53	55
Sorghum	56	133	28	33	88	36	11	61	51	55
White flour	42	71	20	31	79	28	11	42	36	39
Wheat germ	43	66	55	26	65	53	9	52	74	82
Wheat gluten	42	68	17	36	80	24	10	42	31	33

Groundnut flour (peanut)	53	60	35	24	87	27	11	49	64	68
Soy flour	53	77	63	32	82	40	14	52	91	100
Soy protein concentrate[1]	47	80	65	27	91	43	14	50	77	100
Soy protein isolate[2]	48	81	65	27	92	38	14	48	77	100
Sesame seed	48	80	25	51	113	29	15	35	45	49
Sunflower seed	47	64	31	32	68	33	12	52	56	61
Cottonseed meal	36	59	43	30	78	35	12	49	88	84
Potato	42	49	52	25	61	38	12	54	71	70
Navy bean	57	86	74	20	95	44	9	61	57	77
Cassava	19	29	50	10	37	22	21	23	29	38
Bulgur	36	67	27	30	78	30	12	44	49	53
Cornmeal—degermed	29	117	15	29	64	28	5	38	27	29
WSB (wheat soy blend)	48	81	53	44	91	38	17	55	95	100
CSM (corn soy milk)	39	92	63	31	77	39	13	45	89	93
ICSM (instant CSM)	40	95	58	28	77	39	10	45	80	91
Soy fortified bulgur	40	71	37	30	84	34	12	46	67	73
Soy fortified flour 12 percent	37	76	28	34	86	30	10	41	51	55
Wheat protein concentrate and soy	38	72	48	31	77	35	14	43	88	90
Corn soy blend	42	98	45	26	78	37	8	46	74	73
Soy fort. sorghum grits	49	118	41	35	86	38	16	53	75	80
Whey soy drink mix	67	96	76	39	85	53	16	64	100	100
Nonfat dry milk	53	99	72	35	98	42	14	64	100	100
Soy fortified rolled oats	47	68	42	31	78	32	12	51	76	82

Source: Adapted from *The Growing Challenge* 1977.

[1] From Central Soya Co., Fort Wayne, Ind. 46802. *Tech. Bull.* CS-T-776.

[2] Average values from nongelling soy protein isolates of ADM and Ralston Purina.

Table 9-2 The Total Amino Acid Content of a 35.3/64.7 Percent Blend of Cornmeal and Defatted Soy Flour Protein Levels Compared with the Food and Nutrition Board Amino Acid Standard

	Ile	Leu	Lys	Met Cys	Phe Tyr	Thr	Trp	Val
Cornmeal	16.59	46.60	10.24	11.30	37.77	14.12	2.12	18.36
Soy flour	34.29	49.82	40.76	20.70	53.05	25.88	9.06	33.64
Totals	50.88	96.42	51.00	32.00	90.82	40.0	11.18	52.00
FNB Standard	42	70	51	26	73	35	11	48

We can now check out the amino acid content of the product combination and compare it with the FNB standard. To do this we realize, as found by our PS calculations, that 35.3 percent of the protein combination is corn protein and 64.7 percent is soy protein. What must be done is to multiply all the amino acid values for corn by 0.353 and those for soy by 0.647. These should be listed together so that they can be added; the values for each amino acid are added individually. The total then needs to be compared to the FNB standard. The results are shown in Table 9-2.

Hence, the combination of 75 percent cornmeal and 25 percent defatted soy flour brings the amino acid score up to 100 percent, which is obviously good from the nutritional standpoint. This may not be the case from the functionality standpoint because the cornmeal is "diluted" with soy. Cornmeal, a high-starch product, is diluted with a "no-starch" product and the protein level is doubled. We obviously change the character of the cornmeal. Since soy flour contains 50 percent nonprotein material, we might want to consider an additive that is "practically pure" protein, which would certainly cause less of a dilution effect. We now look at the possibility of using soy protein isolate instead of the soy flour.

When comparing the AASs of each of the amino acids of concern, we see the following. The respective scores for soy protein isolate are 127.5 percent, 108.6 percent, 127.3 percent, and 100 percent for lysine, threonine, tryptophane, and valine, respectively. For cornmeal, they are 56.9 percent, 114.3 percent, 54.5 percent, and 108.3 percent. Since cornmeal is deficient in both lysine and tryptophane, these are the main acids to be considered in our calculations. Of the two, tryptophane is the more limiting, so we will use it as our guide when making calculations.

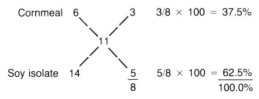

Table 9-3   The Threonine/Valine Content of an Optimum Combination of Cornmeal/Soy Protein Isolate Protein Blend Compared with the FNB Standard

	Threonine	Valine
Cornmeal	15.0	19.5
Soy isolates	23.8	30.0
Totals	38.8	49.5
FNB Standards	37	48

This equates to 407.6 pounds of cornmeal (37.5/0.092) and 69.4 pounds of soy protein isolate (62.5/0.9) for a total of 477 pounds. This is about 85.5 percent cornmeal and 14.5 percent soy protein isolate, which obviously is a lesser dilution of the cornmeal. However, this combination results in a protein content of 20.91 percent [(85.5 × 0.092) + (14.5 × 0.9)] as opposed to 19.4 percent when using soy flour.

Without going through all the calculations, we will now concern ourselves with threonine and valine, the two amino acids in question. To arrive at the total threonine and valine contents, we must multiply those for cornmeal by 0.375 and those for the isolate by 0.625 and then add the values of each. The totals found are then compared with the FNB standard values for the two amino acids (see Table 9-3).

These figures reveal that the levels are slightly higher than the standard; hence, there will be no apparent deficiency. Since our calculations were based on tryptophane, we know that this level is satisfied. What about the remaining questionable amino acid, lysine? Calculations for its level reveal a total of 51.5 milligrams [(29 × 0.375) + (65 × 0.625)], which is above the standard level of 51. Hence, the combination of cornmeal and soy protein isolate has an AAS of at least 100 percent.

This will not always work out in this way. More often than not, we will find that one or more of the amino acid levels will not come up to the standard. In this case, there will be a deficiency. However, we should not lose sight of the fact that the goal in fortification is to increase the AAS to some degree.

With the cornmeal/soy protein isolate combination, we could not hope to fortify the valine level of the cornmeal, but we did find that cornmeal has an excess of valine. This is a good example of the synergistic effect of two proteins fortifying each other.

If a particular combination does not come up to expectations, we can still add a second protein fortifier. In this case, the original combination is treated as a single product. Then, using the calculated amino acid pattern as a guide, the calculations are continued with another protein product. In all likelihood, this second addition will give the desired results.

Last, when using this approach, the PER may or may not be improved because the amino acid requirement for the rat is not the same as that for humans. The chances are that the PER will improve. As far as FDA regulations are concerned, the official protein evaluation method is the regular PER determination. Nevertheless, the exercises we just covered will give us reasonably good combinations that may have good protein quality.

DIETARY USES

Now that we have the basics of protein fortification as a foundation, we are ready to look at special dietary uses for proteins. Again, if proteins are used for this purpose and attention is called to it in advertising and/or on the product label, the FDA regulatory guidelines must be followed. These regulations are spelled out in 21 *CFR,* part 105 (*CFR* 1984) entitled, "Foods for Special Dietary Use." In "Subpart A—General Provisions," sec. 105.3 "Definitions and interpretations," we see the following:

(a)(1) The term "special dietary uses," as applied to food for man, means particular (as distinguished from general) uses of foods, as follows:
(i) Uses for supplying particular dietary needs which exist by reason of a physical, physiological, pathological or other condition, including but not limited to the conditions of diseases, convalescence, pregnancy, lactation, allergic hypersensitivity to food, underweight, and overweight;
(ii) Uses for supplying particular dietary needs which exist by reason of age, including but not limited to the ages of infancy and childhood;
(iii) Uses for supplying or fortifying the ordinary or usual diet with any vitamin, mineral, or other dietary property. Any such particular use of a food is a special dietary use, regardless of whether such food also purports to be or is represented for general use.
(2) The use of an artificial sweetener in a food, except when specifically and solely used for achieving a physical characteristic in the food which cannot be achieved with sugar or other nutritive sweetener, shall be considered a use for regulation of the intake of calories and available carbohydrate, or for use in the diets of diabetics and is therefore a special dietary use.

Subpart B gives labeling guidelines for the various types of foods.

Sec. 105.62   Hypoallergenic foods.
Sec. 105.65   Infant foods.
Sec. 105.66   Label statements relating to usefulness in reducing or maintaining caloric intake or body weight.

Sec. 105.67   Label statement relating to food for use in the diet of diabetics.
Sec. 105.69   Foods used to regulate sodium intake.

We will now consider some of these categories as they may apply to our interest in foodservice applications.

Hypoallergenic Foods

Certain individuals may develop an allergy to specific foods. An adverse physiological reaction in an individual can manifest itself in a number of ways, such as rashes, hives, sneezing, eczema, itching, or stomach upset. In some cases, there may be difficulty in breathing, and, in more serious situations, there may be life-threatening reactions needing emergency medical attention.

According to Anderson et al. (1982), the protein component of a food is considered to be the causative factor in food allergy. The authors reported that some of the more common allergy-producing foods, particularly in children, are oranges, milk, eggs, and sometimes wheat.

A food preparation made to substitute for another to which a person is allergic is called a *hypoallergenic food*. Soy milk preparations have a long history of usage for babies who were allergic to cow's milk. In all cases, the goal in producing a hypoallergenic food is to make a functional substitute for the problem food. In the previous chapters, we talked about making substitutes in specific applications.

From the regulatory standpoint a hypoallergenic food label must state

(a) The common or usual name and the quantity or proportion of each ingredient (including spices, flavoring, and coloring) in case the food is fabricated from two or more ingredients.

(b) A qualification of the name of the food, or the name of each ingredient thereof, in case the food is fabricated from two or more ingredients, to reveal clearly the specific plant or animal that is the source of such food or of such ingredient, if such food or such ingredient consists in whole or in part of plant or animal matter and such name does not reveal clearly the specific plant or animal that is such a source.

(c) An informative statement on the nature and effect of any treatment or processing of the food or any ingredient thereof, if the changed allergenic property results from such treatment or processing.

Low- or Reduced-Calorie Foods

If a food is presented or represented for special dietary use in maintaining or reducing caloric intake, it must be conspicuously labeled stating the basis for the claim(s). If a nonnutritive ingredient is used, the label must identify the ingredient by name and list its percentage by weight in the food. Of course, the ingredient must be safe and suitable.

In the case of a nonnutritive sweetener, its percentage by weight need not be given, but the food must be labeled to alert the consumer that it is present, such as, "Sweetened with nonnutritive sweetener(s)." If the sweetener is used in combination with a sugar, the label must state, "Sweetened with nutritive sweetener(s) and nonnutritive sweetener(s)."

Special guidelines also are offered for use of the terms *low-calorie foods* and *reduced-calorie foods*.

Low-Calorie Foods

This term may be used only if a serving of the food supplies no more than 40 calories and the food provides no more than 0.4 calorie per gram, as consumed, or is a sugar substitute. Then the food can be labeled as "low calorie," "low in calories," or "a low-calorie food." When a food is naturally low in its caloric content, such as celery, it cannot be labeled as "low-calorie celery"; instead, it can be labeled, "celery, a low-calorie food."

Reduced-Calorie Foods

In order to be labeled as such, a food being promoted as a "reduced-calorie" product must have at least one-third fewer calories than the same food as made (prepared) normally. In addition, the label must "clearly and concisely describe" the basis on which the comparative claim is made. "The statement shall either identify a specific food having at least one and a half times as many calories per serving for which the food can substitute, or indicate that the claim of special dietary usefulness is based on a comparison with the same food with the fabrication or alteration of special dietary significance." It is further stated that the food is not nutritionally inferior.

Low-Sodium and/or Salt-Containing Foods

In these cases, the food must show the number of milligrams sodium or sodium chloride per 100 grams of food. This declaration must be to the nearest multiple of 5 milligrams, except that, "if such food contains not more than 10 milligrams of sodium in a specific serving of the food, the label shall bear a statement to that effect" (21 *CFR* 105.62).

SNACK FOODS

Edible items that usually are eaten between meals are referred to as snack foods. They are convenient, tasty, and, to most people, enjoyable. According to Morgan (1983), at least 60 percent of Americans eat some food or beverage between

Table 9-4   Composition of Selected Pizzas

| | 100g Portion | | | | | Percent of Total Calories | | |
Type	Moisture (%)	Energy (Cal.)	Protein (g)	Fat (g)	Carbo-hydrate (g)	Protein	Fat	Carbo-hydrate
Pizza with cheese								
Home recipe, baked								
Cheese topping	48.3	236	12.0	8.3	28.3	20.3	31.7	48.0
Sausage topping	50.6	232	7.8	9.3	29.3	13.4	36.1	50.5
Commercial, baked								
Chilled	45.1	243	9.2	6.8	36.3	15.1	25.2	59.7
Frozen	45.3	244	9.5	7.1	35.4	15.6	26.2	58.2

Source: Adapted from *Handbook No. 8* (USDA/ARS 1963).
Note: Calories calculated on basis of 4 per gram of protein and carbohydrate and 9 per gram of fat.

meals. Most snack items are high in calories and provide little in the way of desirable nutrients. To many nutritionists, they are considered junk foods because their nutrient content certainly is not balanced. The usual criticism is that they are food products that are high in sugar, fat, and/or salt. This is not entirely true; there are some snack foods that are considered to be quite nutritious. A good example is pizza (see Table 9-4).

Of particular note in Table 9-4 is the proportion of calories contributed by protein, fat, and carbohydrate. When the percentage caloric contribution of each of these components is compared with what nutritionists think is a good balance, pizza is found to be a good product. The ideal caloric pattern is 10 percent from protein, 30 percent from fat, and 60 percent from carbohydrate.

Market

According to Schaeder et al. (1969), the snack food industry is an evolutionary industry. Before 1945, the most popular snacks were cookies, crackers, potato chips, pretzels, popcorn, and nuts. In 1980, the number of snack categories doubled. Scales (1982) reported that *Snack Food* magazine breaks the snack-food market down into 13 categories. The categories were broken down into two groups: four were classed as sweet snacks and nine were classed as salty snacks. The dollar size of the market in 1980 was about $10 billion. Table 9-5 gives a breakdown of the various snack items based on their manufacturers' value and/or sales figures for 1980. The table also shows those items that are high in sugar. The remaining snacks are essentially the salty types. Although

Table 9-5   1980 Snack Market

Rank	Snack Category	Dollars (million)
1	Cookies and crackers[1]	3,670
2	Potato chips	1,900
3	Snack nut meats	950
4	Snack cakes and pies[1]	885
5	Corn chips	672
6	Frozen hot snacks pizza hors d'oeuvre types	670
7	Extruded products	270
8	Meat snacks	220
9	Pretzels	211
10	Popcorn[1]	135
11	Imports and miscellaneous	133
12	Toaster pastries[1]	83
13	Fabricated chips	61
	Total market	9,860

[1]High-sugar items (others high salt).
Source: Information obtained from Scales 1982.

popcorn is referred to as a high-sugar product, it also can be one of the salty types. According to Scales, the caramel product had a growth rate of about 23 percent while the growth rate for the regular and cheese-flavored products was about 11 percent.

Cookie and cracker sales were far ahead of the other snack products. Cookies comprised about 60 percent of this market category.

The total market for snack nut meats was $1,350 million instead of the $950 million shown in the table. The higher figure includes all types of uses. Scales reported that $950 million is the correct figure for strictly snack use.

Regular corn chips and tortilla chips make up the second most important salty snack category. Tortilla chips are growing at a faster rate than the regular corn chips. The 1980 breakdown of sales is $415 million versus $258 million.

Pizza is the big seller in the United States. Its sales amount to 70 percent of the total market category.

Scales pointed out that extruded product sales are relatively small compared to the other products. In 1980, these products advanced about 16 percent in dollars and 6 percent in pounds. Most of these snacks were cheese-flavored corn puffs, which amounted to about $100 million. Scales said that the original snacks of this category were corn-based. He reported that there are now more imaginatively formulated products made from a variety of cereal and noncereal products. He revealed that one product uses nonfat dry milk as its chief ingredient. More in keeping with nutritional interests, Scales directed attention to the label of one product; the product was made "of whole wheat and fresh yogurt, not fried (and) no preservatives added." The product was said to be formulated by an internationally known nutritionist. A $1\frac{1}{2}$ ounce serving is claimed to contain 12 percent of the RDA of protein "and appreciable amounts of some vitamins and minerals" (Scales 1982, p. 205).

Four types of products make up the meat snack category. These products, with their dollar sales figures (in millions of dollars), were snack sausages, 78.5; puffed pork, 70; jerky, 59; and pickled products, 13.

One interesting point is that pretzels, a low-moisture food, require more energy to produce than any other bakery product. Their retail price depends a great deal on these energy costs. Another interesting point is that peanuts and pretzels are competitive products. If there is a peanut shortage, the sale of pretzels will increase. Scales stated that pretzel consumption still seems associated with beer more than with any other beverage. "And beer is the unemployed's libation of solace in economic turndowns, such as the one in the spring of 1980" (Scales 1982, p. 204).

Little can be said of the remaining three snack categories, except a comment that should be made about fabricated chips. Scales pointed out that packaging costs of one fabricated chip product were about six times what film packaging would cost. Obviously, this is a real disadvantage when competing with other products. However, products of this type have the potential of becoming whatever we wish from the standpoint of ideal composition, provided that it can be made to appeal to the consumer. The same can be said for the various formulated baked and extruded products.

Fortification

The 1969 White House Conference on Food, Nutrition and Health revealed that, despite American affluence, there is a problem of malnutrition among the poor. However, the problem was not limited to this class (*Snack Foods* 1970). Because of this conference, Americans are becoming more aware of the part nutrition plays in health and disease. Many suggestions were made to correct some of these problems. Not surprisingly, snack foods were singled out as a good place to start making such corrections. It was recommended that snack foods be enriched and fortified, especially since they were so widely used.

Unfortunately, because the ingredient costs of most snack foods are quite low, fortification adds significantly to the cost. Since many of these snacks are made from cereal grains in an extrusion cooking operation, there is also the problem of some adverse effects on texture when proteins are incorporated. With these

Table 9-6 Ingredient Composition of a Snack Food: Conversion from As Is to Dry Basis

Ingredient	As Is Basis				Dry Basis		
	Moisture	Protein	Fat	Carbo-hydrate	Protein	Fat	Carbo-hydrate
Corn grits	12	8.7	0.8	78.1	9.9	0.9	88.8
Cheddar cheese	36.75	24.9	33.14	1.28	39.4	52.4	2.0
Vegetable oil	—	—	100.0	—	—	100.0	—

Source: Compositions found in USDA/ARS (1963 and 1976).

two objections, most processors are not anxious to put out a fortified product. They feel that consumers are not truly interested in buying them.

A popular flavor additive in a number of snack items is dehydrated cheddar cheese. Not only is this product flavorful, but also it contributes to the protein content of the snack. Zick (1969) stated that the balanced finished composition of an expanded corn snack item consists of 60 percent corn grits, 25 percent vegetable oil, 10 to 12 percent cheese flavor, and 2 percent salt. Since the protein level of the dehydrated cheese product is fairly high, it contributes significantly to the total protein content.

We should go through the exercise of calculating the protein, fat, carbohydrate, and caloric composition of a snack so we can make a judgment and then make the necessary changes to obtain a more desirable product.

Compositional Calculations

Three components of food products contribute to the caloric value of foods—protein, fat, and carbohydrate. These also are the same nutritional components in which consumers have an interest. When going through the various steps in making calculations, we will use the snack item to which Zick (1969) referred. The first step is to look at the available information. The snack food is composed of 60 percent corn grits, 25 percent vegetable oil, 10 to 12 percent dehydrated cheddar cheese, and 2 percent salt. The salt does not enter into our calculations, and we need to settle on a specific amount of cheese flavor. We will use 12 percent.

Next, we must have the composition of the various products, which we will get from a reliable source. This can be our own laboratory analysis, or we can go to special tables. In our case, we will use the information published by the USDA (USDA/ARS 1963 and 1976). The information can then be put into a table (see Table 9-6).

Our initial task is to convert all the protein, fat, and carbohydrate contents

Table 9-7   Dry Basis Composition of Cheese-Flavored Snack Food

Ingredient	Percent of Formulation	Dry Basis Composition			Contributed by Each Ingredient			
		Protein	Fat	Carbo-hydrate	Moisture	Protein	Fat	Carbo-hydrate
Corn grits	60	9.9	0.9	88.8	—	5.94	0.54	53.28
Vegetable oil	25	—	100.0	—	—	—	25.0	—
Cheddar cheese	12	39.4	52.4	2.0	—	4.73	6.29	0.24
			Totals		—	10.67	31.83	53.52
		Moisture level adjusted to 2.5%			2.5	10.4	31.0	52.2

from an as-is basis to a dry basis. Note that, in the case of corn grits, the protein content is 8.7 percent. This means that in 100 parts of corn grits, 8.7 parts are protein. Since we want our calculations to be on a dry basis, we must take out the 12 percent, or 12 parts of water, leaving 88 parts of dry material.

When such calculations are made, there are times when we divide and other times when we multiply. Rather than remember when to do which, we can depend on a little logic. If the protein content is 8.7 percent and we take away water, it stands to reason that the protein content will be higher on a percentage basis. Hence, what we will do is divide 8.7 by 0.88 to give us the dry-basis protein content of 9.9 (9.886). If we feel uncomfortable with this, we can always turn to proportions—8.7 parts are to 88 as x is to 100, and then solve for x.

$$\frac{8.7}{88} = \frac{x}{100} \qquad x = \frac{8.7 \times 100}{88} = 9.886$$

We must divide 0.88 into the as-is values in the as-is part of the table to get the dry-basis values. The same approach must be taken with the cheddar cheese flavor ingredient. Since the vegetable oil is already a dry product, no conversion is necessary.

Our next task is to set up a table and show how much protein, fat, and carbohydrate are obtained from each ingredient; these numbers are then totaled to give the composition of the formulated product. This is shown in Table 9-7. On the left side of this table are the amounts of each ingredient with their dry-basis compositions. What needs to be done is to fill in the right-hand portion (amounts contributed by each ingredient) with the appropriate values. Here it is necessary to use multiplication. For corn grits, the formulation calls for only 60 parts of a product that contains 9.9 parts of protein. Thus, each value shown for the three components for corn grits must be multiplied by 0.60 (60 percent), filling in on the right side the values obtained. The same approach must be taken with each of the ingredients.

When this is done, we can see that the totals for the snack for protein, fat, and carbohydrate, on a dry basis, are 10.67, 31.83, and 53.52, respectively. Since the snack is not entirely dry (it does contain a small amount of moisture), it is necessary to make this calculation. We will use the moisture content of 2.5 percent, which means that every item will be diluted by a small amount; the product will now have 2.5 parts water and 97.5 parts of dry material. Knowing that each value will be reduced a small amount, we can multiply each by 0.975. A less accurate way would be again to use the proportion to add 2.5 to 100 parts in setting the proportion, but this would be less than 2.5 percent water ($2.5/102.5 = 2.43$). If this is the approach one would desire, the equation would be:

$$\frac{x}{100 + x} \times 100 = 2.5$$

$$100x = 2.5 \, (100 + X)$$

$$100x = 250 + 2.5X$$

$$100x - 2.5X = 250$$

$$97.5x = 250$$

$$x = \frac{250}{97.5} = 2.564$$

The next thing we want to do is to find the caloric content of the snack. We know that there are approximately 4 Calories in every gram of protein and carbohydrate and 9 Calories in every gram of fat. Since the values shown in the tables for protein, fat, and carbohydrate are percentage figures, they also represent the number of grams of each contained in 100 grams of product. If we multiply the protein and carbohydrate by four and the fat content by nine, then add them together, we obtain the total Calories for 100 grams of product. If we want to know how many Calories are in an ounce of product, we will multiply the number of Calories for 100 grams by 0.2835 because there are 28.35 grams in one ounce.

There will be times when we will need to find the sodium content of a formulation. The same approach can be used. The USDA/ARS (1963 and 1976) also gives the sodium contents of the various foods, usually shown in milligrams. For calculating purposes, if sodium chloride or table salt is used in a formulation, the sodium content is 39.34 percent, or each gram contains 393.4 milligrams of sodium.

Table 9-8 Total Caloric Content Calculation of Expanded Corn Snack Item Referred to by Zick (1969)

	Protein	Fat	Carbohydrate	
	10.4	31.0	52.2	
Cal./gm	4	9	4	
Calories	41.6	279	208.8	= 529.4 Calories in 100 grams

1 oz. = 28.35 grams, or 28.35% of 100 grams
529.2 × 0.2835 = 150 Calories per ounce

MISCELLANEOUS USES

The guidelines given in previous sections apply, for the most part, in the miscellaneous use category. We will now look at the functional benefits, knowing that we always have economic advantages whenever animal proteins are replaced with vegetable protein.

We saw in previous chapters that nonfat dry milk (NFDM) was widely used in many applications. Because of U.S. price supports, NFDM is relatively expensive to use as a protein additive, thus making it advantageous for processors to use an NFDM replacer.

In Chapter 5, we saw how an NFDM replacer could be obtained by blending soy flour with cheese whey. This replacer product is widely used in many baked items. However, this particular replacer product is not used in very many other type systems because of an incompatibility problem. Instead, it was necessary to develop another NFDM replacer composed of 30 percent nongelling soy protein isolate and 70 percent sweet dairy cheese whey solids. Although the product is more expensive than the soy flour/whey blend, it is less expensive than NFDM. The isolate/whey blend product is more compatible in many more systems because it is more soluble than the soy flour product.

When Central Soya was in the business of producing soy protein isolates, they promoted the use of the isolate/whey blend product as a replacer in many different systems. In one piece of their literature (Ag-675), they published the approximate analysis of the blend shown in Table 9-9.

A useful table was included in the same bulletin, in which a number of applications areas were listed along with the normal use level for NFDM and the benefits that the isolate/whey blend provided for each system listed. An adaptation of this table is shown in Table 9-10.

Although the information was published by Central Soya, there are other companies that produce soy protein isolates that may also be used with sweet cheese whey as an NFDM replacer. Most notable of these companies are Archer Daniels Midland, Grain Processing, and Ralston Purina.

Similar NFDM replacer products also are available using sodium casein with

Table 9-9   30 Percent Soy Protein Isolate
and 70 Percent Sweet Dairy
Whey Blend

Ingredient	Percent
Moisture	8.0
Protein (N × 6.25)	
As is	35.0
Dry basis	38.0
Water-soluble protein	45.0[1]
(expressed as % of total protein)	
Fat	0.2
Crude fiber	0.1
Ash	8.0
Carbohydrate (by difference)	48.7

[1] Nitrogen Solubility Index (NSI) AOACS Ball-65 (Central Soya 1975).

Table 9-10   Use Levels for NFDM and NFDM Replacer in Various Food Systems

Food System	Normal Use Level of NFDM (%)	Benefits of SPC/Whey Blend[1]
Compound coatings	22	Reduced bitterness, bulking agent
Caramel	5–12	Body, flavor, color
Aseptic canned pudding	6–8	Color, flavor
Dry mix batters for fried foods	1–20	Color, viscosity control
Gravies	6–12	Color, viscosity control
Sauces	4–8	Viscosity
Soup	2–4	Opacity, flavor
Margarine	1.5	Color in fried products, baking performance
Fudge	5	Body, flavor, color
Waffles and pancake mixes	1–20	Color, viscosity control
Instant mashed potatoes	2	Flavor, body

[1] 30 percent nongelling soy protein isolate and 7 percent sweet cheese whey solids blend.
Source: Courtesy of Central Soya Co., Fort Wayne, Ind.

various combinations of cheese whey. These products often are formulated to work best in specific applications. In all likelihood, other protein products can be used in combination with cheese whey.

Soups, Sauces, and Gravies

Protein additives have functional value in soups, sauces, and gravies because they increase viscosity and provide body. From the emulsion standpoint, they also act as emulsifiers and emulsion stabilizers. When these emulsified products are frozen, certain proteins do a better job than others in preventing syneresis, the separation of water during freeze/thaw cycles, from taking place.

To help us gain a very basic understanding of how proteins can be used advantageously in these applications, we will look at one category only—soups. The principles that apply here will apply in sauces and gravies, too.

The two most important qualities of soups are body and flavor. In all but clear soups, body is a combination of viscosity and thickness (Binsted and Devey 1960). Although starches and gums can contribute to viscosity, they do not contribute to thickness. Binsted and Devey reported that, if used to excess, these agents give soups the effect of "slimness." The desired thickness "can only be achieved with a sufficient proportion of protein and fat dispersed in the aqueous medium made just sufficiently viscous with starch" (Binsted and Devey 1960, p. 30). They also reported that, because it consists of 60 percent protein and fat, a full-fat soy flour is an ideal ingredient for providing the desired thickness for good body in a soup. What makes full-fat soy flour so ideal for this use is that the fat is in a finely dispersed form and is quite stable. The difficulties of emulsifying added fats and insuring that the emulsion remains stable during freezing, canning, or storage are thereby avoided. The fact that the fat is in a stable form is even more important in the preparation of dry soups.

There is another advantage in using full-fat soy flours in soups, according to Binsted and Devey, and that is in the use of additional fat, particularly for canned and frozen soups. They stated that this is possible because of the soy flour's protein and lecithin content, which aids in further fat emulsification. When incorporating extra fat, a roux should be prepared. Binsted and Devey gave a typical recipe for a roux composed of

Clarified margarine	40 pounds
Full-fat soy flour	4 pounds
Wheat flour	68 pounds

The margarine is first heated to 240°F, after which the soy and the flour are blended in by stirring for 10 minutes. The stirring is stopped and the roux is cooked for another 10 minutes. This roux can then be used in the proportion of 1 pound for every gallon of stock.

An interesting point is that a roux made with soy flour has a protein-stabilizing effect in acid-type soups, such as tomato.

It is important to use a soy flour that is cooked to the degree where there is little, if any, enzymatic activity present. Hence, it would be best to use a product that would have an NSI of 50 percent or lower.

It is well known that, in the preparation of a soup stock, soup bones contribute to both body and flavor. Much of the body that is introduced into the stock comes from the conversion of the connective tissue into gelatin. Hence, we can increase the body of the soup through the addition of unflavored gelatin and decrease the time and effort in achieving the desired soup body. A satisfactory body can be obtained with 0.5 ounce of unflavored gelatin for each gallon of soup stock, which should be introduced near the end of the soup-making process.

One of the problems in freezing soups is the separation of water (syneresis), particularly if there are several freeze/thaw cycles. We already saw how soy flour helps in this respect. A number of companies producing soy protein isolates claim that their products also help prevent water separation during freeze/thaw cycles. In most cases, the desired effect can be achieved using about 2 percent of the gelling-type soy protein isolate.

REFERENCES

Anderson, L., M. V. Dibble, P. R. Turkki, H. S. Mitchell, and M. J. Rynbergen. 1982. *Nutrition in Health and Disease,* 17th ed. Philadelphia: J. B. Lippincott.

Binsted, R., and J. D. Devey. 1960. *Soup Manufacture,* 2d ed. London: Food Trade Press.

Central Soya. 1975. Technical Literature: "NFDM Replaces Using Promine-F and Sweet Dairy Whey," Ag-675. Fort Wayne, Ind.

Code of Federal Regulations. 1984. Title 21. Food and Drugs. Parts 100–109 and 170–199.

The Growing Challenge. 1977. Shawnee Mission, Kan.: ADM Milling.

Morgan, K. J. 1983. "The Role of Snacking in the American Diet." *Cereal Foods World* 28:305–6.

Scales, H. 1982. "The U.S. Snack Food Market." *Cereal Foods World* 27:203–5.

Schaeder, W. E., R. B. Fast, J. P. Crimmins, and N. W. Despoisier. 1969. "Evolving Snack Technology." *Cereal Sci. Today* 14:203–4, 208.

Snack Foods. 1970. "Much Ado About Nutrition." (Jan.):45–9.

USDA/ARS. 1963. *Composition of Foods.* Agricultural Handbook No. 8. Washington, D.C.: U.S. Government Printing Office.

———. 1976. *Composition of Foods—Dairy and Egg Products.* Agricultural Handbook No. 8-1. Washington, D.C.: U.S. Government Printing Office.

Zick, W. F. 1969. "Lipid- and Protein-Derived Flavors for Snack Foods Applications." *Cereal Sci. Today* 14:205.

Index